11-1/11-2 WORK TOGETHER, pp. 304 and 309 — S0-AAC-240

Journalizing transactions for starting a corporation

Journalizing transactions for stock subscriptions and preparing a balance sheet

[7, 3]

CASH PAYMENTS JOURNAL PAGE 1

	DATE	ACCOUNT TITLE	CK. NO.	POST. REF.	GENERAL DEBIT	GENERAL CREDIT	ACCOUNTS PAYABLE DEBIT	PURCHASES DISCOUNT CREDIT	CASH CREDIT	
1	20-- Apr. 4	Organization Costs	1		10 0 0 0 00				10 0 0 0 00	1
2										2
3										3
4										4
5										5
6										6
7										7
8										8
9										9

WT 11-1

CASH RECEIPTS JOURNAL PAGE 1

	DATE	ACCOUNT TITLE	DOC. NO.	POST. REF.	GENERAL DEBIT	GENERAL CREDIT	ACCOUNTS RECEIVABLE CREDIT	SALES CREDIT	SALES TAX PAYABLE DEBIT	SALES TAX PAYABLE CREDIT	SALES DISCOUNT DEBIT	CASH DEBIT	
1	20-- Apr. 3	Capital Stock—Common	R1-4			600 0 0 0 00						600 0 0 0 00	1
2	24	Subscription Receivable	R5			100 0 0 0 00						100 0 0 0 00	2
3													3
4													4
5													5
6													6
7													7
8													8
9													9

WT 11-1 / *WT 11-2*

GENERAL JOURNAL PAGE 1

	DATE	ACCOUNT TITLE	DOC. NO.	POST. REF.	DEBIT	CREDIT	
1	20-- Apr. 7	Subscriptions Receivable	M1		100 0 0 0 00		1
2		Stock Subscribed—Common				100 0 0 0 00	2
3	25	Stock Subscribed—Common	M2		100 0 0 0 00		3
4		Capital Stock—Common				100 0 0 0 00	4
5							5
6							6
7							7
8							8
9							9

WT 11-2

11-1/11-2 WORK TOGETHER (concluded)

[4]

Presidential Limousine, Inc.

Balance Sheet

April 30, 20--

ASSETS												
Current Assets:												
Cash										690	0 0 0	00
Intangible Assets:												
Organization Costs										10	0 0 0	00
Total Assets										700	0 0 0	00
STOCKHOLDERS' EQUITY												
Paid-in Capital:												
Capital Stock—Common (35,000												
shares, $20.00 stated value)										700	0 0 0	00
Total Stockholders' Equity										700	0 0 0	00

11-1/11-2 ON YOUR OWN, pp. 305 and 309

Journalizing transactions for starting a corporation   [8, 5]
Journalizing transactions for stock subscriptions and preparing a balance sheet

CASH PAYMENTS JOURNAL   PAGE 1

	DATE		ACCOUNT TITLE	CK. NO.	POST. REF.	GENERAL DEBIT	GENERAL CREDIT	ACCOUNTS PAYABLE DEBIT	PURCHASES DISCOUNT CREDIT	CASH CREDIT	
1	20-- June	5	Organization Costs	1		15 0 0 0 00				15 0 0 0 00	1
2											2
3											3
4											4
5											5
6											6
7											7
8											8
9											9

(OYO 11-1)

CASH RECEIPTS JOURNAL   PAGE 1

	DATE		ACCOUNT TITLE	DOC. NO.	POST. REF.	GENERAL DEBIT	GENERAL CREDIT	ACCOUNTS RECEIVABLE CREDIT	SALES CREDIT	SALES TAX PAYABLE DEBIT	SALES TAX PAYABLE CREDIT	SALES DISCOUNT DEBIT	CASH DEBIT	
1	20-- June	3	Capital Stock—Common	R1-3			400 0 0 0 00						400 0 0 0 00	1
2		24	Subscriptions Receivable	R4			10 0 0 0 00						10 0 0 0 00	2
3														3
4														4
5														5
6														6
7														7
8														8
9														9

(OYO 11-1, OYO 11-2)

GENERAL JOURNAL   PAGE 1

	DATE		ACCOUNT TITLE	DOC. NO.	POST. REF.	DEBIT	CREDIT	
1	20-- June	11	Subscriptions Receivable	M1		10 0 0 0 00		1
2			Stock Subscribed—Common				10 0 0 0 00	2
3		19	Subscriptions Receivable	M2		30 0 0 0 00		3
4			Stock Subscribed—Common				30 0 0 0 00	4
5		25	Stock Subscribed—Common	M3		10 0 0 0 00		5
6			Capital Stock—Common				10 0 0 0 00	6
7								7
8								8
9								9

(OYO 11-2)

11-1/11-2 ON YOUR OWN (concluded)

[6]

Sierra Corporation																
Balance Sheet																
June 30, 20--																

ASSETS																
Current Assets:																
Cash	395	0	0	0	00											
Subscriptions Receivable	30	0	0	0	00											
Total Current Assets						425	0	0	0	00						
Intangible Asset:																
Organization Costs						15	0	0	0	00						
Total Assets											440	0	0	0	00	
STOCKHOLDERS' EQUITY																
Paid-in Capital:																
Capital Stock—Common (41,000 shares,						410	0	0	0	00						
$10.00 stated value)																
Stock Subscribed—Common (3,000 shares)						30	0	0	0	00						
Total Paid-in Capital											440	0	0	0	00	
Total Stockholders' Equity											440	0	0	0	00	

11-3 WORK TOGETHER, p. 313

Calculating and journalizing the dividends for a corporation

[4]

Value of preferred stock:

2,000 shares	×	$100.00 par value	=	$200,000.00

[5]

Preferred stock dividend:

$200,000	×	6%	=	$12,000.00

Common stock dividend:

$60,000.00	–	$12,000.00	=	$48,000.00

[6]

GENERAL JOURNAL

PAGE 4

	DATE		ACCOUNT TITLE	DOC. NO.	POST. REF.	DEBIT	CREDIT	
1	20-- Jan.	10	Dividends—Common	M29		48 00 0 00		1
2			Dividends—Preferred			12 00 0 00		2
3			Dividends Payable				60 00 0 00	3
4								4
5								5
6								6

11-3   WORK TOGETHER (concluded)

[7]

CASH PAYMENTS JOURNAL   PAGE 11

				1	2	3	4	5
				GENERAL		ACCOUNTS PAYABLE DEBIT	PURCHASES DISCOUNT CREDIT	CASH CREDIT
DATE	ACCOUNT TITLE	CK. NO.	POST. REF.	DEBIT	CREDIT			
20-- Jan. 30	Dividends Payable	124		6000000				6000000

11-3 ON YOUR OWN, p. 313

Calculating and journalizing the dividends for a corporation [8]

Value of preferred stock:

3,500 shares × $80.00 par value = $280,000.00

[9]

Preferred stock dividend:

$280,000 × 8% = $22,400.00

Common stock dividend:

$90,000.00 − $22,400.00 = $67,600.00

[10]

GENERAL JOURNAL   PAGE 7

	DATE		ACCOUNT TITLE	DOC. NO.	POST. REF.	DEBIT	CREDIT	
1	20-- July	2	Dividends—Common	M87		67 6 0 0 00		1
2			Dividends—Preferred			22 4 0 0 00		2
3			Dividends Payable				90 0 0 0 00	3
4								4
5								5
6								6

11-3 ON YOUR OWN (concluded)

[11]

CASH PAYMENTS JOURNAL

PAGE 14

DATE	ACCOUNT TITLE	CK. NO.	POST. REF.	1 GENERAL DEBIT	2 GENERAL CREDIT	3 ACCOUNTS PAYABLE DEBIT	4 PURCHASES DISCOUNT CREDIT	5 CASH CREDIT	
20-- Aug. 2	Dividends Payable	326		9000000				9000000	1
									2
									3
									4
									5
									6
									7
									8
									9
									10
									11
									12
									13
									14
									15
									16
									17
									18
									19
									20
									21
									22
									23
									24
									25

11-1/11-2 APPLICATION PROBLEMS, p. 315

Journalizing transactions for starting a corporation
Journalizing transactions for stock subscriptions and preparing a balance sheet

CASH PAYMENTS JOURNAL

PAGE 1

	DATE		ACCOUNT TITLE	CK. NO.	POST. REF.	GENERAL DEBIT	GENERAL CREDIT	ACCOUNTS PAYABLE DEBIT	PURCHASES DISCOUNT CREDIT	CASH CREDIT	
1	20-- Jan.	4	Organization Costs	1		2 0 0 0 00				2 0 0 0 00	1
2											2
3											3
4											4
5											5
6											6
7											7

CASH RECEIPTS JOURNAL

PAGE 1

	DATE		ACCOUNT TITLE	DOC. NO.	POST. REF.	GENERAL DEBIT	GENERAL CREDIT	ACCOUNTS RECEIVABLE CREDIT	SALES CREDIT	SALES TAX PAYABLE DEBIT	SALES TAX PAYABLE CREDIT	SALES DISCOUNT DEBIT	CASH DEBIT	
1	20-- Jan.	4	Capital Stock—Common	R1-3			480 0 0 0 00						480 0 0 0 00	1
2	Feb.	1	Subscriptions Receivable	R4			20 0 0 0 00						20 0 0 0 00	2
3		8	Subscriptions Receivable	R5			50 0 0 0 00						50 0 0 0 00	3
4	Mar.	1	Subscriptions Receivable	R6			50 0 0 0 00						50 0 0 0 00	4
5														5
6														6

GENERAL JOURNAL

PAGE 1

	DATE		ACCOUNT TITLE	DOC. NO.	POST. REF.	DEBIT	CREDIT	
1	20-- Jan.	5	Subscriptions Receivable	M1		20 0 0 0 00		1
2			Stock Subscribed—Common				20 0 0 0 00	2
3		16	Subscriptions Receivable	M2		100 0 0 0 00		3
4			Stock Subscribed—Common				100 0 0 0 00	4
5	Feb.	1	Stock Subscribed—Common	M3		20 0 0 0 00		5
6			Capital Stock—Common				20 0 0 0 00	6
7		15	Subscriptions Receivable	M4		3 0 0 0 00		7
8			Stock Subscribed—Common				3 0 0 0 00	8
9	Mar.	1	Stock Subscribed—Common	M5		100 0 0 0 00		9
10			Capital Stock—Common				100 0 0 0 00	10
11								11
12								12
13								13

11-1/11-2 APPLICATION PROBLEMS (concluded)

[2]

Pacific Technologies

Balance Sheet

March 2, 20--

ASSETS														
Current Assets:														
Cash	598	0	0	0	00									
Subscriptions Receivable	3	0	0	0	00									
Total Current Assets						601	0	0	0	00				
Intangible Asset:														
Organization Costs						2	0	0	0	00				
Total Assets											603	0	0	0	00
STOCKHOLDERS' EQUITY														
Paid-in Capital:														
Capital Stock—Common (60,000 shares,														
$10.00 stated value)	600	0	0	0	00									
Stock Subscribed—Common (300 shares)	3	0	0	0	00									
Total Paid-in Capital						603	0	0	0	00				
Total Stockholders' Equity											603	0	0	0	00

11-3 APPLICATION PROBLEM, p. 315

Calculating dividends for a corporation   [1]

	Edison	Carmac
Number of Preferred Shares	2,000	10,000
Par Value	$100.00	$50.00
Total Value of Preferred Stock	$200,000.00	$500,000.00
Dividend Rate	10%	8%
Total Annual Dividend—Preferred	$20,000.00	$40,000.00

[2]

Edison Corporation

Year	Total Dividends	Preferred Dividends	Common Dividends
1	$25,000.00	$20,000.00	$ 5,000.00
2	$30,000.00	$20,000.00	$10,000.00
3	$35,000.00	$20,000.00	$15,000.00

Carmac Corporation

Year	Total Dividends	Preferred Dividends	Common Dividends
1	$50,000.00	$40,000.00	$10,000.00
2	$60,000.00	$40,000.00	$20,000.00
3	$75,000.00	$40,000.00	$35,000.00

11-3 APPLICATION PROBLEM

Extra forms

Number of Preferred Shares		
Par Value		
Total Value of Preferred Stock		
Dividend Rate		
Total Annual Dividend—Preferred		

Year	Total Dividends	Preferred Dividends	Common Dividends
1			
2			
3			

Year	Total Dividends	Preferred Dividends	Common Dividends
1			
2			
3			

11-4 APPLICATION PROBLEM, p. 316

Journalizing transactions for declaring and paying dividends

GENERAL JOURNAL   PAGE 8

	DATE		ACCOUNT TITLE	DOC. NO.	POST. REF.	DEBIT	CREDIT	
1	20– Aug.	12	Dividends—Common	M65		130 00 00 00		1
2			Dividends—Preferred			50 00 00 00		2
3			Dividends Payable				180 00 00 00	3
4								4
5								5
6								6
7								7
8								8
9								9
10								10
11								11
12								12
13								13
14								14
15								15
16								16
17								17
18								18
19								19
20								20
21								21
22								22
23								23
24								24
25								25
26								26
27								27
28								28
29								29
30								30
31								31

11-4 APPLICATION PROBLEM (concluded)

CASH PAYMENTS JOURNAL

PAGE 21

DATE	ACCOUNT TITLE	CK. NO.	POST. REF.	GENERAL DEBIT	GENERAL CREDIT	ACCOUNTS PAYABLE DEBIT	PURCHASES DISCOUNT CREDIT	CASH CREDIT	
				1	**2**	**3**	**4**	**5**	
20-- Nov. 15	Dividends Payable	139		1800000 0				1800000 0	1
									2
									3
									4
									5
									6
									7
									8
									9
									10
									11
									12
									13
									14
									15
									16
									17
									18
									19
									20
									21
									22
									23
									24
									25

11-5 MASTERY PROBLEM, p. 316

Journalizing transactions for starting a corporation, declaring and paying dividends, and preparing a balance sheet

[1, 3]

CASH PAYMENTS JOURNAL

PAGE 1

	DATE		ACCOUNT TITLE	CK. NO.	POST. REF.	GENERAL DEBIT	GENERAL CREDIT	ACCOUNTS PAYABLE DEBIT	PURCHASES DISCOUNT CREDIT	CASH CREDIT	
1	20X2 Aug.	4	Organization Costs	1		6 50 00 00				6 50 00 00	1
2	20X4 Jan.	15	Dividends Payable	339		40 00 00 00				40 00 00 00	2
3											3
4											4

CASH RECEIPTS JOURNAL

PAGE 1

	DATE		ACCOUNT TITLE	DOC. NO.	POST. REF.	GENERAL DEBIT	GENERAL CREDIT	ACCOUNTS RECEIVABLE CREDIT	SALES CREDIT	SALES TAX PAYABLE DEBIT	SALES TAX PAYABLE CREDIT	SALES DISCOUNT DEBIT	CASH DEBIT	
1	20X2 Aug.	4	Capital Stock—Common	R1-10			250 00 00 00						250 00 00 00	1
2	Sept.	16	Subscriptions Receivable	R11			2 50 00 00						2 50 00 00	2
3	Oct.	1	Subscriptions Receivable	R12			7 50 00 00						7 50 00 00	3
4	Nov.	1	Subscriptions Receivable	R13			7 50 00 00						7 50 00 00	4
5														5
6														6

GENERAL JOURNAL

PAGE 1

	DATE		ACCOUNT TITLE	DOC. NO.	POST. REF.	DEBIT	CREDIT	
1	20X2 Aug.	6	Subscriptions Receivable	M1		2 50 00 00		1
2			Stock Subscribed—Common				2 50 00 00	2
3		21	Subscriptions Receivable	M2		15 00 00 00		3
4			Stock Subscribed—Common				15 00 00 00	4
5	Sept.	16	Stock Subscribed—Common	M3		2 50 00 00		5
6			Capital Stock—Common				2 50 00 00	6
7	Oct.	15	Subscriptions Receivable	M4		30 00 00 00		7
8			Stock Subscribed—Common				30 00 00 00	8
9	Nov.	1	Stock Subscribed—Common	M5		15 00 00 00		9
10			Capital Stock—Common				15 00 00 00	10
11	20X3 Nov.	15	Dividends—Common	M206		30 00 00 00		11
12			Dividends—Preferred			10 00 00 00		12
13			Dividends Payable				40 00 00 00	13
14								14
15								15

11-5 MASTERY PROBLEM (concluded)

[2]

SkyPark, Inc.

Balance Sheet

November 2, 20--

ASSETS				
Current Assets:				
Cash	261 0 0 0 00			
Subscriptions Receivable	30 0 0 0 00			
Total Current Assets		291 0 0 0 00		
Intangible Asset:				
Organization Costs		6 5 0 0 00		
Total Assets			297 5 0 0 00	
STOCKHOLDERS' EQUITY				
Paid-in Capital:				
Capital Stock—Common (53,500 shares,				
$5.00 stated value)	267 5 0 0 00			
Stock Subscribed—Common (6,000 shares)	30 0 0 0 00			
Total Paid-in Capital		297 5 0 0 00		
Total Stockholders' Equity			297 5 0 0 00	

11-6 CHALLENGE PROBLEM, p. 317

Journalizing transactions for a corporation

CASH RECEIPTS JOURNAL

PAGE 12

				GENERAL		ACCOUNTS RECEIVABLE CREDIT	SALES CREDIT	SALES TAX PAYABLE		SALES DISCOUNT DEBIT	CASH DEBIT
DATE	ACCOUNT TITLE	DOC. NO.	POST. REF.	DEBIT	CREDIT			DEBIT	CREDIT		
20X1 Oct. 15	Subscriptions Receivable	R245			1000000						1000000
20X2 Feb. 21	Subscriptions Receivable	R296			1000000						1000000
20X3 May 12	Subscriptions Receivable	R312			1000000						1000000

CASH PAYMENTS JOURNAL

PAGE 14

				GENERAL		ACCOUNTS PAYABLE DEBIT	PURCHASES DISCOUNT CREDIT	CASH CREDIT
DATE	ACCOUNT TITLE	CK. NO.	POST. REF.	DEBIT	CREDIT			
20X2 Jan. 15	Dividends Payable	1489		40000000				40000000
20X3 Jan. 15	Dividends Payable	1654		45000000				45000000

11-6 CHALLENGE PROBLEM (concluded)

GENERAL JOURNAL
PAGE 6

	DATE		ACCOUNT TITLE	DOC. NO.	POST. REF.	DEBIT	CREDIT	
1	20X1 Jun.	7	Subscriptions Receivable	M234		20 000 00		1
2			Stock Subscribed—Common				20 000 00	2
3	Nov.	1	Dividends—Common	M245		160 000 00		3
4			Dividends—Preferred			240 000 00		4
5			Dividends Payable				400 000 00	5
6	20X2 Feb.	21	Stock Subscribed—Common	M262		20 000 00		6
7			Capital Stock—Common				20 000 00	7
8	Oct.	12	Subscriptions Receivable	M289		100 000 00		8
9			Stock Subscribed—Preferred				100 000 00	9
10	Nov.	1	Dividends—Common	M292		210 000 00		10
11			Dividends—Preferred			240 000 00		11
12			Dividends Payable				450 000 00	12
13	20X3 May	12	Stock Subscribed—Preferred	M324		100 000 00		13
14			Capital Stock—Preferred				100 000 00	14
15	Nov.	1	Dividends—Common	M364		198 000 00		15
16			Dividends—Preferred			252 000 00		16
17			Dividends Payable				450 000 00	17
18								18
19								19
20								20
21								21
22								22
23								23
24								24
25								25
26								26
27								27
28								28
29								29
30								30
31								31

12-1 WORK TOGETHER, p. 327

Journalizing capital stock transactions [6]

CASH RECEIPTS JOURNAL PAGE 4

	DATE	ACCOUNT TITLE	DOC. NO.	POST. REF.	GENERAL DEBIT	GENERAL CREDIT	ACCOUNTS RECEIVABLE CREDIT	SALES CREDIT	SALES TAX PAYABLE DEBIT	SALES TAX PAYABLE CREDIT	SALES DISCOUNT DEBIT	CASH DEBIT	
1	20-- May 2	Capital Stock—Preferred	R234			1000000						1200000	1
2		Paid-in Capital in Excess											2
3		of Par Value—Preferred				200000							3
4	3	Discount on Sale of			50000								4
5		Preferred Stock	R235			500000						450000	5
6		Capital Stock—Preferred											6
7	5	Capital Stock—Common	R236			240000						300000	7
8		Paid-in Capital in Excess											8
9		of Stated Value—Common				60000							9
10	7	Capital Stock—Common	R237			80000						80000	10
11													11
12													12
13													13
14													14
15													15
16													16
17													17
18													18
19													19
20													20
21													21
22													22
23													23
24													24
25													25

12-1 WORK TOGETHER (concluded)

[6]

GENERAL JOURNAL   PAGE 2

	DATE		ACCOUNT TITLE	DOC. NO.	POST. REF.	DEBIT	CREDIT	
1	20-- May	5	Office Equipment	M103		5 0 0 0 00		1
2			Capital Stock—Preferred				5 0 0 0 00	2
3								3
4								4
5								5
6								6
7								7
8								8
9								9
10								10
11								11
12								12
13								13
14								14
15								15
16								16
17								17
18								18
19								19
20								20
21								21
22								22
23								23
24								24
25								25
26								26
27								27
28								28
29								29
30								30
31								31

12-1 ON YOUR OWN, p. 328

Journalizing capital stock transactions [7]

CASH RECEIPTS JOURNAL PAGE 5

	DATE	ACCOUNT TITLE	DOC. NO.	POST. REF.	GENERAL DEBIT	GENERAL CREDIT	ACCOUNTS RECEIVABLE CREDIT	SALES CREDIT	SALES TAX PAYABLE DEBIT	SALES TAX PAYABLE CREDIT	SALES DISCOUNT DEBIT	CASH DEBIT
1	20— June 3	Capital Stock—Preferred	R174			1600000						1700000
2		Paid in Capital in Excess										
3		of Par Value—Preferred				100000						
4		6 Discount on Sale of										
5		Preferred Stock	R175		40000	1600000						1560000
6		Capital stock—Preferred				1600000						
7		9 Capital Stock—Common	R176			150000						1500000
8		11 Capital Stock—Common	R177			150000						160000
9		Paid in Capital in Excess										
10		of Stated Value—Common				10000						
11		12 Capital Stock—Preferred	R178			1600000						1600000
12												
13												
14												
15												
16												
17												
18												
19												
20												
21												
22												
23												
24												
25												

12-1 ON YOUR OWN (concluded)

[7]

GENERAL JOURNAL   PAGE 3

	DATE		ACCOUNT TITLE	DOC. NO.	POST. REF.	DEBIT	CREDIT	
1	20-- June	8	Land	M223		3200000		1
2			Capital Stock—Preferred				3200000	2
3		14	Office Furniture	M224		800000		3
4			Capital Stock—Preferred				800000	4
5								5
6								6
7								7
8								8
9								9
10								10
11								11
12								12
13								13
14								14
15								15
16								16
17								17
18								18
19								19
20								20
21								21
22								22
23								23
24								24
25								25
26								26
27								27
28								28
29								29
30								30
31								31

12-2 WORK TOGETHER, p. 333

Journalizing treasury stock transactions [4]

CASH RECEIPTS JOURNAL

PAGE 11

	DATE	ACCOUNT TITLE	DOC. NO.	POST. REF.	GENERAL DEBIT	GENERAL CREDIT	ACCOUNTS RECEIVABLE CREDIT	SALES CREDIT	SALES TAX PAYABLE DEBIT	SALES TAX PAYABLE CREDIT	SALES DISCOUNT DEBIT	CASH DEBIT	
1	Mar. 12	Treasury Stock	R409			220000						240000	1
2		Paid-in Capital from Sale											2
3		of Treasury Stock				20000							3
4	13	Treasury Stock	R410			220000						220000	4
5	16	Paid-in Capital from			100000								5
6		Sale of Treasury Stock	R411									210000	6
7		Treasury Stock				220000							7
8													8
9													9
10													10
11													11
12													12
13													13
14													14
15													15
16													16
17													17
18													18
19													19
20													20
21													21
22													22
23													23
24													24
25													25

12-2 WORK TOGETHER (concluded)

[4]

CASH PAYMENTS JOURNAL

PAGE 8

DATE		ACCOUNT TITLE	CK. NO.	POST. REF.	GENERAL DEBIT	GENERAL CREDIT	ACCOUNTS PAYABLE DEBIT	PURCHASES DISCOUNT CREDIT	CASH CREDIT	
20-- Mar.	9	Treasury Stock	753		660000				660000	1
										2
										3
										4
										5
										6
										7
										8
										9
										10
										11
										12
										13
										14
										15
										16
										17
										18
										19
										20
										21
										22
										23
										24
										25

12-2 ON YOUR OWN, p. 333

Journalizing treasury stock transactions

[5]

CASH RECEIPTS JOURNAL PAGE 7

	DATE	ACCOUNT TITLE	DOC. NO.	POST. REF.	GENERAL DEBIT	GENERAL CREDIT	ACCOUNTS RECEIVABLE CREDIT	SALES CREDIT	SALES TAX PAYABLE DEBIT	SALES TAX PAYABLE CREDIT	SALES DISCOUNT DEBIT	CASH DEBIT	
1	20-- Aug. 23	Paid-in Capital from											1
2		Sale of Treasury Stock	R85		25000							350000	2
3		Treasury Stock				375000							3
4	25	Treasury Stock	R86			375000						375000	4
5	27	Treasury Stock	R87			160000						170000	5
6		Paid-in Capital from Sale											6
7		of Treasury Stock				10000							7
8													8
9													9
10													10
11													11
12													12
13													13
14													14
15													15
16													16
17													17
18													18
19													19
20													20
21													21
22													22
23													23
24													24
25													25

12-2 ON YOUR OWN (concluded)

CASH PAYMENTS JOURNAL   PAGE 6

DATE	ACCOUNT TITLE	CK. NO.	POST. REF.	GENERAL DEBIT	GENERAL CREDIT	ACCOUNTS PAYABLE DEBIT	PURCHASES DISCOUNT CREDIT	CASH CREDIT	
Aug. 22	Treasury Stock	172		7500000				7500000	1
26	Treasury Stock	173		12000000				12000000	2
									3
									4
									5
									6
									7
									8
									9
									10
									11
									12
									13
									14
									15
									16
									17
									18
									19
									20
									21
									22
									23
									24
									25

12-3 WORK TOGETHER, p. 339

Journalizing bonds payable transactions

[4]

CASH RECEIPTS JOURNAL

PAGE 4

	DATE	ACCOUNT TITLE	DOC. NO.	POST. REF.	1 GENERAL DEBIT	2 GENERAL CREDIT	3 ACCOUNTS RECEIVABLE CREDIT	4 SALES CREDIT	5 SALES TAX PAYABLE DEBIT	6 SALES TAX PAYABLE CREDIT	7 SALES DISCOUNT DEBIT	8 CASH DEBIT	
1	20X1 Feb. 1	Bonds Payable	R135			30000000						30000000	1
2													2
3													3
4													4
5													5
6													6
7													7
8													8
9													9
10													10

CASH PAYMENTS JOURNAL

PAGE 5

	DATE	ACCOUNT TITLE	CK. NO.	POST. REF.	1 GENERAL DEBIT	2 GENERAL CREDIT	3 ACCOUNTS PAYABLE DEBIT	4 PURCHASES DISCOUNT CREDIT	5 CASH CREDIT	
1	20X2 Feb. 1	Interest Expense	201		3000000				3000000	1
2	1	Bond Sinking Fund	202		37500000				37500000	2
3	20X3 Feb. 1	Interest Expense	313		3000000				3000000	3
4	1	Bond Sinking Fund	314		37500000				36000000	4
5		Interest Income				150000				5
6										6
7										7
8										8
9										9
10										10

12-3 WORK TOGETHER (concluded)

[4]

GENERAL JOURNAL   PAGE 2

	DATE		ACCOUNT TITLE	DOC. NO.	POST. REF.	DEBIT	CREDIT	
1	20X9 Feb.	3	Bonds Payable	M87		300 00 0 00		1
2			Bond Sinking Fund				300 00 0 00	2
3								3
4								4
5								5
6								6
7								7
8								8
9								9
10								10
11								11
12								12
13								13
14								14
15								15
16								16
17								17
18								18
19								19
20								20
21								21
22								22
23								23
24								24
25								25
26								26
27								27
28								28
29								29
30								30
31								31

12-3 ON YOUR OWN, p. 340

Journalizing bonds payable transactions [5]

CASH RECEIPTS JOURNAL PAGE 11

DATE	ACCOUNT TITLE	DOC. NO.	POST. REF.	GENERAL DEBIT	GENERAL CREDIT	ACCOUNTS RECEIVABLE CREDIT	SALES CREDIT	SALES TAX PAYABLE DEBIT	SALES TAX PAYABLE CREDIT	SALES DISCOUNT DEBIT	CASH DEBIT	
20X1 May 1	Bonds Payable	R63			5000000 00						5000000 00	1
												2
												3
												4
												5
												6
												7
												8
												9
												10

CASH PAYMENTS JOURNAL PAGE 10

DATE	ACCOUNT TITLE	CK. NO.	POST. REF.	GENERAL DEBIT	GENERAL CREDIT	ACCOUNTS PAYABLE DEBIT	PURCHASES DISCOUNT CREDIT	CASH CREDIT	
20X2 May 1	Interest Expense	71		400000 00				400000 00	1
1	Bond Sinking Fund	72		1000000 00				1000000 00	2
20X3 May 1	Interest Expense	173		400000 00				400000 00	3
1	Bond Sinking Fund	174		1000000 00				950000 00	4
1	Interest Income				50000 00				5
									6
									7
									8
									9
									10

12-3 ON YOUR OWN (concluded)

[5]

GENERAL JOURNAL   PAGE 9

	DATE		ACCOUNT TITLE	DOC. NO.	POST. REF.	DEBIT	CREDIT	
1	20X6 May	2	Bonds Payable	M33		500 00 0 00		1
2			Bond Sinking Fund				500 00 0 00	2
3								3
4								4
5								5
6								6
7								7
8								8
9								9
10								10
11								11
12								12
13								13
14								14
15								15
16								16
17								17
18								18
19								19
20								20
21								21
22								22
23								23
24								24
25								25
26								26
27								27
28								28
29								29
30								30
31								31

12-1 APPLICATION PROBLEM, p. 342

Journalizing capital stock transactions

CASH RECEIPTS JOURNAL   PAGE 2

	DATE	ACCOUNT TITLE	DOC. NO.	POST. REF.	1 GENERAL DEBIT	2 GENERAL CREDIT	3 ACCOUNTS RECEIVABLE CREDIT	4 SALES CREDIT	5 SALES TAX PAYABLE DEBIT	6 SALES TAX PAYABLE CREDIT	7 SALES DISCOUNT DEBIT	8 CASH DEBIT
1	Feb. 8	Capital Stock—Common	R398			2500000						2500000
2	Apr. 15	Capital Stock—Preferred	R518			4000000						4000000
3	Aug. 25	Discount on Sale of										
4		Preferred Stock	R601		200000							4800000
5		Capital Stock—Preferred				5000000						
6	Dec. 11	Capital Stock—Preferred	R698			2000000						2040000
7		Paid-in Capital in Excess										
8		of Par Value—Preferred				40000						
9												
10												
11												
12												
13												
14												
15												
16												
17												
18												
19												
20												
21												
22												
23												
24												
25												

12-1 APPLICATION PROBLEM (concluded)

GENERAL JOURNAL   PAGE 2

	DATE		ACCOUNT TITLE	DOC. NO.	POST. REF.	DEBIT	CREDIT	
1	20-- Feb.	26	Land	M67		30 00 0 00		1
2			Capital Stock—Preferred				30 00 0 00	2
3								3
4								4
5								5
6								6
7								7
8								8
9								9
10								10
11								11
12								12
13								13
14								14
15								15
16								16
17								17
18								18
19								19
20								20
21								21
22								22
23								23
24								24
25								25
26								26
27								27
28								28
29								29
30								30
31								31

12-2 APPLICATION PROBLEM, p. 342

Journalizing treasury stock transactions

CASH RECEIPTS JOURNAL — PAGE 2

| | | | | GENERAL | | ACCOUNTS RECEIVABLE CREDIT | SALES CREDIT | SALES TAX PAYABLE | | SALES DISCOUNT DEBIT | CASH DEBIT |
DATE	ACCOUNT TITLE	DOC. NO.	POST. REF.	DEBIT	CREDIT			DEBIT	CREDIT		
20-- Feb. 27	Treasury Stock	R126			1 2 5 0 0 0						1 2 5 0 0 0
Apr. 15	Treasury Stock	R151			2 7 5 0 0 0						3 3 0 0 0 0
	Paid-in Capital from										
	Sale of Treasury Stock				5 5 0 0 0						
July 30	Paid-in Capital from			3 0 0 0 0 0							
	Sale of Treasury Stock	R203			3 3 0 0 0 0						3 0 0 0 0 0
	Treasury Stock										

12-2 APPLICATION PROBLEM (concluded)

CASH PAYMENTS JOURNAL

PAGE 3

	DATE	ACCOUNT TITLE	CK. NO.	POST. REF.	GENERAL DEBIT	GENERAL CREDIT	ACCOUNTS PAYABLE DEBIT	PURCHASES DISCOUNT CREDIT	CASH CREDIT	
1	20-- Feb. 21	Treasury Stock	87		4 000 00				4 000 00	1
2	Mar. 22	Treasury Stock	138		8 250 00				8 250 00	2
3										3
4										4
5										5
6										6
7										7
8										8
9										9
10										10
11										11
12										12
13										13
14										14
15										15
16										16
17										17
18										18
19										19
20										20
21										21
22										22
23										23
24										24
25										25

12-3 APPLICATION PROBLEM, p. 343

Journalizing bonds payable transactions

CASH RECEIPTS JOURNAL

PAGE 1

	DATE	ACCOUNT TITLE	DOC. NO.	POST. REF.	GENERAL DEBIT	GENERAL CREDIT	ACCOUNTS RECEIVABLE CREDIT	SALES CREDIT	SALES TAX PAYABLE DEBIT	SALES TAX PAYABLE CREDIT	SALES DISCOUNT DEBIT	CASH DEBIT	
1	20X1 Jan. 1	Bonds Payable	R104			20000000						20000000	1
2													2
3													3
4													4
5													5
6													6
7													7
8													8
9													9
10													10

CASH PAYMENTS JOURNAL

PAGE 8

	DATE	ACCOUNT TITLE	CK. NO.	POST. REF.	GENERAL DEBIT	GENERAL CREDIT	ACCOUNTS PAYABLE DEBIT	PURCHASES DISCOUNT CREDIT	CASH CREDIT	
1	20X1 July 1	Interest Expense	294		900000				900000	1
2	1	Bond Sinking Fund	295		20000000				20000000	2
3	20X2 Jan. 1	Interest Expense	504		900000				900000	3
4	1	Bond Sinking Fund	505		20000000				1920000	4
5		Interest Income				80000				5
6										6
7										7
8										8
9										9
10										10

12-3 APPLICATION PROBLEM (concluded)

GENERAL JOURNAL

	DATE		ACCOUNT TITLE	DOC. NO.	POST. REF.	DEBIT	CREDIT	
1	20X6 Jan.	4	Bonds Payable	M290		200 00 0 00		1
2			Bond Sinking Fund				200 00 0 00	2
3								3
4								4
5								5
6								6
7								7
8								8
9								9
10								10
11								11
12								12
13								13
14								14
15								15
16								16
17								17
18								18
19								19
20								20
21								21
22								22
23								23
24								24
25								25
26								26
27								27
28								28
29								29
30								30
31								31

12-4 MASTERY PROBLEM, p. 343

Journalizing stock and bonds transactions

CASH RECEIPTS JOURNAL PAGE 1

	DATE	ACCOUNT TITLE	DOC. NO.	POST. REF.	GENERAL DEBIT	GENERAL CREDIT	ACCOUNTS RECEIVABLE CREDIT	SALES CREDIT	SALES TAX PAYABLE DEBIT	SALES TAX PAYABLE CREDIT	SALES DISCOUNT DEBIT	CASH DEBIT
1	20X1 Jan. 1	Bonds Payable	R198			5000000						5000000
2	12	Capital Stock—Common	R210			1000000						1000000
3	Feb. 28	Treasury Stock	R215			600000						600000
4	Mar. 13	Capital Stock—Common	R220			200000						300000
5		Paid-in Capital in Excess										
6		of Stated Value—Common				100000						
7	Apr. 8	Capital Stock—Preferred	R226			1000000						1010000
8		Paid-in Capital in Excess										
9		of Par Value—Preferred				10000						
10	Apr. 15	Treasury Stock	R231			360000						540000
11		Paid-in Capital from										
12		Sale of Treasury Stock				180000						
13	May 15	Disc. on Sale of Preferred Stock	R232		200000							7800000
14		Capital Stock—Preferred				8000000						
15	July 23	Paid-in Capital from										
16		Sale of Treasury Stock	R353		20000	440000						420000
17		Treasury Stock										
18												
19												
20												
21												
22												
23												
24												
25												

12-4 MASTERY PROBLEM (concluded)

CASH PAYMENTS JOURNAL

PAGE 8

	DATE	ACCOUNT TITLE	CK. NO.	POST. REF.	GENERAL DEBIT (1)	GENERAL CREDIT (2)	ACCOUNTS PAYABLE DEBIT (3)	PURCHASES DISCOUNT CREDIT (4)	CASH CREDIT (5)
1	20X1 Feb. 21	Treasury Stock	97		1080000				1080000
2	Mar. 22	Treasury Stock	138		3200000				3200000
3	July 1	Interest Expense	200		300000				300000
4	July 1	Bond Sinking Fund	201		500000				500000
5	20X2 Jan. 1	Interest Expense	504		300000				300000
6	Jan. 1	Bond Sinking Fund	505		500000				460000
7		Interest Income				400000			
8									
9									
10									
11									

GENERAL JOURNAL

PAGE 1

	DATE	ACCOUNT TITLE	DOC. NO.	POST. REF.	DEBIT	CREDIT
1	20X1 July 14	Delivery Equipment	M148		20000000	
2		Capital Stock—Preferred				20000000
3	20X6 Jan. 1	Bonds Payable	M491		50000000	
4		Bond Sinking Fund				50000000
5						
6						
7						
8						
9						

12-5   CHALLENGE PROBLEM, p. 344

Journalizing stock and bond transactions

CASH RECEIPTS JOURNAL

PAGE 1

	DATE	DOC. NO.	POST. REF.	ACCOUNT TITLE	GENERAL DEBIT	GENERAL CREDIT	ACCOUNTS RECEIVABLE CREDIT	SALES CREDIT	SALES TAX PAYABLE DEBIT	SALES TAX PAYABLE CREDIT	SALES DISCOUNT DEBIT	CASH DEBIT	
1	20X1 Jan. 1	R51		Bonds Payable		200000000						200000000	1
2	Feb. 12	R64		Capital Stock—Common		1500000						1800000	2
3				Paid-in Capital in Excess of									3
4				Stated Value—Common		300000							4
5	20	R105		Capital Stock—Preferred		5000000						5000000	5
6	Apr. 3			Paid-in Capital from Sale									6
7		R210		of Treasury Stock	100000							1500000	7
8				Treasury Stock		160000							8
9	May 10	R387		Disc. on Sale of Preferred Stock	300000							2970000	9
10				Capital Stock—Preferred		3000000							10
11	Sept. 18	R561		Treasury Stock		400000						500000	11
12				Paid-in Capital from Sale of									12
13				Treasury Stock		100000							13
14	Oct. 14	R600		Capital Stock—Preferred		1500000						1545000	14
15				Paid-in Capital in Excess of									15
16				Par Value—Preferred		45000							16
17													17
18													18
19													19
20													20
21													21
22													22
23													23
24													24
25													25

12-5 CHALLENGE PROBLEM (concluded)

CASH PAYMENTS JOURNAL

PAGE 2

	DATE	ACCOUNT TITLE	CK. NO.	POST. REF.	GENERAL DEBIT	GENERAL CREDIT	ACCOUNTS PAYABLE DEBIT	PURCHASES DISCOUNT CREDIT	CASH CREDIT	
1	20X1 Feb. 5	Treasury Stock	120		8000000				8000000	1
2	July 1	Interest Expense	389		1000000				1000000	2
3	1	Bond Sinking Fund	390		2000000				2000000	3
4	20X2 Jan. 1	Interest Expense	634		1000000				1000000	4
5	1	Bond Sinking Fund	635		2000000				1920000	5
6		Interest Income				800000				6
7										7
8										8
9										9
10										10
11										11

GENERAL JOURNAL

PAGE 1

	DATE	ACCOUNT TITLE	DOC. NO.	POST. REF.	DEBIT	CREDIT	
1	20X1 Mar. 14	Office Equipment	M195		7000000		1
2		Capital Stock—Common				5000000	2
3		Paid-in Cap. in Exc. of Stated Val.—Common				2000000	3
4	20X6 Jan. 2	Bonds Payable	M428		200000000		4
5		Bond Sinking Fund				200000000	5
6							6
7							7
8							8
9							9

13-1 WORK TOGETHER

The work sheet for this problem begins on page 42.

Extra form

ACCOUNT TITLE	TRIAL BALANCE		ADJUSTMENTS		INCOME STATEMENT		BALANCE SHEET	
	DEBIT	CREDIT	DEBIT	CREDIT	DEBIT	CREDIT	DEBIT	CREDIT
	1	2	3	4	5	6	7	8
34								
35								
36								
37								
38								
39								
40								
41								
42								
43								
44								
45								
46								
47								
48								
49								
50								
51								
52								
53								
54								
55								
56								
57								
58								
59								
60								
61								
62								
63								
64								
65								
66								

13-1 WORK TOGETHER, p. 354

Calculating federal income tax expense, recording the adjustment, and completing a work sheet

[3–7]

Provident Electronics
Work Sheet
For Year Ended December 31, 20--

#	ACCOUNT TITLE	TRIAL BALANCE DEBIT	TRIAL BALANCE CREDIT	ADJUSTMENTS DEBIT	ADJUSTMENTS CREDIT	INCOME STATEMENT DEBIT	INCOME STATEMENT CREDIT	BALANCE SHEET DEBIT	BALANCE SHEET CREDIT
1	Cash	2128012						2128012	
2	Petty Cash	25000						25000	
3	Notes Receivable	1073100						1073100	
4	Interest Receivable			(a) 13809				13809	
5	Accounts Receivable	3802943						3802943	
6	Allowance for Uncollectible Accts.		11025		(b) 106722				117747
7	Merchandise Inventory	4407220			(c) 13715			4393505	
8	Supplies—Sales	804428			(d) 363376			441052	
9	Supplies—Administrative	514130			(e) 343121			171009	
10	Prepaid Insurance	343037			(f) 120544			222493	
11	Store Equipment	4297458						4297458	
12	Accum. Depr.—Store Equipment		516400		(g) 482100				998500
13	Office Equipment	5214294						5214294	
14	Accum. Depr.—Office Equipment		110448		(h) 159224				269672
15	Building	24000000						24000000	
16	Accum. Depr.—Building		261400		(i) 130700				392100
17	Land	4100000						4100000	
18	Notes Payable		152000						152000
19	Interest Payable				(j) 15200				15200
20	Accounts Payable		523427						523427
21	Employee Income Tax Payable		20800						20800
22	Federal Income Tax Payable				(m) 609229				609229
23	Social Security Tax Payable		10065		(k) 5745				15810
24	Medicare Tax Payable		2687		(k) 1342				4029
25	Salaries Payable				(l) 67434				67434
26	Sales Tax Payable		31450						31450
27	Unemploy. Tax Payable—Federal		1834		(k) 201				2035
28	Unemploy. Tax Payable—State		28582		(k) 4890				33472
29	Health Ins. Premiums Payable		7306						7306
30	Dividends Payable		746288						746288
31	Capital Stock		12837600						12837600
32	Paid-in Capital in Exc. St. Val.		1590100						1590100
33	Retained Earnings		4014397						4014397

13-1 WORK TOGETHER (concluded)

[3–7]

#	ACCOUNT TITLE	TB Debit	TB Credit	Adj Debit	Adj Credit	IS Debit	IS Credit	BS Debit	BS Credit
34	Dividends	7456 00						7456 00	
35	Income Summary			(c) 1377 15		1377 15			
36	Sales		298372 50				298372 50		
37	Sales Discount	2944 00				2944 00			
38	Sales Returns & Allowances	457 69				457 69			
39	Purchases	147332 99				147332 99			
40	Purchases Discount		1323 15				1323 15		
41	Purchases Returns & Allowances		472 64				472 64		
42	Advertising Expense	2590 45				2590 45			
43	Credit Card Fee Expense	2241 03				2241 03			
44	Depr. Expense—Store Equip.			(g) 4821 00		4821 00			
45	Miscellaneous Exp.—Sales	3426 00				3426 00			
46	Salary Expense—Sales	17072 30		(l) 674 34		17746 64			
47	Supplies Expense—Sales			(d) 3633 76		3633 76			
48	Depr. Expense—Office Equip.	3156 90		(h) 1592 24		4749 14			
49	Depr. Expense—Building	1200 00		(i) 1307 00		2507 00			
50	Insurance Expense			(f) 1205 44		1205 44			
51	Miscellaneous Exp.—Administrative	3244 12				3244 12			
52	Payroll Taxes Expense	2205 22		(k) 121 78		2327 00			
53	Property Tax Expense	1100 00				1100 00			
54	Salary Expense—Administrative	4509 00				4509 00			
55	Supplies Expense—Administrative			(e) 3431 21		3431 21			
56	Uncollectible Accounts Expense			(b) 1067 22		1067 22			
57	Utilities Expense	9239 46				9239 46			
58	Interest Income				(a) 138 09		138 09		
59	Interest Expense	2205 00		(j) 152 00		2357 00			
60	Federal Income Tax Expense	10000 00		(m) 6092 29		16092 29			
61		508826 38	508826 38	24373 52	24373 52	234509 59	300306 38	290282 75	224485 96
62	Net Income after Fed. Income Tax					65796 79			65796 79
63						300306 38	300306 38	290282 75	290282 75
64									
65									
66									

13-1 WORK TOGETHER

Extra form

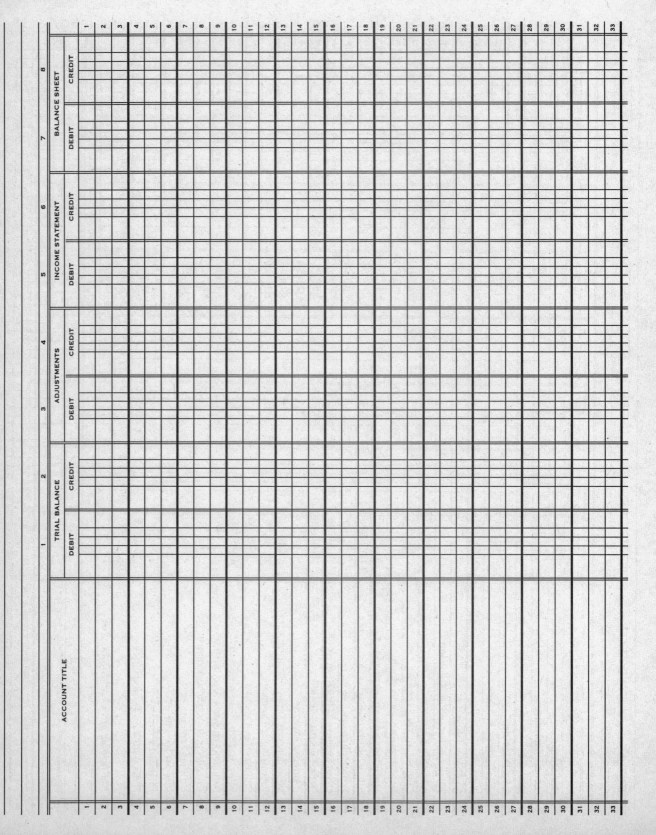

13-1 ON YOUR OWN

The work sheet for this problem begins on page 46.

Extra form

| | TRIAL BALANCE | | ADJUSTMENTS | | INCOME STATEMENT | | BALANCE SHEET | |
ACCOUNT TITLE	DEBIT	CREDIT	DEBIT	CREDIT	DEBIT	CREDIT	DEBIT	CREDIT

13-1 ON YOUR OWN, p. 354

Calculating federal income tax expense, recording the adjustment, and completing a work sheet [8–12]

BRE Corporation
Work Sheet
For Year Ended December 31, 20--

#	Account Title	Trial Balance Debit	Trial Balance Credit	Adjustments Debit	Adjustments Credit	Income Statement Debit	Income Statement Credit	Balance Sheet Debit	Balance Sheet Credit
1	Cash	4256024						4256024	
2	Petty Cash	50000						50000	
3	Notes Receivable	2146200						2146200	
4	Interest Receivable			(a) 13809				13809	
5	Accounts Receivable	7605886						7605886	
6	Allowance for Uncollectible Accts.		220050		(b) 1067722				1287772
7	Merchandise Inventory	8814440			(c) 13715			8800725	
8	Supplies—Sales	1608856			(d) 363376			1245480	
9	Supplies—Administrative	1028260			(e) 343121			685139	
10	Prepaid Insurance	686074			(f) 120544			565530	
11	Store Equipment	8594916						8594916	
12	Accum. Depr.—Store Equipment		1032800		(g) 482100				1514900
13	Office Equipment	10428588						10428588	
14	Accum. Depr.—Office Equipment		2208896		(h) 1592224				3801120
15	Building	4800000						4800000	
16	Accum. Depr.—Building		5228800		(i) 1306700				6535500
17	Land	8200000						8200000	
18	Notes Payable		304000						304000
19	Interest Payable				(j) 15200				15200
20	Accounts Payable		10468854						10468854
21	Employee Income Tax Payable		41600						41600
22	Federal Income Tax Payable				(m) 1414545				1414545
23	Social Security Tax Payable		201130		(k) 5745				206875
24	Medicare Tax Payable		53374		(k) 13342				66716
25	Salaries Payable				(l) 67434				67434
26	Sales Tax Payable		62900						62900
27	Unemploy. Tax Payable—Federal		3668		(k) 201				3869
28	Unemploy. Tax Payable—State		57164		(k) 4890				62054
29	Health Ins. Premiums Payable		146112						146112
30	Dividends Payable	1492576						1492576	
31	Capital Stock		25675000						25675000
32	Paid-in Capital in Exc. St. Val.		3180400						3180400
33	Retained Earnings		10028794						10028794

13-1 ON YOUR OWN (concluded)

[8–12]

#	ACCOUNT TITLE	TRIAL BALANCE DEBIT	TRIAL BALANCE CREDIT	ADJUSTMENTS DEBIT	ADJUSTMENTS CREDIT	INCOME STATEMENT DEBIT	INCOME STATEMENT CREDIT	BALANCE SHEET DEBIT	BALANCE SHEET CREDIT
34	Dividends	14912 00						14912 00	
35	Income Summary			(c) 137 15		137 15			
36	Sales		596745 00				596745 00		
37	Sales Discount	588 00				588 00			
38	Sales Returns & Allowances	915 38				915 38			
39	Purchases	294665 98				294665 98			
40	Purchases Discount		2646 30				2646 30		
41	Purchases Returns & Allowances		945 28				945 28		
42	Advertising Expense	5180 90				5180 90			
43	Credit Card Fee Expense	4482 06				4482 06			
44	Depr. Expense—Store Equip.			(g) 4821 00		4821 00			
45	Miscellaneous Exp.—Sales	6852 00				6852 00			
46	Salary Expense—Sales	34144 60		(j) 674 34		34818 94			
47	Supplies Expense—Sales			(d) 3633 76		3633 76			
48	Depr. Expense—Office Equip.	6313 80		(h) 1592 24		7906 04			
49	Depr. Expense—Building	2400 00		(i) 1307 00		3707 00			
50	Insurance Expense			(f) 1205 44		1205 44			
51	Miscellaneous Exp.—Administrative	6488 24				6488 24			
52	Payroll Taxes Expense	4410 44		(k) 121 78		4532 22			
53	Property Tax Expense	2200 00				2200 00			
54	Salary Expense—Administrative	9018 00				9018 00			
55	Supplies Expense—Administrative			(e) 3431 21		3431 21			
56	Uncollectible Accounts Expense			(b) 1067 22		1067 22			
57	Utilities Expense	18478 92				18478 92			
58	Interest Income				(a) 138 09		138 09		
59	Interest Expense	4410 00		(l) 152 00		4562 00			
60	Federal Income Tax Expense	40000 00		(m) 14145 45		54145 45			
61		1037652 76	1037652 76	32426 68	32426 68	472836 91	600474 67	588834 97	461197 21
62	Net Income after Fed. Income Tax					127637 76			127637 76
63						600474 67	600474 67	588834 97	588834 97
64									
65									
66									

13-1 ON YOUR OWN

Extra form

ACCOUNT TITLE	TRIAL BALANCE		ADJUSTMENTS		INCOME STATEMENT		BALANCE SHEET	
	DEBIT	CREDIT	DEBIT	CREDIT	DEBIT	CREDIT	DEBIT	CREDIT

13-2 WORK TOGETHER, p. 362

Analyzing financial statements [4]

The work sheet prepared in Work Together 13-1 is needed to complete this problem.

Provident Electronics

Income Statement

For Year Ended December 31, 20--

						% OF NET SALES
Operating Revenue:						
Sales				298 3 7 2 50		
Less: Sales Discount		2 9 4 00				
Sales Ret. & Allow.		4 5 7 69		7 5 1 69		
Net Sales					297 6 2 0 81	100.0
Cost of Merchandise Sold:						
Mdse. Inventory, January 1, 20--				44 0 7 2 20		
Purchases		147 3 3 2 99				
Less: Purchases Discount	1 3 2 3 15					
Purch. Ret. & Allow.	4 7 2 64	1 7 9 5 79				
Net Purchases				145 5 3 7 20		
Total Cost of Mdse. Avail for Sale				189 6 0 9 40		
Less Mdse. Inventory, Dec. 31, 20--				43 9 3 5 05		
Cost of Merchandise Sold					145 6 7 4 35	48.9
Gross Profit on Operations					151 9 4 6 46	51.1
Operating Expenses:						
Selling Expenses:						
Advertising Expense		2 5 9 0 45				
Credit Card Fee Expense		2 2 4 1 03				
Depr. Expense—Store Equip.		4 8 2 1 00				
Miscellaneous Expense—Sales		3 4 2 6 00				
Salary Expense—Sales		17 7 4 6 64				
Supplies Expense—Sales		3 6 3 3 76				
Total Selling Expenses				34 4 5 8 88		11.6
Administrative Expenses:						
Depr. Expense—Office Equip.		4 7 4 9 14				
Depr. Expense—Building		2 5 0 7 00				
Insurance Expense		1 2 0 5 44				
Miscellaneous Expense—Admin.		3 2 4 4 12				
Payroll Taxes Expense		2 3 2 7 00				

13-2 WORK TOGETHER (continued)

[4]

Provident Electronics

Income Statement (continued)

For Year Ended December 31, 20--

									% OF NET SALES
Property Tax Expense			1 1 0 0 00						
Salary Expense—Admin.			4 5 0 9 00						
Supplies Expense—Admin.			3 4 3 1 21						
Uncoll. Accounts Expense			1 0 6 7 22						
Utilities Expense			9 2 3 9 46						
Total Admin. Expense					33 3 7 9 59				11.2
Total Operating Expenses							67 8 3 8 47		22.8
Income from Operations							84 1 0 7 99		28.3
Other Revenue:									
Interest Income					1 3 8 09				
Other Expenses:									
Interest Expense					2 3 5 7 00				
Net Deduction							2 2 1 8 91		0.7
Net Income before Fed. Income Tax							81 8 8 9 08		27.5
Less Federal Income Tax Expense							16 0 9 2 29		5.4
Net Income after Fed. Income Tax							65 7 9 6 79		22.1

[5]

Earnings per share:

Net Income	÷	*Shares Outstanding*	=	*Earnings per Share*
$65,796.79	÷	*10,698*	=	*$6.15*

13-2 WORK TOGETHER (continued)

Provident Electronics

Statement of Stockholders' Equity

For Year Ended December 31, 20--

Paid-in Capital:						
Capital Stock, $12.00 Stated Value:						
January 1, 20--, 10,000 Shares Issued	120 0 0 0 00					
Issued during Current Year, 698 Shares	8 3 7 6 00					
Balance, Dec. 31, 20--, 10, 698 Shares Issued		128 3 7 6 00				
Total Value of Capital Stock Issued			128 3 7 6 00			
Additional Paid-in Capital:						
Pd.-in-Cap. in Exc. of St. Value			15 9 0 1 00			
Total Paid-in Capital			144 2 7 7 00			
Retained Earnings:						
Balance, January 1, 20--		40 1 4 3 97				
Net Income after Federal Income Tax for 20--	65 7 9 6 79					
Less Dividends Declared during 20--	7 4 5 6 00					
Net Increase during 20--		58 3 4 0 79				
Balance, December 31, 20--			98 4 8 4 76			
Total Stockholders' Equity, Dec. 31, 20--			242 7 6 1 76			

[6a]

Equity per share:

Equity	÷	Shares Outstanding	=	Equity per Share
$242,761.76	÷	10,698	=	$22.69

[6b]

Price-earnings ratio:

Market Price	÷	Earnings per Share	=	Price–Earnings Ratio
$31.75	÷	$6.15	=	5.2 times

Name _____ Date _____ Class _____

Provident Electronics

Balance Sheet

December 31, 20--

ASSETS					
Current Assets:					
Cash			21 2 8 0 12		
Petty Cash			2 5 0 00		
Notes Receivable			10 7 3 1 00		
Interest Receivable			1 3 8 09		
Accounts Receivable	38 0 2 9 43				
Less Allow. for Uncollectible Accounts	1 1 7 7 47		36 8 5 1 96		
Merchandise Inventory			43 9 3 5 05		
Supplies—Sales			4 4 1 0 52		
Supplies—Administrative			1 7 1 0 09		
Prepaid Insurance			2 2 2 4 93		
Total Current Assets				121 5 3 1 76	
Plant Assets:					
Store Equipment	42 9 7 4 58				
Less Accum. Depr.—Store Equip.	9 9 8 5 00		32 9 8 9 58		
Office Equipment	52 1 4 2 94				
Less Accum. Depr.—Office Equipment	2 6 9 6 72		49 4 4 6 22		
Building	24 0 0 0 00				
Less Accum. Depr.—Building	3 9 2 1 00		20 0 7 9 00		
Land			41 0 0 0 00		
Total Plant Assets				143 5 1 4 80	
Total Assets				265 0 4 6 56	

13-2 WORK TOGETHER (continued)

Provident Electronics

Balance Sheet (continued)

December 31, 20--

LIABILITIES																		
Current Liabilities:																		
Notes Payable						1	5	2	0	00								
Interest Payable							1	5	2	00								
Accounts Payable						5	2	3	4	27								
Employee Income Tax Payable							2	0	8	00								
Federal Income Tax Payable						6	0	9	2	29								
Social Security Tax Payable							1	5	8	10								
Medicare Tax Payable								4	0	29								
Salaries Payable							6	7	4	34								
Sales Tax Payable							3	1	4	50								
Unemploy. Tax Payable—Federal								2	0	35								
Unemploy. Tax Payable—State							3	3	4	72								
Health Insurance Premiums Payable								7	3	06								
Dividends Payable						7	4	6	2	88								
Total Liabilities												22	2	8	4	80		
STOCKHOLDERS' EQUITY																		
Total Stockholders' Equity												242	7	6	1	76		
Total Liabilities & Stockholders' Equity												265	0	4	6	56		

13-2 WORK TOGETHER (concluded)

[7a]

Accounts receivable turnover ratio:

(January 1 Book Value	+	December 31 Book Value)	÷	2	=	Average
($42,684.28	+	$36,851.96)	÷	2	=	$39,768.12

Net Sales on Account	÷	Average Book Value	=	Ratio
$238,698.00	÷	$39,768.12	=	6.0 times

[7b]

Rate earned on average stockholders' equity:

(January 1 Equity	+	December 31 Equity)	÷	2	=	Average
($171,613.97	+	$242,761.76)	÷	2	=	$207,187.87

Net Income	÷	Average Equity	=	Rate
$65,796.79	÷	$207,187.87	=	31.8%

[7c]

Rate earned on average total assets:

(January 1 Assets	+	December 31 Assets)	÷	2	=	Average
($249,980.25	+	$265,046.56)	÷	2	=	$257,513.41

(Net Income	÷	Average Assets)	=	Rate
($65,796.79	÷	$257,513.41)	=	25.6%

13-2 ON YOUR OWN, p. 362

Analyzing financial statements [8]

The work sheet prepared in On Your Own 13-1 is needed to complete this problem.

BRE Corporation

Income Statement

For Year Ended December 31, 20--

						% OF NET SALES
Operating Revenue:						
Sales				596 7 4 5 00		
Less: Sales Discount			5 8 8 00			
Sales Ret. & Allow.			9 1 5 38	1 5 0 3 38		
Net Sales					595 2 4 1 62	100.0
Cost of Merchandise Sold:						
Mdse. Inventory, January 1, 20--				88 1 4 4 40		
Purchases		294 6 6 5 98				
Less: Purchases Discount	2 6 4 6 30					
Purch. Ret. & Allow.	9 4 5 28	3 5 9 1 58				
Net Purchases				291 0 7 4 40		
Total Cost of Mdse. Avail for Sale				379 2 1 8 80		
Less Mdse. Inventory, Dec. 31, 20--				88 0 0 7 25		
Cost of Merchandise Sold					291 2 1 1 55	48.9
Gross Profit on Operations					304 0 3 0 07	51.1
Operating Expenses:						
Selling Expenses:						
Advertising Expense		5 1 8 0 90				
Credit Card Fee Expense		4 4 8 2 06				
Depr. Expense—Store Equip.		4 8 2 1 00				
Miscellaneous Expense—Sales		6 8 5 2 00				
Salary Expense—Sales		34 8 1 8 94				
Supplies Expense—Sales		3 6 3 3 76				
Total Selling Expenses				59 7 8 8 66		10.0
Administrative Expenses:						
Depr. Expense—Office Equip.		7 9 0 6 04				
Depr. Expense—Building		3 7 0 7 00				
Insurance Expense		1 2 0 5 44				
Miscellaneous Expense—Admin.		6 4 8 8 24				
Payroll Taxes Expense		4 5 3 2 22				

13-2 ON YOUR OWN (continued)

[8]

BRE Corporation
Income Statement (continued)
For Year Ended December 31, 20--

							% OF NET SALES
Property Tax Expense			2 2 0 0 00				
Salary Expense—Admin.			9 0 1 8 00				
Supplies Expense—Admin.			3 4 3 1 21				
Uncoll. Accounts Expense			1 0 6 7 22				
Utilities Expense			18 4 7 8 92				
Total Admin. Expense				58 0 3 4 29			9.7
Total Operating Expenses						117 8 2 2 95	19.8
Income from Operations						186 2 0 7 12	31.3
Other Revenue:							
Interest Income				1 3 8 09			
Other Expenses:							
Interest Expense				4 5 6 2 00			
Net Deduction						4 4 2 3 91	0.7
Net Income before Fed. Income Tax						181 7 8 3 21	30.5
Less Federal Income Tax Expense						54 1 4 5 45	9.1
Net Income after Fed. Income Tax						127 6 3 7 76	21.4

[9]

Earnings per share:

Net Income	÷	Shares Outstanding	=	Earnings per Share
$127,637.76	÷	25,675	=	$4.97

13-2 ON YOUR OWN (continued)

BRE Corporation

Statement of Stockholders' Equity

For Year Ended December 31, 20--

Paid-in Capital:				
Capital Stock, $10.00 Stated Value:				
January 1, 20--, 20,000 Shares Issued	200 0 0 0 00			
Issued during Current Year, 5,675 Shares	56 7 5 0 00			
Balance, Dec. 31, 20--, 25,675 Shares Issued		256 7 5 0 00		
Total Value of Capital Stock Issued			256 7 5 0 00	
Additional Paid-in Capital:				
Pd.-in-Cap. in Exc. of St. Value			31 8 0 4 00	
Total Paid-in Capital			288 5 5 4 00	
Retained Earnings:				
Balance, January 1, 20--		100 2 8 7 94		
Net Income after Federal Income Tax for 20--	127 6 3 7 76			
Less Dividends Declared during 20--	14 9 1 2 00			
Net Increase during 20--		112 7 2 5 76		
Balance, December 31, 20--			213 0 1 3 70	
Total Stockholders' Equity, Dec. 31, 20--			501 5 6 7 70	

[10a]

Equity per share:

Equity	÷	Shares Outstanding	=	Equity per Share
$501,567.70	÷	25,675	=	$19.54

[10b]

Price-earnings ratio:

Market Price	÷	Earnings per Share	=	Price–Earnings Ratio
$48.25	÷	$4.97	=	9.7 times

13-2 ON YOUR OWN (continued)

BRE Corporation

Balance Sheet

December 31, 20--

ASSETS													
Current Assets:													
Cash						42	5	6	0	24			
Petty Cash							5	0	0	00			
Notes Receivable						21	4	6	2	00			
Interest Receivable							1	3	8	09			
Accounts Receivable	76	0	5	8	86								
Less Allow. for Uncoll. Accounts	1	2	8	7	72	74	7	7	1	14			
Merchandise Inventory						88	0	0	7	25			
Supplies—Sales						12	4	5	4	80			
Supplies—Administrative						6	8	5	1	39			
Prepaid Insurance						5	6	5	5	30			
Total Current Assets											252	4	0	0	21
Plant Assets:													
Store Equipment	85	9	4	9	16								
Less Accum. Depr.—Store Equip.	15	1	4	9	00	70	8	0	0	16			
Office Equipment	104	2	8	5	88								
Less Accum. Depr.—Office Equipment	3	8	0	1	20	100	4	8	4	68			
Building	48	0	0	0	00								
Less Accum. Depr.—Building	6	5	3	5	00	41	4	6	5	00			
Land						82	0	0	0	00			
Total Plant Assets											294	7	4	9	84
Total Assets											547	1	5	0	05

13-2 ON YOUR OWN (continued)

BRE Corporation

Balance Sheet (continued)

December 31, 20--

LIABILITIES																		
Current Liabilities:																		
Notes Payable							3	0	4	0	00							
Interest Payable								1	5	2	00							
Accounts Payable							10	4	6	8	54							
Employee Income Tax Payable								4	1	6	00							
Federal Income Tax Payable							14	1	4	5	45							
Social Security Tax Payable								2	5	8	75							
Medicare Tax Payable									6	7	16							
Salaries Payable								6	7	4	34							
Sales Tax Payable								6	2	9	00							
Unemploy. Tax Payable—Federal									3	8	69							
Unemploy. Tax Payable—State								6	2	0	54							
Health Insurance Premiums Payable								1	4	6	12							
Dividends Payable							14	9	2	5	76							
Total Liabilities													45	5	8	2	35	
STOCKHOLDERS' EQUITY																		
Total Stockholders' Equity													501	5	6	7	70	
Total Liabilities & Stockholders' Equity													547	1	5	0	05	

13-2 ON YOUR OWN (concluded)

[11a]

Accounts receivable turnover ratio:

(January 1 Book Value	+	December 31 Book Value)	÷	2	=	Average
($69,250.50	+	$74,771.14)	÷	2	=	$72,010.82

Net Sales on Account	÷	Average Book Value	=	Ratio
$505,955.30	÷	$72,010.82	=	7.0 times

[11b]

Rate earned on average stockholders' equity:

(January 1 Equity	+	December 31 Equity)	÷	2	=	Average
($300,287.94	+	$501,567.70)	÷	2	=	$400,927.82

Net Income	÷	Average Equity	=	Rate
$127,637.76	÷	$400,927.82	=	31.8%

[11c]

Rate earned on average total assets:

(January 1 Assets	+	December 31 Assets)	÷	2	=	Average
($538,140.20	+	$547,150.05)	÷	2	=	$542,645.13

Net Income	÷	Average Assets	=	Rate
$127,637.76	÷	$542,645.13	=	23.5%

13-3 WORK TOGETHER, p. 369

End-of-fiscal period work for a corporation   **[4]**

The work sheet from Work Together 13-1 is needed to complete this problem.

GENERAL JOURNAL   PAGE 14

	DATE		ACCOUNT TITLE	DOC. NO.	POST. REF.	DEBIT	CREDIT	
1			*Adjusting Entries*					1
2	20-- Dec.	31	*Interest Receivable*			1 3 8 09		2
3			*Interest Income*				1 3 8 09	3
4		31	*Uncollectible Accounts Expense*			1 0 6 7 22		4
5			*Allowance for Uncollectible Accts.*				1 0 6 7 22	5
6		31	*Income Summary*			1 3 7 15		6
7			*Merchandise Inventory*				1 3 7 15	7
8		31	*Supplies Expense—Sales*			3 6 3 3 76		8
9			*Supplies—Sales*				3 6 3 3 76	9
10		31	*Supplies Expense—Administrative*			3 4 3 1 21		10
11			*Supplies—Administrative*				3 4 3 1 21	11
12		31	*Insurance Expense*			1 2 0 5 44		12
13			*Prepaid Insurance*				1 2 0 5 44	13
14		31	*Depr. Expense—Store Equip.*			4 8 2 1 00		14
15			*Accum. Depr.—Store Equip.*				4 8 2 1 00	15
16		31	*Depr. Expense—Office Equip.*			1 5 9 2 24		16
17			*Accum. Depr.—Office Equip.*				1 5 9 2 24	17
18		31	*Depr. Expense—Building*			1 3 0 7 00		18
19			*Accum. Depr.—Building*				1 3 0 7 00	19
20		31	*Interest Expense*			1 5 2 00		20
21			*Interest Payable*				1 5 2 00	21
22		31	*Payroll Taxes Expense*			1 2 1 78		22
23			*Social Security Tax Payable*				5 7 45	23
24			*Medicare Tax Payable*				1 3 42	24
25			*Unemploy. Tax Payable—Federal*				2 01	25
26			*Unemploy. Tax Payable—State*				4 8 90	26
27		31	*Salary Expense—Sales*			6 7 4 34		27
28			*Salaries Payable*				6 7 4 34	28
29		31	*Federal Income Tax Expense*			6 0 9 2 29		29
30			*Federal Income Tax Payable*				6 0 9 2 29	30
31								31

13-3 WORK TOGETHER (continued)

[5]

GENERAL JOURNAL   PAGE 15

	DATE		ACCOUNT TITLE	DOC. NO.	POST. REF.	DEBIT	CREDIT	
1			*Closing Entries*					1
2	20-- Dec.	31	*Sales*			298 372 50		2
3			*Purchases Discount*			1 323 15		3
4			*Purchases Returns and Allowances*			472 64		4
5			*Interest Income*			138 09		5
6			*Income Summary*				300 306 38	6
7		31	*Income Summary*			234 372 44		7
8			*Sales Discount*				2 940 00	8
9			*Sales Returns and Allowances*				457 69	9
10			*Purchases*				147 332 99	10
11			*Advertising Expense*				2 590 45	11
12			*Credit Card Fee Expense*				2 241 03	12
13			*Depr. Expense—Store Equip.*				4 821 00	13
14			*Miscellaneous Expense—Sales*				3 426 00	14
15			*Salary Expense—Sales*				17 746 64	15
16			*Supplies Expense—Sales*				3 633 76	16
17			*Depr. Expense—Office Equip.*				4 749 14	17
18			*Depr. Expense—Building*				2 507 00	18
19			*Insurance Expense*				1 205 44	19
20			*Miscellaneous Exp.—Admin.*				3 244 12	20
21			*Payroll Taxes Expense*				2 327 00	21
22			*Property Tax Expense*				1 100 00	22
23			*Salary Expense—Admin.*				4 509 00	23
24			*Supplies Expense—Admin.*				3 431 21	24
25			*Uncollectible Accts. Exp.*				1 067 22	25
26			*Utilities Expense*				9 239 46	26
27			*Interest Expense*				2 357 00	27
28			*Federal Income Tax Expense*				16 092 29	28
29		31	*Income Summary*			65 796 79		29
30			*Retained Earnings*				65 796 79	30
31		31	*Retained Earnings*			7 456 00		31
32			*Dividends*				7 456 00	32

13-3 WORK TOGETHER (continued)

[6]

Provident Electronics

Post-Closing Trial Balance

December 31, 20--

ACCOUNT TITLE	DEBIT	CREDIT
Cash	21 2 8 0 12	
Petty Cash	2 5 0 00	
Notes Receivable	10 7 3 1 00	
Interest Receivable	1 3 8 09	
Accounts Receivable	38 0 2 9 43	
Allowance for Uncollectible Accounts		1 1 7 7 47
Merchandise Inventory	43 9 3 5 05	
Supplies—Sales	4 4 1 0 52	
Supplies—Administrative	1 7 1 0 09	
Prepaid Insurance	2 2 2 4 93	
Store Equipment	42 9 7 4 58	
Accum. Depr.—Store Equipment		9 9 8 5 00
Office Equipment	52 1 4 2 94	
Accum. Depr.—Office Equipment		2 6 9 6 72
Building	24 0 0 0 00	
Accum. Depr.—Building		3 9 2 1 00
Land	41 0 0 0 00	
Notes Payable		1 5 2 0 00
Interest Payable		1 5 2 00
Accounts Payable		5 2 3 4 27
Employee Income Tax Payable		2 0 8 00
Federal Income Tax Payable		6 0 9 2 29
Social Security Tax Payable		1 5 8 10
Medicare Tax Payable		4 0 29
Salaries Payable		6 7 4 34
Sales Tax Payable		3 1 4 50
Unemploy. Tax Payable—Federal		2 0 35
Unemploy. Tax Payable—State		3 3 4 72
Health Inc. Premiums Payable		7 3 06
Dividends Payable		7 4 6 2 88
Capital Stock		128 3 7 6 00
Paid-in Capital in Excess of Stated Value		15 9 0 1 00
Retained Earnings		98 4 8 4 76
Totals	282 8 2 6 75	282 8 2 6 75

13-3 WORK TOGETHER (concluded)

[7]

GENERAL JOURNAL   PAGE 16

	DATE		ACCOUNT TITLE	DOC. NO.	POST. REF.	DEBIT	CREDIT	
1			*Reversing Entries*					1
2	20-- Jan.	1	Interest Income			1 3 8 09		2
3			Interest Receivable				1 3 8 09	3
4		1	Interest Payable			1 5 2 00		4
5			Interest Expense				1 5 2 00	5
6		1	Social Security Tax Payable			5 7 45		6
7			Medicare Tax Payable			1 3 42		7
8			Unemploy. Tax Payable—Federal			2 01		8
9			Unemploy. Tax Payable—State			4 8 90		9
10			Payroll Taxes Expense				1 2 1 78	10
11		1	Salaries Payable			6 7 4 34		11
12			Salary Expense—Sales				6 7 4 34	12
13								13
14								14
15								15
16								16
17								17
18								18
19								19
20								20
21								21
22								22
23								23
24								24
25								25
26								26
27								27
28								28
29								29
30								30
31								31

Name _____ Date _____ Class _____

13-3 ON YOUR OWN, p. 369

End-of-fiscal period work for a corporation   **[8]**

The work sheet from On Your Own 13-1 is needed to complete this problem.

GENERAL JOURNAL   PAGE 14

	DATE		ACCOUNT TITLE	DOC. NO.	POST. REF.	DEBIT	CREDIT	
1			*Adjusting Entries*					1
2	20-- Dec.	31	Interest Receivable			1 3 8 09		2
3			Interest Income				1 3 8 09	3
4		31	Uncollectible Accounts Expense			1 0 6 7 22		4
5			Allowance for Uncollectible Accts.				1 0 6 7 22	5
6		31	Income Summary			1 3 7 15		6
7			Merchandise Inventory				1 3 7 15	7
8		31	Supplies Expense—Sales			3 6 3 3 76		8
9			Supplies—Sales				3 6 3 3 76	9
10		31	Supplies Expense—Administrative			3 4 3 1 21		10
11			Supplies—Administrative				3 4 3 1 21	11
12		31	Insurance Expense			1 2 0 5 44		12
13			Prepaid Insurance				1 2 0 5 44	13
14		31	Depr. Expense—Store Equip.			4 8 2 1 00		14
15			Accum. Depr.—Store Equip.				4 8 2 1 00	15
16		31	Depr. Expense—Office Equip.			1 5 9 2 24		16
17			Accum. Depr.—Office Equip.				1 5 9 2 24	17
18		31	Depr. Expense—Building			1 3 0 7 00		18
19			Accum. Depr.—Building				1 3 0 7 00	19
20		31	Interest Expense			1 5 2 00		20
21			Interest Payable				1 5 2 00	21
22		31	Payroll Taxes Expense			1 2 1 78		22
23			Social Security Tax payable				5 7 45	23
24			Medicare Tax Payable				1 3 42	24
25			Unemploy. Tax Payable—Federal				2 01	25
26			Unemploy. Tax Payable—State				4 8 90	26
27		31	Salary Expense—Sales			6 7 4 34		27
28			Salaries Payable				6 7 4 34	28
29		31	Federal Income Tax Expense			14 1 4 5 45		29
30			Federal Income Tax Payable				14 1 4 5 45	30

13-3 ON YOUR OWN (continued)

[9]

GENERAL JOURNAL   PAGE 15

	DATE		ACCOUNT TITLE	DOC. NO.	POST. REF.	DEBIT	CREDIT	
1			*Closing Entries*					1
2	20-- Dec.	31	Sales			5967 45 00		2
3			Purchases Discount			2646 30		3
4			Purchases Returns and Allowances			945 28		4
5			Interest Income			138 09		5
6			Income Summary				60047 46 67	6
7		31	Income Summary			47269 99 76		7
8			Sales Discount				588 00	8
9			Sales Returns and Allowances				915 38	9
10			Purchases				29466 59 98	10
11			Advertising Expense				5180 90	11
12			Credit Card Fee Expense				4482 06	12
13			Depr. Exp.—Store Equip.				4821 00	13
14			Miscellaneous Expense—Sales				6852 00	14
15			Salary Expense—Sales				34818 94	15
16			Supplies Expense—Sales				3633 76	16
17			Depr. Expense—Office Equip.				7906 04	17
18			Depr. Expense—Building				3707 00	18
19			Insurance Expense				1205 44	19
20			Miscellaneous Exp.—Admin.				6488 24	20
21			Payroll Taxes Expense				4532 22	21
22			Property Tax Expense				2200 00	22
23			Salary Expense—Admin.				9018 00	23
24			Supplies Expense—Admin.				3431 21	24
25			Uncollectible Accts. Expense				1067 22	25
26			Utilities Expense				18478 92	26
27			Interest Expense				4562 00	27
28			Federal Income Tax Expense				54145 45	28
29		31	Income Summary			12763 77 6		29
30			Retained Earnings				12763 77 6	30
31		31	Retained Earnings			14912 00		31
32			Dividends				14912 00	32

13-3 ON YOUR OWN (continued)

[10]

BRE Corporation

Post-Closing Trial Balance

December 31, 20--

ACCOUNT TITLE	DEBIT	CREDIT
Cash	42 5 6 0 24	
Petty Cash	5 0 0 00	
Notes Receivable	21 4 6 2 00	
Interest Receivable	1 3 8 09	
Accounts Receivable	76 0 5 8 86	
Allowance for Uncollectible Accts.		1 2 8 7 72
Merchandise Inventory	88 0 0 7 25	
Supplies—Sales	12 4 5 4 80	
Supplies—Administrative	6 8 5 1 39	
Prepaid Insurance	5 6 5 5 30	
Store Equipment	85 9 4 9 16	
Accum. Depr.—Store Equipment		15 1 4 9 00
Office Equipment	104 2 8 5 88	
Accum. Depr.—Office Equipment		3 8 0 1 20
Building	48 0 0 0 00	
Accum. Depr.—Building		6 5 3 5 00
Land	82 0 0 0 00	
Notes Payable		3 0 4 0 00
Interest Payable		1 5 2 00
Accounts Payable		10 4 6 8 54
Employee Income Tax Payable		4 1 6 00
Federal Income Tax Payable		14 1 4 5 45
Social Security Tax Payable		2 5 8 75
Medicare Tax Payable		6 7 16
Salaries Payable		6 7 4 34
Sales Tax Payable		6 2 9 00
Unemploy. Tax Payable—Federal		3 8 69
Unemploy. Tax Payable—State		6 2 0 54
Health Inc. Premiums Payable		1 4 6 12
Dividends Payable		14 9 2 5 76
Capital Stock		256 7 5 0 00
Paid-in Capital in Excess of Stated Value		31 8 0 4 00
Retained Earnings		213 0 1 3 70
Total	573 9 2 2 97	573 9 2 2 97

13-3 ON YOUR OWN (concluded)

[11]

GENERAL JOURNAL   PAGE 16

	DATE		ACCOUNT TITLE	DOC. NO.	POST. REF.	DEBIT	CREDIT	
1			*Reversing Entries*					1
2	20-- Jan.	1	Interest Income			1 3 8 09		2
3			Interest Receivable				1 3 8 09	3
4		1	Interest Payable			1 5 2 00		4
5			Interest Expense				1 5 2 00	5
6		1	Social Security Tax Payable			5 7 45		6
7			Medicare Tax Payable			1 3 42		7
8			Unemploy. Tax Payable—Federal			2 01		8
9			Unemploy. Tax Payable—State			4 8 90		9
10			Payroll Taxes Expense				1 2 1 78	10
11		1	Salaries Payable			6 7 4 34		11
12			Salary Expense—Sales				6 7 4 34	12
13								13
14								14
15								15
16								16
17								17
18								18
19								19
20								20
21								21
22								22
23								23
24								24
25								25
26								26
27								27
28								28
29								29
30								30
31								31

13-1 APPLICATION PROBLEM, p. 371
The work sheet for this problem begins on page 70.

Preparing a work sheet for a corporation

	TRIAL BALANCE		ADJUSTMENTS		INCOME STATEMENT		BALANCE SHEET	
ACCOUNT TITLE	DEBIT	CREDIT	DEBIT	CREDIT	DEBIT	CREDIT	DEBIT	CREDIT
59 Depr. Expense—Office Equip.			(j) 301864		301864			
60 Insurance Expense			(f) 263304		263304			
61 Miscellaneous Expense—Admin.	326803				326803			
62 Payroll Taxes Expense	238186		(n) 7313		245499			
63 Property Tax Expense	230000				230000			
64 Salary Expense—Admin.	539533		(m) 59349		598882			
65 Supplies Expense—Admin.			(e) 406552		406552			
66 Uncollectible Accounts Expense			(b) 126405		126405			
67 Utilities Expense	551866				551866			
68 Interest Income		12333	(a) 16017			28350		
69 Interest Expense	262059		(l) 400257	(g) 185	662131			
70 Organization Expense			(k) 5000		5000			
71 Federal Income Tax Expense	550000		(o) 50150		600150			
72	44662426	44662426	2256786	2256786	16279923	19680774	29778712	26377861
73 Net Income after Federal Income Tax					3400851			3400851
74					19680774	19680774	29778712	29778712
75								
76								
77								
78								
79								
80								
81								
82								
83								
84								
85								
86								

13-1 APPLICATION PROBLEM (continued)

The work sheet prepared in Application Problem 13-1 is needed to complete Application Problems 13-3 and 13-4.

Trexler, Inc.
Work Sheet
For Year Ended December 31, 20--

#	ACCOUNT TITLE	TRIAL BALANCE DEBIT	TRIAL BALANCE CREDIT	ADJUSTMENTS DEBIT	ADJUSTMENTS CREDIT	INCOME STATEMENT DEBIT	INCOME STATEMENT CREDIT	BALANCE SHEET DEBIT	BALANCE SHEET CREDIT
1	Cash	42789960						42789960	
2	Petty Cash	50000						50000	
3	Notes Receivable	1892491						1892491	
4	Interest Receivable			(a) 16017				16017	
5	Accounts Receivable	3083048						3083048	
6	Allowance for Uncollectible Accts.		9249		(b) 126405				135654
7	Merchandise Inventory	5161022			(c) 15999			5145023	
8	Supplies—Sales	289807			(d) 169537			120270	
9	Supplies—Administrative	502537			(e) 406552			95985	
10	Prepaid Insurance	406962			(f) 263304			143658	
11	Prepaid Interest			(g) 185				185	
12	Bond Sinking Fund	400000						400000	
13	Store Equipment	1362707						1362707	
14	Accum. Depr.—Store Equip.		130820		(h) 129457				260277
15	Building	5800000						5800000	
16	Accum. Depr.—Building		321900		(i) 290000				611900
17	Office Equipment	3049134						3049134	
18	Accum. Depr.—Office Equip.		307963		(j) 301864				609827
19	Land	3148884						3148884	
20	Organization Costs	200000			(k) 5000			150000	
21	Notes Payable		30830						30830
22	Interest Payable				(l) 400257				400257
23	Accounts Payable		194276						194276
24	Employee Income Tax Payable		24664						24664
25	Federal Income Tax Payable				(o) 50150				50150
26	Social Security Tax Payable		12090		(n) 4859				16949
27	Medicare Tax Payable		2790		(n) 1121				3911
28	Salaries Payable				(m) 74746				74746

APPLICATION PROBLEM (continued)

#	ACCOUNT TITLE	TRIAL BALANCE DEBIT	TRIAL BALANCE CREDIT	ADJUSTMENTS DEBIT	ADJUSTMENTS CREDIT	INCOME STATEMENT DEBIT	INCOME STATEMENT CREDIT	BALANCE SHEET DEBIT	BALANCE SHEET CREDIT
29	Sales Tax Payable		43163						43163
30	Unemploy. Tax Payable—Federal		4921		(n) 172				5093
31	Unemploy. Tax Payable—State		33278		(n) 1161				34439
32	Health Insur. Prem. Payable		9249						9249
33	Dividends Payable		907350						907350
34	Bonds Payable		4000000						4000000
35	Capital Stock—Common		10900000						10900000
36	Pd.-in Cap. in Exc. St. Val.—Common		2400000						2400000
37	Capital Stock—Preferred		4200000						4200000
38	Pd.-in.Cap. in Exc. Par—Preferred		110000						110000
39	Disc. on Sale of Preferred Stock	200000						200000	
40	Treasury Stock	70000						70000	
41	Pd.-in Cap. from Sale of Tr. Stock		14000						14000
42	Retained Earnings		1341126						1341126
43	Dividends—Common	487350						487350	
44	Dividends—Preferred	420000						420000	
45	Income Summary			(c) 15999		15999			
46	Sales		19440119				19440119		
47	Sales Discount	38880				38880			
48	Sales Returns & Allowances	58320				58320			
49	Purchases	9230646				9230646			
50	Purchases Discount		156921				156921		
51	Purchases Returns & Allowances		55384				55384		
52	Advertising Expense	234312				234312			
53	Credit Card Fee Expense	265142				265142			
54	Depr. Expense—Store Equip.			(h) 129457		129457			
55	Miscellaneous Expense—Sales	114073				114073			
56	Salary Expense—Sales	1399704		(m) 15397		1415101			
57	Supplies Expense—Sales			(d) 169537		169537			
58	Depr. Expense—Building			(i) 290000		290000			

13-1 APPLICATION PROBLEM (concluded)

Extra form

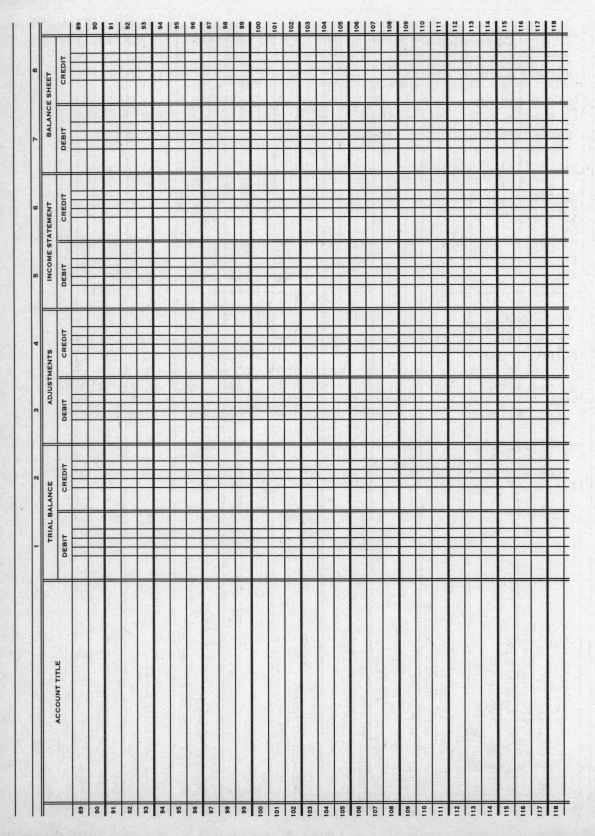

13-2 APPLICATION PROBLEM, p. 371

Calculating federal income taxes

Corporation A	Net Income Before Taxes	Tax Rate	Federal Income Tax Amount
15% of the first $50,000	$50,000.00	15%	$ 7,500.00
25% of the next $25,000	23,932.56	25%	5,983.14
34% of the next $25,000	0.00	34%	0.00
39% of the next $235,000	0.00	39%	0.00
34% of the net income about $335,000	0.00	34%	0.00
Totals	$73,932.56		$13,483.14

Corporation B	Net Income Before Taxes	Tax Rate	Federal Income Tax Amount
15% of the first $50,000	$50,000.00	15%	$ 7,500.00
25% of the next $25,000	25,000.00	25%	6,250.00
34% of the next $25,000	25,000.00	34%	8,500.00
39% of the next $235,000	235,000.00	39%	91,650.00
34% of the net income about $335,000	132,032.45	34%	44,891.03
Totals	$467,032.45		$158,791.03

Corporation C	Net Income Before Taxes	Tax Rate	Federal Income Tax Amount
15% of the first $50,000	$38,296.44	15%	$5,744.47
25% of the next $25,000	0.00	25%	0.00
34% of the next $25,000	0.00	34%	0.00
39% of the next $235,000	0.00	39%	0.00
34% of the net income about $335,000	0.00	34%	0.00
Totals	$38,296.44		$5,744.47

13-2 APPLICATION PROBLEM

Extra forms

	Net Income Before Taxes	Tax Rate	Federal Income Tax Amount
15% of the first $50,000			
25% of the next $25,000			
34% of the next $25,000			
39% of the next $235,000			
34% of the net income about $335,000			
Totals			

	Net Income Before Taxes	Tax Rate	Federal Income Tax Amount
15% of the first $50,000			
25% of the next $25,000			
34% of the next $25,000			
39% of the next $235,000			
34% of the net income about $335,000			
Totals			

	Net Income Before Taxes	Tax Rate	Federal Income Tax Amount
15% of the first $50,000			
25% of the next $25,000			
34% of the next $25,000			
39% of the next $235,000			
34% of the net income about $335,000			
Totals			

13-3 APPLICATION PROBLEM, p. 371

Preparing financial statements for a corporation   [1]

The work sheet prepared in Application Problem 13-1 is needed to complete this problem.

Trexler, Inc.

Income Statement

For Year Ended December 31, 20--

					% OF NET SALES
Operating Revenue:					
Sales			194 4 0 1 19		
Less: Sales Discount		3 8 8 80			
Sales Ret. & Allow.		5 8 3 20	9 7 2 00		
Net Sales				193 4 2 9 19	100.0
Cost of Merchandise Sold:					
Mdse. Inventory, January 1, 20--			51 6 1 0 22		
Purchases		92 3 0 6 46			
Less: Purchases Discount	1 5 6 9 21				
Purch. Ret. & Allow.	5 5 3 84	2 1 2 3 05			
Net Purchases			90 1 8 3 41		
Total Cost of Mdse. Avail. for Sale			141 7 9 3 63		
Less Mdse. Inventory, Dec. 31, 20--			51 4 5 0 23		
Cost of Merchandise Sold				90 3 4 3 40	46.7
Gross Profit on Operations				103 0 8 5 79	53.3
Operating Expenses:					
Selling Expenses:					
Advertising Expense		2 3 4 3 12			
Credit Card Fee Expense		2 6 5 1 42			
Depr. Expense—Store Equip.		1 2 9 4 57			
Miscellaneous Expense—Sales		1 1 4 0 73			
Salary Expense—Sales		14 1 5 1 01			
Supplies Expense—Sales		1 6 9 5 37			
Total Selling Expenses			23 2 7 6 22		12.0
Administrative Expenses:					
Depr. Expense—Building		2 9 0 0 00			
Depr. Expense—Office Equip.		3 0 1 8 64			
Insurance Expense		2 6 3 3 04			
Miscellaneous Expense—Admin.		3 2 6 8 03			
Payroll Taxes Expense		2 4 5 4 99			

13-3 APPLICATION PROBLEM (continued)

[1]

Trexler, Inc.

Income Statement (continued)

For Year Ended December 31, 20--

			% OF NET SALES
Property Tax Expense	2 3 0 0 00		
Salary Expense—Admin.	5 9 8 8 82		
Supplies Expense—Admin.	4 0 6 5 52		
Uncoll. Accounts Expense	1 2 6 4 05		
Utilities Expense	5 5 1 8 66		
Total Admin. Expense		33 4 1 1 75	17.3
Total Operating Expenses		56 6 8 7 97	29.3
Income from Operations		46 3 9 7 82	24.0
Other Revenue:			
Interest Income		2 8 3 50	
Other Expenses:			
Interest Expense	6 6 2 1 31		
Organization Expense	5 0 00		
Total Other Expenses		6 6 7 1 31	
Net Deduction		6 3 8 7 81	3.3
Net Income before Fed. Income Tax		40 0 1 0 01	20.7
Less Federal Income Tax Expense		6 0 0 1 50	3.1
Net Income after Fed. Income Tax		34 0 0 8 51	17.6

[4]

Earnings per share:

Stock	Share of Net Income	÷	Shares Outstanding	=	Earnings per Share
Preferred	$ 4,200.00	÷	420	=	$10.00
Common	$29,808.51	÷	10,830	=	$ 2.75

13-3 APPLICATION PROBLEM (continued)

Income statement analysis   [2, 3]

		Acceptable %	Actual %	Positive Result		Recommended Action If Needed
				Yes	No	
a.	Cost of merchandise sold	Not more than 40.0%	46.7%		✓	*Increase selling prices and/or analyze purchases and inventory controls and correct any negative situations.*
b.	Gross profit on operations	Not less than 60.0%	53.3%		✓	*Correcting cost of merchandise sold will correct gross profit.*
c.	Total selling expenses	Not more than 13.5%	12.0%	✓		*None*
d.	Total administrative expenses	Not more than 18.5%	17.3%	✓		*None*
e.	Total operating expenses	Not more than 32.0%	29.3%	✓		*None*
f.	Income from operations	Not less than 28.0%	24.0%		✓	*Correcting cost of merchandise sold will correct income from operations.*
g.	Net deduction from other revenue and expenses	Not more than 4.0%	3.3%	✓		*None*
h.	Net income before federal income tax	Not less than 24.0%	20.7%		✓	*Correcting cost of merchandise sold will correct net income.*

13-3 APPLICATION PROBLEM (continued)

[5]

Trexler, Inc.

Statement of Stockholders' Equity

For Year Ended December 31, 20--

Paid-in Capital:			
Common Stock, *$10.00* Stated Value:			
January 1, 20--, *8,000* Shares Issued	80 0 0 0 00		
Issued during Current Year, *2,900* Shares	29 0 0 0 00		
Balance, Dec. 31, 20--, *10,900* Shares Issued		109 0 0 0 00	
Preferred Stock, *10.0%, $100.00* Par Value:			
January 1, 20--, *150* Shares Issued	15 0 0 0 00		
Issued during Current Year, *270* Shares	27 0 0 0 00		
Balance, Dec. 31, 20--, *420* Shares Issued		42 0 0 0 00	
Total Value of Capital Stock Issued			151 0 0 0 00
Additional Paid-in Capital:			
Pd.-in-Cap. in Exc. of St. Value—Common	24 0 0 0 00		
Pd.-in-Cap. in Exc. of Par—Preferred	1 1 0 0 00		
Pd.-in-Cap. from Sale of Treasury Stock	1 4 0 00	25 2 4 0 00	
Less Disc. on Sale of Preferred Stock		2 0 0 0 00	
Total Additional Paid-in Capital			23 2 4 0 00
Total Paid-in Capital			174 2 4 0 00
Retained Earnings:			
Balance, January 1, 20--		13 4 1 1 26	
Net Income after Federal Income Tax for 20--	34 0 0 8 51		
Less Dividends Declared during 20--	9 0 7 3 50		
Net Increase during 20--		24 9 3 5 01	
Balance, December 31, 20--			38 3 4 6 27
Total Pd.-in Capital & Retained Earnings			212 5 8 6 27
Less Treasury Stock, *70* Shares of			
Common Stock, December 31, 20--			7 0 0 00
Total Stockholders' Equity, Dec. 31, 20--			211 8 8 6 27

13-3 APPLICATION PROBLEM (continued)

[6a]

Equity per share:

Stock	Equity	÷	Shares Outstanding	=	Earnings per Share
Preferred	$ 42,000.00	÷	420	=	$100.00
Common	$169,886.27	÷	10,830	=	$ 15.69

[6b]

Price-earnings ratio:

Stock	Market Price	÷	Earnings per Share	=	Price-earnings Ratio
Common	$24.00	÷	$2.75	=	8.7 times

[7]

Trexler, Inc.

Balance Sheet

December 31, 20--

ASSETS					
Current Assets:					
Cash			42 7 8 9 60		
Petty Cash			5 0 0 00		
Notes Receivable			18 9 2 4 91		
Interest Receivable			1 6 0 17		
Accounts Receivable	30 8 3 0 48				
Less Allow. for Uncoll. Accounts	1 3 5 6 54		29 4 7 3 94		
Merchandise Inventory			51 4 5 0 23		
Supplies—Sales			1 2 0 2 70		
Supplies—Administrative			9 5 9 85		
Prepaid Insurance			1 4 3 6 58		
Prepaid Interest			1 85		
Total Current Assets				146 8 9 9 83	
Long-Term Investment:					
Bond Sinking Fund				4 0 0 0 00	
Plant Assets:					
Store Equipment	13 6 2 7 07				
Less Accum. Depr.—Store Equip.	2 6 0 2 77		11 0 2 4 30		

13-3 APPLICATION PROBLEM (continued)

Trexler, Inc.

Balance Sheet (continued)

December 31, 20--

Building	58 0 0 0 00					
Less Accum. Depr.—Building Equipment	6 1 1 9 00	51 8 8 1 00				
Office	30 4 9 1 34					
Less Accum. Depr.—Office	6 0 9 8 27	24 3 9 3 07				
Land		31 4 8 8 84				
Total Plant Assets			118 7 8 7 21			
Intangible Asset:						
Organization Costs			1 5 0 00			
Total Assets			269 8 3 7 04			
LIABILITIES						
Current Liabilities:						
Notes Payable		3 0 8 30				
Interest Payable		4 0 0 2 57				
Accounts Payable		1 9 4 2 76				
Employee Income Tax Payable		2 4 6 64				
Federal Income Tax Payable		5 0 1 50				
Social Security Tax Payable		1 6 9 49				
Medicare Tax Payable		3 9 11				
Salaries Payable		7 4 7 46				
Sales Tax Payable		4 3 1 63				
Unemploy. Tax Payable—Federal		5 0 93				
Unemploy. Tax Payable—State		3 4 4 39				
Health Insurance Premiums Payable		9 2 49				
Dividends Payable		9 0 7 3 50				
Total Current Liabilities			17 9 5 0 77			
Long-Term Liability:						
Bonds Payable			40 0 0 0 00			
Total Liabilities			57 9 5 0 77			
STOCKHOLDERS' EQUITY						
Total Stockholders' Equity			211 8 8 6 27			
Total Liabilities & Stockholders' Equity			269 8 3 7 04			

13-3 APPLICATION PROBLEM (continued)

[8a]

Accounts receivable turnover ratio:

(January 1 Book Value	+	*December 31 Book Value)*	÷	*2*	=	*Average*
($25,353.35	+	*$29,473.94)*	÷	*2*	=	*$27,413.65*

Net Sales on Account	÷	*Average Book Value*	=	*Ratio*
$126,405.00	÷	*$27,413.65*	=	*4.6 times*

[8b]

Rate earned on average stockholders' equity:

(January 1 Equity	+	*December 31 Equity)*	÷	*2*	=	*Average*
($106,951.26	+	*$211,886.27)*	÷	*2*	=	*$159,418.77*

Net Income	÷	*Average Equity*	=	*Rate*
$34,008.51	÷	*$159,418.77*	=	*21.3%*

[8c]

Rate earned on average total assets:

(January 1 Assets	+	*December 31 Assets)*	÷	*2*	=	*Average*
($233,699.75	+	*$269,837.04)*	÷	*2*	=	*$251,768.40*

Net Income	÷	*Average Assets*	=	*Rate*
$34,008.51	÷	*$251,768.40*	=	*13.5%*

13-3 APPLICATION PROBLEM

Extra form

13-4 APPLICATION PROBLEM, p. 372

[1]

The work sheet prepared in Application Problem 13-1 is needed to complete this problem.

GENERAL JOURNAL   PAGE 13

	DATE		ACCOUNT TITLE	DOC. NO.	POST. REF.	DEBIT	CREDIT	
1			*Adjusting Entries*					1
2	20– Dec.	31	Interest Receivable			1 6 0 17		2
3			Interest Income				1 6 0 17	3
4		31	Uncollectible Accounts Expense			1 2 6 4 05		4
5			Allowance for Uncollectible Accounts				1 2 6 4 05	5
6		31	Income Summary			1 5 9 99		6
7			Merchandise Inventory				1 5 9 99	7
8		31	Supplies Expense—Sales			1 6 9 5 37		8
9			Supplies—Sales				1 6 9 5 37	9
10		31	Supplies Expense—Administrative			4 0 6 5 52		10
11			Supplies—Administrative				4 0 6 5 52	11
12		31	Insurance Expense			2 6 3 3 04		12
13			Prepaid Insurance				2 6 3 3 04	13
14		31	Prepaid Interest			1 85		14
15			Interest Expense				1 85	15
16		31	Depreciation Expense—Store Equipment			1 2 9 4 57		16
17			Accum. Depr.—Store Equipment				1 2 9 4 57	17
18		31	Depreciation Expense—Building			2 9 0 0 00		18
19			Accum. Depr.—Building				2 9 0 0 00	19
20		31	Depreciation Expense—Office Equipment			3 0 1 8 64		20
21			Accum. Depr.—Office Equipment				3 0 1 8 64	21
22		31	Organization Expense			5 0 00		22
23			Organization Costs				5 0 00	23
24		31	Interest Expense			4 0 0 2 57		24
25			Interest Payable				4 0 0 2 57	25
26		31	Salary Expense—Sales			1 5 3 97		26
27			Salary Expense—Administrative			5 9 3 49		27
28			Salaries Payable				7 4 7 46	28
29		31	Payroll Taxes Expense			7 3 13		29
30			Social Security Tax Payable				4 8 59	30
31			Medicare Tax Payable				1 1 21	31
32			Unemployment Tax Payable—Federal				1 72	32
33			Unemployment Tax Payable—State				1 1 61	33
34		31	Federal Income Tax Expense			5 0 1 50		34
35			Federal Income Tax Payable				5 0 1 50	35

13-4 APPLICATION PROBLEM (continued)

[2]

GENERAL JOURNAL — PAGE 14

	DATE		ACCOUNT TITLE	DOC. NO.	POST. REF.	DEBIT	CREDIT	
1			*Closing Entries*					1
2	20-- Dec.	31	Sales			19 440 1 19		2
3			Purchases Discount			1 569 21		3
4			Purchases Returns and Allowances			5 53 84		4
5			Interest Income			2 83 50		5
6			Income Summary				19 680 7 74	6
7		31	Income Summary			162 639 24		7
8			Sales Discount				3 888 0	8
9			Sales Returns and Allowances				5 832 0	9
10			Purchases				92 306 46	10
11			Advertising Expense				2 343 12	11
12			Credit Card Fee Expense				2 651 42	12
13			Depreciation Expense—Store Equip.				1 294 57	13
14			Miscellaneous Expense—Sales				1 140 73	14
15			Salary Expense—Sales				14 151 01	15
16			Supplies Expense—Sales				1 695 37	16
17			Depreciation Expense—Building				2 900 00	17
18			Depreciation Expense—Office Equip.				3 018 64	18
19			Insurance Expense				2 633 04	19
20			Miscellaneous Expense—Admin.				3 268 03	20
21			Payroll Taxes Expense				2 454 99	21
22			Property Tax Expense				2 300 00	22
23			Salary Expense—Administrative				5 988 82	23
24			Supplies Expense—Administrative				4 065 52	24
25			Uncollectible Accounts Expense				1 264 05	25
26			Utilities Expense				5 518 66	26
27			Interest Expense				6 621 31	27
28			Organization Expense				50 00	28
29			Federal Income Tax Expense				6 001 50	29
30		31	Income Summary			34 008 51		30
31			Retained Earnings				34 008 51	31
32		31	Retained Earnings			9 073 50		32
33			Dividends—Common				4 873 50	33
34			Dividends—Preferred				4 200 00	34
35								35

13-4 APPLICATION PROBLEM (concluded)

[3]

GENERAL JOURNAL   PAGE 1

	DATE		ACCOUNT TITLE	DOC. NO.	POST. REF.	DEBIT	CREDIT	
1			*Reversing Entries*					1
2	20-- Jan.	1	Interest Income			1 6 0 17		2
3			Interest Receivable				1 6 0 17	3
4		1	Interest Expense			1 85		4
5			Prepaid Interest				1 85	5
6		1	Interest Payable			4 0 0 2 57		6
7			Interest Expense				4 0 0 2 57	7
8		1	Salaries Payable			7 4 7 46		8
9			Salary Expense—Sales				1 5 3 97	9
10			Salary Expense—Administrative				5 9 3 49	10
11		1	Social Security Tax Payable			4 8 59		11
12			Medicare Tax Payable			1 1 21		12
13			Unemployment Tax Payable—Federal			1 72		13
14			Unemployment Tax Payable—State			1 1 61		14
15			Payroll Taxes Expense				7 3 13	15
16								16
17								17
18								18
19								19
20								20
21								21
22								22
23								23
24								24
25								25
26								26
27								27
28								28
29								29
30								30
31								31
32								32
33								33
34								34
35								35

13-4 APPLICATION PROBLEM

Extra form

GENERAL JOURNAL   PAGE _____

	DATE		ACCOUNT TITLE	DOC. NO.	POST. REF.	DEBIT	CREDIT	
1								1
2								2
3								3
4								4
5								5
6								6
7								7
8								8
9								9
10								10
11								11
12								12
13								13
14								14
15								15
16								16
17								17
18								18
19								19
20								20
21								21
22								22
23								23
24								24
25								25
26								26
27								27
28								28
29								29
30								30
31								31
32								32
33								33
34								34
35								35

13-5 MASTERY PROBLEM

Extra form

GENERAL JOURNAL   PAGE _____

	DATE	ACCOUNT TITLE	DOC. NO.	POST. REF.	DEBIT	CREDIT	
1							1
2							2
3							3
4							4
5							5
6							6
7							7
8							8
9							9
10							10
11							11
12							12
13							13
14							14
15							15
16							16
17							17
18							18
19							19
20							20
21							21
22							22
23							23
24							24
25							25
26							26
27							27
28							28
29							29
30							30
31							31
32							32
33							33
34							34
35							35

13-5 MASTERY PROBLEM, p. 373

Completing end-of-fiscal period work for a corporation [1]

Lander, Inc.
Work Sheet
For Year Ended December 31, 20--

#	ACCOUNT TITLE	TRIAL BALANCE DEBIT	TRIAL BALANCE CREDIT	ADJUSTMENTS DEBIT	ADJUSTMENTS CREDIT	INCOME STATEMENT DEBIT	INCOME STATEMENT CREDIT	BALANCE SHEET DEBIT	BALANCE SHEET CREDIT
1	Cash	4256024						4256024	
2	Petty Cash	50000						50000	
3	Notes Receivable	2156177						2156177	
4	Interest Receivable			(a) 27718				27718	
5	Accounts Receivable	5605886						5605886	
6	Allowance for Uncollectible Accounts		15618		(b) 213441				229059
7	Merchandise Inventory	8714653			(c) 27015			8687638	
8	Supplies—Sales	1708854			(d) 727975			980879	
9	Supplies—Administrative	1048559			(e) 686484			362075	
10	Prepaid Insurance	687177			(f) 450783			236394	
11	Prepaid Interest			(g) 312				312	
12	Bond Sinking Fund	700000						700000	
13	Store Equipment	6797477						6797477	
14	Accum. Depr.—Store Equip.		8035591		(h) 974600				9010191
15	Building	4800000						4800000	
16	Accum. Depr.—Building		5328000		(i) 2400000				7728000
17	Office Equipment	5301002						5301002	
18	Accum. Depr.—Office Equip.		2208960		(j) 2185950				4394910
19	Land	10428503						10428503	
20	Organization Costs	300000			(k) 7500			22500	
21	Notes Payable		52059						52059
22	Interest Payable				(l) 700434				700434
23	Accounts Payable		1046853						1046853
24	Employee Income Tax Payable		41647						41647
25	Federal Income Tax Payable				(o) 12697				12697
26	Social Security Tax Payable		20415		(n) 8955				29370
27	Medicare Tax Payable		4711		(n) 2067				6778
28	Salaries Payable				(m) 137778				137778

13-5 MASTERY PROBLEM (continued)

[1]

#	ACCOUNT TITLE	Trial Balance Debit	Trial Balance Credit	Adjustments Debit	Adjustments Credit	Income Statement Debit	Income Statement Credit	Balance Sheet Debit	Balance Sheet Credit
29	Sales Tax Payable		72882						72882
30	Unemploy. Tax Payable—Federal		8309		(n) 127				8436
31	Unemploy. Tax Payable—State		56192		(n) 859				57051
32	Health Ins. Prem. Payable		15618						15618
33	Dividends Payable		1492280						1492280
34	Bonds Payable		7000000						7000000
35	Capital Stock—Common		18400000						18400000
36	Pd.-in Cap. in Exc. St. Val.—Common		3000000						3000000
37	Capital Stock—Preferred		7200000						7200000
38	Pd.-in.Cap. in Exc. Par—Preferred		180000						180000
39	Disc. on Sale of Preferred Stock	300000						300000	
40	Treasury Stock	1200000						1200000	
41	Pd.-in Cap. from Sale of Tr. Stock		24000						24000
42	Retained Earnings		2264560						2264560
43	Dividends—Common	772280						772280	
44	Dividends—Preferred	720000						720000	
45	Income Summary			(c) 27015		27015			
46	Sales		37673550				37673550		
47	Sales Discount	59347				59347			
48	Sales Returns & Allowances	89021				89021			
49	Purchases	15565599				15565599			
50	Purchases Discount		264615				264615		
51	Purchases Returns & Allow.		93394				93394		
52	Advertising Expense	395647				395647			
53	Credit Card Fee Expense	447706				447706			
54	Depr. Expense—Store Equip.			(h) 974600		974600			
55	Miscellaneous Expense—Sales	6975889				6975889			
56	Salary Expense—Sales	3415061		(m) 37565		3452626			
57	Supplies Expense—Sales			(d) 727975		727975			
58	Depr. Expense—Building			(i) 240000		240000			

13-5 MASTERY PROBLEM (continued)

[1]

	ACCOUNT TITLE	TRIAL BALANCE DEBIT	TRIAL BALANCE CREDIT	ADJUSTMENTS DEBIT	ADJUSTMENTS CREDIT	INCOME STATEMENT DEBIT	INCOME STATEMENT CREDIT	BALANCE SHEET DEBIT	BALANCE SHEET CREDIT	
59	Depr. Expense—Office Equip.			(j) 218595		218595				59
60	Insurance Expense			(f) 450783		450783				60
61	Miscellaneous Expense—Admin.	651824				651824				61
62	Payroll Taxes Expense	471044		(n) 12008		483052				62
63	Property Tax Expense	230000				230000				63
64	Salary Expense—Admin.	911030		(m) 100213		1011243				64
65	Supplies Expense—Admin.			(e) 686484		686484				65
66	Uncollectible Accounts Expense			(b) 213441		213441				66
67	Utilities Expense	931854			(a) 27718	931854				67
68	Interest Income		20824				48542			68
69	Interest Expense	442500		(l) 700434	(g) 312	1142622				69
70	Organization Expense			(k) 7500		7500				70
71	Federal Income Tax Expense	2000000		(o) 12697		2012697				71
72		80504814	80504814	4437340	4437340	30717220	38080101	52324865	44961984	72
73	Net Income after Federal Income Tax					7362881			7362881	73
74						38080101	38080101	52324865	52324865	74

13-5 MASTERY PROBLEM (continued)

[2–4]

Lander, Inc.

Income Statement

For Year Ended December 31, 20--

									% OF NET SALES
Operating Revenue:									
Sales						376 7 3 5 50			
Less: Sales Discount			5 9 3 47						
Sales Ret. & Allow.			8 9 0 21		1 4 8 3 68				
Net Sales							375 2 5 1 82		100.0
Cost of Merchandise Sold:									
Mdse. Inventory, January 1, 20--						87 1 4 6 53			
Purchases			155 6 5 5 99						
Less: Purchases Discount	2 6 4 6 15								
Purch. Ret. & Allow.	9 3 3 94		3 5 8 0 09						
Net Purchases						152 0 7 5 90			
Total Cost of Mdse. Avail. for Sale						239 2 2 2 43			
Less Mdse. Inventory, Dec. 31, 20--						86 8 7 6 38			
Cost of Merchandise Sold							152 3 4 6 05		40.6
Gross Profit on Operations							222 9 0 5 77		59.4
Operating Expenses:									
Selling Expenses:									
Advertising Expense			3 9 5 6 47						
Credit Card Fee Expense			4 4 7 7 06						
Depr. Expense—Store Equip.			9 7 4 6 00						
Miscellaneous Expense—Sales			6 9 7 5 89						
Salary Expense—Sales			34 5 2 6 26						
Supplies Expense—Sales			7 2 7 9 75						
Total Selling Expenses						66 9 6 1 43			17.8
Administrative Expenses:									
Depr. Expense—Building			2 4 0 0 00						
Depr. Expense—Office Equip.			2 1 8 5 95						
Insurance Expense			4 5 0 7 83						
Miscellaneous Expense—Admin.			6 5 1 8 24						
Payroll Taxes Expense			4 8 3 0 52						
Property Tax Expense			2 3 0 0 00						
Salary Expense—Admin.			10 1 1 2 43						

13-5 MASTERY PROBLEM (continued)

[2]

Lander, Inc.

Income Statement (continued)

For Year Ended December 31, 20--

					% OF NET SALES
Supplies Expense—Admin.		6 8 6 4 84			
Uncollectible Accounts Expense		2 1 3 4 41			
Utilities Expense		9 3 1 8 54			
Total Admin. Expense			51 1 7 2 76		13.6
Total Operating Expenses				118 1 3 4 19	31.5
Income from Operations				104 7 7 1 58	27.9
Other Revenue:					
Interest Income			4 8 5 42		
Other Expenses:					
Interest Expense		11 4 2 6 22			
Organization Expense		7 5 00			
Total Other Expenses			11 5 0 1 22		
Net Deduction				11 0 1 5 80	2.9
Net Income before Fed. Income Tax				93 7 5 5 78	25.0
Less Federal Income Tax Expense				20 1 2 6 97	5.4
Net Income after Fed. Income Tax				73 6 2 8 81	19.6

[4]

Earnings per share:

Stock	Share of Net Income	÷	Shares Outstanding	=	Earnings per Share
Preferred	$ 7,200.00	÷	720	=	$10.00
Common	$66,428.81	÷	18,310	=	$ 3.63

13-5 MASTERY PROBLEM (continued)

Income statement analysis   [3]

		Acceptable %	Actual %	Positive Result		Recommended Action If Needed
				Yes	No	
a.	Cost of merchandise sold	Not more than 42.0%	**40.6%**	✓		*None*
b.	Gross profit on operations	Not less than 58.0%	**59.4%**	✓		*None*
c.	Total selling expenses	Not more than 13.0%	**17.8%**		✓	*Review and identify excessive expenses so they may be controlled.*
d.	Total administrative expenses	Not more than 15.5%	**13.6%**	✓		*None*
e.	Total operating expenses	Not more than 28.5%	**31.5%**		✓	*Correcting selling expenses will correct total expenses.*
f.	Income from operations	Not less than 29.5%	**27.9%**		✓	*Correcting selling expenses will correct income from operations.*
g.	Net deduction from other revenue and expenses	Not more than 3.5%	**2.9%**	✓		*None*
h.	Net income before federal income tax	Not less than 26.0%	**25.0%**		✓	*Correcting selling expenses will correct net income.*

13-5 MASTERY PROBLEM (continued)

[5]

Lander, Inc.

Statement of Stockholders' Equity

For Year Ended December 31, 20--

Paid-in Capital:				
Common Stock, *$10.00* Stated Value:				
January 1, 20--, *18,000* Shares Issued	180 0 0 0 00			
Issued during Current Year, *400* Shares	4 0 0 0 00			
Balance, Dec. 31, 20--, *18,400* Shares Issued		184 0 0 0 00		
Preferred Stock, *10.0%*, *$100.00* Par Value:				
January 1, 20--, *600* Shares Issued	60 0 0 0 00			
Issued during Current Year, *120* Shares	12 0 0 0 00			
Balance, Dec. 31, 20--, *720* Shares Issued		72 0 0 0 00		
Total Value of Capital Stock Issued			256 0 0 0 00	
Additional Paid-in Capital:				
Pd.-in-Cap. in Exc. of St. Value—Common	30 0 0 0 00			
Pd.-in-Cap. in Exc. of Par—Preferred	1 8 0 0 00			
Pd.-in-Cap. from Sale of Treasury Stock	2 4 0 00	32 0 4 0 00		
Less Disc. on Sale of Preferred Stock		3 0 0 0 00		
Total Additional Paid-in Capital			29 0 4 0 00	
Total Paid-in Capital			285 0 4 0 00	
Retained Earnings:				
Balance, January 1, 20--		22 6 4 5 60		
Net Income after Federal Income Tax for 20--	73 6 2 8 81			
Less Dividends Declared during 20--	14 9 2 2 80			
Net Increase during 20--		58 7 0 6 01		
Balance, December 31, 20--			81 3 5 1 61	
Total Pd.-in Capital & Retained Earnings			366 3 9 1 61	
Less Treasury Stock, *90* Shares of				
Common Stock, December 31, 20--			1 2 0 0 00	
Total Stockholders' Equity, Dec. 31, 20--			365 1 9 1 61	

13-5 MASTERY PROBLEM (continued)

[6a]

Equity per share:

Stock	Equity	÷	Shares Outstanding	=	Earnings per Share
Preferred	$ 72,000.00	÷	720	=	$100.00
Common	$293,191.61	÷	18,310	=	$ 16.01

[6b]

Price-earnings ratio:

Stock	Market Price	÷	Earnings per Share	=	Price-earnings Ratio
Common	$30.00	÷	$3.63	=	8.3 times

[7]

Lander, Inc.

Balance Sheet

December 31, 20--

ASSETS					
Current Assets:				
Cash			42 5 6 0 24		
Petty Cash			5 0 0 00		
Notes Receivable			21 5 6 1 77		
Interest Receivable			2 7 7 18		
Accounts Receivable	56 0 5 8 86				
Less Allow. for Uncoll. Accounts	2 2 9 0 59		53 7 6 8 27		
Merchandise Inventory			86 8 7 6 38		
Supplies—Sales			9 8 0 8 79		
Supplies—Administrative			3 6 2 0 75		
Prepaid Insurance			2 3 6 3 94		
Prepaid Interest			3 12		
Total Current Assets				221 3 4 0 44	
Long-Term Investment:					
Bond Sinking Fund				7 0 0 0 00	
Plant Assets:					
Store Equipment	67 9 7 4 77				
Less Accum. Depr.—Store Equip.	17 7 8 1 91		50 1 9 2 86		

13-5 MASTERY PROBLEM (continued)

[7]

Lander, Inc.

Balance Sheet (continued)

December 31, 20--

Building	48 0 0 0 00			
Less Accum. Depr.—Building	7 7 2 8 00	40 2 7 2 00		
Office Equipment	53 0 1 0 02			
Less Accum. Depr.—Office Equip.	4 3 9 4 91	48 6 1 5 11		
Land		104 2 8 5 03		
Total Plant Assets			243 3 6 5 00	
Intangible Asset:				
Organization Costs			2 2 5 00	
Total Assets			471 9 3 0 44	
LIABILITIES				
Current Liabilities:				
Notes Payable		5 2 0 59		
Interest Payable		7 0 0 4 34		
Accounts Payable		10 4 6 8 53		
Employee Income Tax Payable		4 1 6 47		
Federal Income Tax Payable		1 2 6 97		
Social Security Tax Payable		2 9 3 70		
Medicare Tax Payable		6 7 78		
Salaries Payable		1 3 7 7 78		
Sales Tax Payable		7 2 8 82		
Unemploy. Tax Payable—Federal		8 4 36		
Unemploy. Tax Payable—State		5 7 0 51		
Health Insurance Premiums Payable		1 5 6 18		
Dividends Payable		14 9 2 2 80		
Total Current Liabilities			36 7 3 8 83	
Long-Term Liability:				
Bonds Payable			70 0 0 0 00	
Total Liabilities			106 7 3 8 83	
STOCKHOLDERS' EQUITY				
Total Stockholders' Equity			365 1 9 1 61	
Total Liabilities & Stockholders' Equity			471 9 3 0 44	

13-5 MASTERY PROBLEM (continued)

[8a]

Accounts receivable turnover ratio:

(January 1 Book Value	+	December 31 Book Value)	÷	2	=	Average
($47,288.92	+	$53,768.27)	÷	2	=	$50,528.60

Net Sales on Account	÷	Average Book Value	=	Ratio
$213,441.00	÷	$50,528.60	=	4.2 times

[8b]

Rate earned on average stockholders' equity:

(January 1 Equity	+	December 31 Equity)	÷	2	=	Average
($290,485.60	+	$365,191.61)	÷	2	=	$327,838.61

Net Income	÷	Average Equity	=	Rate
$73,628.81	÷	$327,838.61	=	22.5%

[8c]

Rate earned on average total assets:

(January 1 Assets	+	December 31 Assets)	÷	2	=	Average
($392,691.70	+	$471,930.44)	÷	2	=	$432,311.07

Net Income	÷	Average Assets	=	Rate
$73,628.81	÷	$432,311.07	=	17.0%

13-5 MASTERY PROBLEM (continued)

[9]

GENERAL JOURNAL   PAGE 13

	DATE		ACCOUNT TITLE	DOC. NO.	POST. REF.	DEBIT	CREDIT	
1			*Adjusting Entries*					1
2	20-- Dec.	31	*Interest Receivable*			2 7 7 18		2
3			*Interest Income*				2 7 7 18	3
4		31	*Uncollectible Accounts Expense*			2 1 3 4 41		4
5			*Allowance for Uncollectible Accounts*				2 1 3 4 41	5
6		31	*Income Summary*			2 7 0 15		6
7			*Merchandise Inventory*				2 7 0 15	7
8		31	*Supplies Expense—Sales*			7 2 7 9 75		8
9			*Supplies—Sales*				7 2 7 9 75	9
10		31	*Supplies Expense—Administrative*			6 8 6 4 84		10
11			*Supplies—Administrative*				6 8 6 4 84	11
12		31	*Insurance Expense*			4 5 0 7 83		12
13			*Prepaid Insurance*				4 5 0 7 83	13
14		31	*Prepaid Interest*			3 12		14
15			*Interest Expense*				3 12	15
16		31	*Depreciation Expense—Store Equipment*			9 7 4 6 00		16
17			*Accum. Depr.—Store Equipment*				9 7 4 6 00	17
18		31	*Depreciation Expense—Building*			2 4 0 0 00		18
19			*Accum. Depr.—Building*				2 4 0 0 00	19
20		31	*Depreciation Expense—Office Equipment*			2 1 8 5 95		20
21			*Accum. Depr.—Office Equipment*				2 1 8 5 95	21
22		31	*Organization Expense*			7 5 00		22
23			*Organization Costs*				7 5 00	23
24		31	*Interest Expense*			7 0 0 4 34		24
25			*Interest Payable*				7 0 0 4 34	25
26		31	*Salary Expense—Sales*			3 7 5 65		26
27			*Salary Expense—Administrative*			1 0 0 2 13		27
28			*Salaries Payable*				1 3 7 7 78	28
29		31	*Payroll Taxes Expense*			1 2 0 08		29
30			*Social Security Tax Payable*				8 9 55	30
31			*Medicare Tax Payable*				2 0 67	31
32			*Unemployment Tax Payable—Federal*				1 27	32
33			*Unemployment Tax Payable—State*				8 59	33
34		31	*Federal Income Tax Expense*			1 2 6 97		34
35			*Federal Income Tax Payable*				1 2 6 97	35

13-5 MASTERY PROBLEM (continued)

[10]

GENERAL JOURNAL   PAGE 14

	DATE		ACCOUNT TITLE	DOC. NO.	POST. REF.	DEBIT	CREDIT	
1			*Closing Entries*					1
2	20-- Dec.	31	Sales			376 735 50		2
3			Purchases Discount			2 646 15		3
4			Purchases Returns and Allowances			933 94		4
5			Interest Income			485 42		5
6			Income Summary				380 801 01	6
7		31	Income Summary			306 902 05		7
8			Sales Discount				593 47	8
9			Sales Returns and Allowances				890 21	9
10			Purchases				155 655 99	10
11			Advertising Expense				3 956 47	11
12			Credit Card Fee Expense				4 477 06	12
13			Depreciation Expense—Store Equip.				9 746 00	13
14			Miscellaneous Expense—Sales				6 975 89	14
15			Salary Expense—Sales				34 526 26	15
16			Supplies Expense—Sales				7 279 75	16
17			Depreciation Expense—Building				2 400 00	17
18			Depreciation Expense—Office Equip.				2 185 95	18
19			Insurance Expense				4 507 83	19
20			Miscellaneous Expense—Admin.				6 518 24	20
21			Payroll Taxes Expense				4 830 52	21
22			Property Tax Expense				2 300 00	22
23			Salary Expense—Administrative				10 112 43	23
24			Supplies Expense—Administrative				6 864 84	24
25			Uncollectible Accounts Expense				2 134 41	25
26			Utilities Expense				9 318 54	26
27			Interest Expense				11 426 22	27
28			Organization Expense				75 00	28
29			Federal Income Tax Expense				20 126 97	29
30		31	Income Summary			73 628 81		30
31			Retained Earnings				73 628 81	31
32		31	Retained Earnings			14 922 80		32
33			Dividends—Common				7 722 80	33
34			Dividends—Preferred				7 200 00	34
35								35

13-5 MASTERY PROBLEM (concluded)

[11]

GENERAL JOURNAL   PAGE 1

	DATE		ACCOUNT TITLE	DOC. NO.	POST. REF.	DEBIT	CREDIT	
1			*Reversing Entries*					1
2	20-- Jan.	1	*Interest Income*			2 7 7 18		2
3			*Interest Receivable*				2 7 7 18	3
4		1	*Interest Expense*			3 12		4
5			*Prepaid Interest*				3 12	5
6		1	*Interest Payable*			7 0 0 4 34		6
7			*Interest Expense*				7 0 0 4 34	7
8		1	*Salaries Payable*			1 3 7 7 78		8
9			*Salary Expense—Sales*				3 7 5 65	9
10			*Salary Expense—Administrative*				1 0 0 2 13	10
11		1	*Social Security Tax Payable*			8 9 55		11
12			*Medicare Tax Payable*			2 0 67		12
13			*Unemployment Tax Payable—Federal*			1 27		13
14			*Unemployment Tax Payable—State*			8 59		14
15			*Payroll Taxes Expense*				1 2 0 08	15
16								16
17								17
18								18
19								19
20								20
21								21
22								22
23								23
24								24
25								25
26								26
27								27
28								28
29								29
30								30
31								31
32								32
33								33
34								34
35								35

13-6 CHALLENGE PROBLEM, p. 374

Preparing a Form 1120, U.S. Corporation Income Tax Return

Goldstein, Inc.

Income Statement

For Year Ended December 31, 20--

			% OF NET SALES
Operating Revenue:			
Sales		873 9 0 2 40	
Less: Sales Discount	1 8 8 7 45		
Sales Ret. & Allow.	3 0 0 0 45	4 8 8 7 90	
Net Sales		869 0 1 4 50	100.0
Cost of Merchandise Sold:			
Mdse. Inventory, January 1, 20--		267 4 5 3 09	
Purchases	426 5 9 6 48		
Less: Purchases Discount	3 6 2 5 65		
Purch. Ret. & Allow.	5 7 5 4 70	9 3 8 0 35	
Net Purchases		417 2 1 6 13	
Total Cost of Mdse. Avail. for Sale		684 6 6 9 22	
Less Mdse. Inventory, Dec. 31, 20--		258 7 5 5 19	
Cost of Merchandise Sold		425 9 1 4 03	49.0
Gross Profit on Operations		443 1 0 0 47	51.0
Operating Expenses:			
Selling Expenses:			
Advertising Expense	8 0 2 1 20		
Credit Card Fee Expense	12 6 3 2 30		
Depr. Expense—Store Equip.	14 2 5 6 30		
Miscellaneous Expense—Sales	17 3 5 2 30		
Salary Expense—Sales	48 6 4 3 40		
Supplies Expense—Sales	18 4 6 4 31		
Total Selling Expenses		119 3 6 9 81	13.7
Administrative Expenses:			
Depr. Expense—Building	10 5 0 0 00		
Depr. Expense—Office Equip.	5 8 5 4 50		
Insurance Expense	6 2 3 4 20		
Miscellaneous Expense—Admin.	17 4 3 2 20		
Payroll Taxes Expense	7 5 2 3 30		
Property Tax Expense	16 9 1 8 84		
Salary Expense—Admin.	21 7 5 4 30		

13-6 CHALLENGE PROBLEM (continued)

Goldstein, Inc.

Income Statement (continued)

For Year Ended December 31, 20--

										% OF NET SALES
Supplies Expense—Admin.		16 4 3 2 60					
Uncoll. Accounts Expense		3 7 4 5 20					
Utilities Expense		20 5 3 2 60					
Total Admin. Expense			126 9 2 7 74			14.6
Total Operating Expenses				246 2 9 7 55		28.3
Income from Operations				196 8 0 2 92		22.6
Other Revenue:						
Interest Income			5 1 1 33			
Other Expenses:						
Interest Expense		35 7 5 5 45				
Organization Expense		7 2 0 00				
Total Other Expenses			36 4 7 5 45			
Net Deduction from Other Rev. & Exp.				35 9 6 4 12		4.1
Net Income before Fed. Income Tax				160 8 3 8 80		18.5
Less Federal Income Tax Expense				45 9 7 7 13		5.3
Net Income after Fed. Income Tax				114 8 6 1 67		13.2

13-6 CHALLENGE PROBLEM (concluded)

[1–6]

Form 1120	**U.S. Corporation Income Tax Return**		OMB No. 1545-0123		

Form **1120**
Department of the Treasury
Internal Revenue Service

U.S. Corporation Income Tax Return

For calendar year 20-- or tax year beginning ...., 20--, ending ...., 20 ...
▶ Instructions are separate. See page 1 for Paperwork Reduction Act Notice.

OMB No. 1545-0123

20--

A Check if a:
(1) Consolidated return (attach Form 851) ☐
(2) Personal holding co. (attach Sch. PH) ☐
(3) Personal service corp. (as defined in Temporary Regs. sec. 1.441-4T— see instructions) ☐

Use IRS label. Otherwise, please print or type.

Name *Goldstein, Inc.*

Number, street, and room or suite no. (If a P.O. box, see page 6 of instructions.) *7834 Industrial Road*

City or town, state, and ZIP code *Oxford, MS 38655-1550*

B Employer identification number *65-074738*

C Date incorporated *1/5/--*

D Total assets (see Specific Instructions) $ *786,986 50*

E Check applicable boxes: (1) ☐ Initial return (2) ☐ Final return (3) ☐ Change in address

Income

			Amount	
1a	Gross receipts or sales *872,014 95* b Less returns and allowances *3,000 45* c Bal ▶	1c	869,014	50
2	Cost of goods sold (Schedule A, line 8)	2	425,914	03
3	Gross profit. Subtract line 2 from line 1c	3	443,100	47
4	Dividends (Schedule C, line 19)	4	-0-	
5	Interest	5	511	33
6	Gross rents	6	-0-	
7	Gross royalties	7	-0-	
8	Capital gain net income (attach Schedule D (Form 1120))	8	-0-	
9	Net gain or (loss) from Form 4797, Part II, line 20 (attach Form 4797)	9	-0-	
10	Other income (see instructions—attach schedule)	10	-0-	
11	**Total income.** Add lines 3 through 10 ▶	11	443,611	80

Deductions (See instructions for limitations on deductions.)

			Amount	
12	Compensation of officers (Schedule E, line 4)	12	7,217	60
13a	Salaries and wages *63,180 10* b Less jobs credit *-0-* c Balance ▶	13c	63,180	10
14	Repairs	14		
15	Bad debts	15	3,745	20
16	Rents	16	-0-	
17	Taxes	17	24,442	14
18	Interest	18	35,755	45
19	Charitable contributions (**see instructions for 10% limitation**)	19	-0-	
20	Depreciation (attach Form 4562) 20 *30,610 80*			
21	Less depreciation claimed on Schedule A and elsewhere on return 21a *-0-*	21b	30,610	80
22	Depletion	22	-0-	
23	Advertising	23	8,021	20
24	Pension, profit-sharing, etc., plans	24	-0-	
25	Employee benefit programs	25	-0-	
26	Other deductions (attach schedule)	26	109,800	51
27	**Total deductions.** Add lines 12 through 26 ▶	27	282,773	00
28	Taxable income before net operating loss deduction and special deductions. Subtract line 27 from line 11	28	160,838	80
29	**Less:** a Net operating loss deduction (see instructions) 29a *-0-*			
	b Special deductions (Schedule C, line 20) 29b *-0-*	29c	-0-	

Tax and Payments

			Amount	
30	**Taxable income.** Subtract line 29c from line 28	30	160,838	80
31	Total tax (Schedule J, line 10)	31	45,977	13
32	**Payments:** a 20-- overpayment credited to 20-- 32a *-0-*			
b	20-- estimated tax payments 32b *42,000 00*			
c	Less 20-- refund applied for on Form 4466 32c (*-0-*) d Bal ▶ 32d *42,000 00*			
e	Tax deposited with Form 7004 32e *-0-*			
f	Credit from regulated investment companies (attach Form 2439) 32f *-0-*			
g	Credit for Federal tax on fuels (attach Form 4136). See instructions 32g *-0-*	32h	42,000	00
33	Estimated tax penalty (see instructions). Check if Form 2220 is attached ▶ ☐	33	-0-	
34	**Tax due.** If line 32h is smaller than the total of lines 31 and 33, enter amount owed	34	3,977	13
35	**Overpayment.** If line 32h is larger than the total of lines 31 and 33, enter amount overpaid	35	-0-	
36	Enter amount of line 35 you want: **Credited to 20-- estimated tax** ▶ **Refunded** ▶	36	-0-	

Please Sign Here

Under penalties of perjury, I declare that I have examined this return, including accompanying schedules and statements, and to the best of my knowledge and belief, it is true, correct, and complete. Declaration of preparer (other than taxpayer) is based on all information of which preparer has any knowledge.

▶ _____ Signature of officer   Date _____   Title _____

Paid Preparer's Use Only

Preparer's signature ▶	Date _____ Check if self-employed ☐	Preparer's social security number
Firm's name (or yours if self-employed) and address ▶		E.I. No. ▶
		ZIP code ▶

13-6 CHALLENGE PROBLEM

Extra form

Form **1120**	**U.S. Corporation Income Tax Return**	OMB No. 1545-0123
Department of the Treasury Internal Revenue Service	For calendar year 20-- or tax year beginning .... , 20--, ending .... , 20 ... ▶ Instructions are separate. See page 1 for Paperwork Reduction Act Notice.	20--

A Check if a:
(1) Consolidated return (attach Form 851) ☐
(2) Personal holding co. (attach Sch. PH) ☐
(3) Personal service corp. (as defined in Temporary Regs. sec. 1.441-4T— see instructions) ☐

Use IRS label. Otherwise, please print or type.

Name

Number, street, and room or suite no. (If a P.O. box, see page 6 of instructions.)

City or town, state, and ZIP code

B Employer identification number

C Date incorporated

D Total assets (see Specific Instructions)

$

E Check applicable boxes: (1) ☐ Initial return (2) ☐ Final return (3) ☐ Change in address

Income

1a	Gross receipts or sales _____ b Less returns and allowances _____ c Bal ▶	1c	
2	Cost of goods sold (Schedule A, line 8)	2	
3	Gross profit. Subtract line 2 from line 1c	3	
4	Dividends (Schedule C, line 19)	4	
5	Interest	5	
6	Gross rents	6	
7	Gross royalties	7	
8	Capital gain net income (attach Schedule D (Form 1120)) . .	8	
9	Net gain or (loss) from Form 4797, Part II, line 20 (attach Form 4797)	9	
10	Other income (see instructions—attach schedule)	10	
11	**Total income.** Add lines 3 through 10 . . . . ▶	11	

Deductions (See instructions for limitations on deductions.)

12	Compensation of officers (Schedule E, line 4)	12	
13a	Salaries and wages _____ b Less jobs credit _____ c Balance ▶	13c	
14	Repairs	14	
15	Bad debts	15	
16	Rents	16	
17	Taxes	17	
18	Interest	18	
19	Charitable contributions (**see instructions for 10% limitation**) . .	19	
20	Depreciation (attach Form 4562) 20		
21	Less depreciation claimed on Schedule A and elsewhere on return 21a	21b	
22	Depletion	22	
23	Advertising	23	
24	Pension, profit-sharing, etc., plans	24	
25	Employee benefit programs	25	
26	Other deductions (attach schedule)	26	
27	**Total deductions.** Add lines 12 through 26 . . . . . . ▶	27	
28	Taxable income before net operating loss deduction and special deductions. Subtract line 27 from line 11	28	
29	**Less:** a Net operating loss deduction (see instructions) . . 29a		
	b Special deductions (Schedule C, line 20) 29b	29c	

Tax and Payments

30	**Taxable income.** Subtract line 29c from line 28	30	
31	**Total tax** (Schedule J, line 10)	31	
32	Payments: a 20-- overpayment credited to 20-- 32a		
b	20-- estimated tax payments . . 32b		
c	Less 20-- refund applied for on Form 4466 32c ( ) d Bal ▶ 32d		
e	Tax deposited with Form 7004 . . . . . 32e		
f	Credit from regulated investment companies (attach Form 2439) . 32f		
g	Credit for Federal tax on fuels (attach Form 4136). See instructions . . 32g	32h	
33	Estimated tax penalty (see instructions). Check if Form 2220 is attached . . . ▶ ☐	33	
34	**Tax due.** If line 32h is smaller than the total of lines 31 and 33, enter amount owed . .	34	
35	**Overpayment.** If line 32h is larger than the total of lines 31 and 33, enter amount overpaid . . .	35	
36	Enter amount of line 35 you want: **Credited to 20-- estimated tax** ▶ _____ **Refunded** ▶	36	

Please Sign Here

Under penalties of perjury, I declare that I have examined this return, including accompanying schedules and statements, and to the best of my knowledge and belief, it is true, correct, and complete. Declaration of preparer (other than taxpayer) is based on all information of which preparer has any knowledge.

▶ _____ Signature of officer   Date _____   ▶ _____ Title

Paid Preparer's Use Only

Preparer's signature ▶ _____	Date _____	Check if self-employed ☐	Preparer's social security number
Firm's name (or yours if self-employed) and address ▶ _____		E.I. No. ▶	
		ZIP code ▶	

2   REINFORCEMENT ACTIVITY, p. 378

[1, 2]

CASH RECEIPTS JOURNAL

PAGE 23

	DATE	ACCOUNT TITLE	DOC. NO.	POST. REF.	GENERAL DEBIT	GENERAL CREDIT	ACCOUNTS RECEIVABLE CREDIT	SALES CREDIT	SALES TAX PAYABLE DEBIT	SALES TAX PAYABLE CREDIT	SALES DISCOUNT DEBIT	CASH DEBIT	
1	20-- Dec. 1	Rent Income	R126			240000						240000	1
2	5	Notes Payable	NP6			1000000						1000000	2
3	6	Capital Stock—Common	R134			700000						770000	3
4		Paid-in Capital in Exc. of											4
5		Stated Value—Common				70000							5
6	7	Notes Receivable	R136			15000						15247	6
7		Interest Income				247							7
8	11	Accum. Depr.—Office Equip.	R138		60000							7000	8
9		Loss on Plant Assets			3000								9
10		Office Equipment				70000							10
11	13	Capital Stock—Common	R140			200000						200000	11
12	14	Notes Receivable	R141			24750						25157	12
13		Interest Income				407							13
14	20	Susan Vine	R143				42750					42750	14
15	27	Interest Expense	NP7		10000							490000	15
16		Notes Payable				500000							16
17	28	Treasury Stock	R146			9000						13000	17
18		Paid-in Capital from Sale											18
19		of Treasury Stock				4000							19
20	29	Accum. Depr.—Store Equip.	R147		104000							80000	20
21		Store Equipment				160000							21
22		Gain on Plant Assets				24000							22
23													23

2   REINFORCEMENT ACTIVITY (continued)

[1, 2]

CASH RECEIPTS JOURNAL

PAGE 23

	DATE	ACCOUNT TITLE	DOC. NO.	POST. REF.	GENERAL DEBIT	GENERAL CREDIT	ACCOUNTS RECEIVABLE CREDIT	SALES CREDIT	SALES TAX PAYABLE DEBIT	SALES TAX PAYABLE CREDIT	SALES DISCOUNT DEBIT	CASH DEBIT
24	Dec. 29	Patrick Carson	R148				15125					15230
25		Interest Income				105						
26	29	Subscriptions Receivable	R149			300000						300000
27	31	Totals			1770000	3317509	57875					3198384
28												
29												
30												

CASH PAYMENTS JOURNAL

PAGE 23

	DATE	ACCOUNT TITLE	CK. NO.	POST. REF.	GENERAL DEBIT	GENERAL CREDIT	ACCOUNTS PAYABLE DEBIT	PURCHASES DISCOUNT CREDIT	CASH CREDIT
1	Dec. 2	Office Equipment	476		265000				265000
2	5	Interest Expense	482		2400000				2400000
3	5	Bond Sinking Fund	487		2000000				1840000
4		Interest Income				160000			
5	11	Treasury Stock	502		54000				54000
6	12	Notes Payable	503		300000				306000
7		Interest Expense			600				
8	16	Notes Payable	509		100000				101644
9		Interest Expense			1644				
10	21	Office Equipment	515		270000				200000
11		Accum. Depr.—Office Equipment			280000				
12		Office Equipment				350000			
13	30	Dividends Payable	519		1582000				1582000
14	31	Totals			6983244	5100000			6473244

2   REINFORCEMENT ACTIVITY (continued)

[1]

GENERAL JOURNAL   PAGE 12

	DATE		ACCOUNT TITLE	DOC. NO.	POST. REF.	DEBIT	CREDIT	
1	20-- Dec.	1	Dividends—Common	M316		11 78 00 0		1
2			Dividends—Preferred			4 04 00 0		2
3			Dividends Payable				15 82 00 0	3
4		1	Allowance for Uncollectible Accounts	M317		4 27 50		4
5			Accounts Receivable/Susan Vine		/		4 27 50	5
6		1	Depreciation Expense—Store Equipment	M318		2 10 00		6
7			Accum. Depr.—Store Equipment				2 10 00	7
8		1	Accum. Depr.—Store Equipment	M318		1 05 00 0		8
9			Store Equipment				1 05 00 0	9
10		1	Subscriptions Receivable	M319		3 00 00 0		10
11			Stock Subscribed—Preferred				3 00 00 0	11
12		4	Accounts Receivable/Patrick Carson	M320	/	1 51 25		12
13			Notes Receivable				1 50 00	13
14			Interest income				1 25	14
15		4	Depreciation Expense—Office Equipment	M321		50 00		15
16			Accum. Depr.—Office Equipment				50 00	16
17		4	Accum. Depr.—Office Equipment	M321		2 00 00		17
18			Loss on Plant Assets			50 00		18
19			Office Equipment				2 50 00	19
20		4	Notes Receivable	NR5		5 00 00		20
21			Accounts Receivable/Leigh Calhoun		/		5 00 00	21
22		11	Depreciation Expense—Office Equipment	M322		1 00 00		22
23			Accum. Depr.—Office Equipment				1 00 00	23
24		19	Office Equipment	M323		1 00 00 0		24
25			Capital Stock—Preferred				1 00 00 0	25
26		20	Accounts Receivable/Susan Vine	M324	/	4 27 50		26
27			Allowance for Uncollectible Accounts				4 27 50	27
28		21	Depreciation Expense—Office Equipment	M325		7 00 00		28
29			Accum. Depr.—Office Equipment				7 00 00	29
30		29	Depreciation Expense—Store Equipment	M326		1 44 00		30
31			Accum. Depr.—Store Equipment				1 44 00	31
32		29	Stock Subscribed—Preferred	M327		3 00 00 0		32
33			Capital Stock—Preferred				3 00 00 0	33

2 REINFORCEMENT ACTIVITY (continued)

[3]

Whitehurst, Inc.
Work Sheet
For Year Ended December 31, 20--

		ACCOUNT TITLE	TRIAL BALANCE DEBIT	TRIAL BALANCE CREDIT	ADJUSTMENTS DEBIT	ADJUSTMENTS CREDIT	INCOME STATEMENT DEBIT	INCOME STATEMENT CREDIT	BALANCE SHEET DEBIT	BALANCE SHEET CREDIT
1	Cash		2486159						2486159	
2	Petty Cash		30000						30000	
3	Notes Receivable		50000						50000	
4	Interest Receivable				(a) 9570				9570	
5	Accounts Receivable		4095765						4095765	
6	Allowance for Uncollectible Accounts			41928		(b) 34347				76275
7	Subscriptions Receivable									
8	Merchandise Inventory		21884633			(c)12222770			20661863	
9	Supplies—Sales		340678			(d) 195072			145606	
10	Supplies—Administrative		194728			(e) 121728			73000	
11	Prepaid Insurance		176400			(f) 79400			97000	
12	Prepaid Interest				(g) 9333				9333	
13	Bond Sinking Fund		6000000						6000000	
14	Store Equipment		9340000						9340000	
15	Accum. Depr.—Store Equip.			2802000		(h) 830000				3632000
16	Building		8000000						8000000	
17	Accum. Depr.—Building			4500000		(i) 1500000				6000000
18	Office Equipment		3156800						3156800	
19	Accum. Depr.—Office Equip.			947040		(j) 115000				1062040
20	Land		2000000						2000000	
21	Organization Costs		600000			(k) 30000			30000	
22	Notes Payable			15000000						15000000
23	Interest Payable					(l) 202500				202500
24	Accounts Payable			1242000						1242000
25	Employee Inc. Tax Payable			163440						163440
26	Federal Income Tax Payable					(p) 239570				239570
27	Social Security Tax Payable			15252		(m) 25665				40917
28	Medicare Tax Payable			3520		(n) 5923				9443

2   REINFORCEMENT ACTIVITY (continued)

[3]

	ACCOUNT TITLE	TRIAL BALANCE DEBIT	TRIAL BALANCE CREDIT	ADJUSTMENTS DEBIT	ADJUSTMENTS CREDIT	INCOME STATEMENT DEBIT	INCOME STATEMENT CREDIT	BALANCE SHEET DEBIT	BALANCE SHEET CREDIT
29	Salaries Payable				(m) 394854				394854
30	Sales Tax Payable		95142						95142
31	Unearned Rent				(o) 1200000				1200000
32	Unemploy. Tax Pay.—Federal		1072		(n) 1579				2651
33	Unemploy. Tax Pay.—State		7236		(n) 10658				17894
34	Health Ins. Prem. Payable		21540						21540
35	Dividends Payable								
36	Bonds Payable		200000000						200000000
37	Capital Stock—Common		126800000						126800000
38	Stock Subscribed—Common								
39	Pd.-in Cap. in Exc. Stated Va.—Common		3000000						3000000
40	Capital Stock—Preferred		4440000						4440000
41	Stock Subscribed—Preferred								
42	Pd.-in Cap. in Exc. Stated Val.—Preferred		1500000						1500000
43	Treasury Stock	450000						450000	
44	Pd.-in Cap. from Sale of Tr. Stock		4000						4000
45	Retained Earnings		2675939						2675939
46	Dividends—Common	1178000						1178000	
47	Dividends—Preferred	404000						404000	
48	Income Summary			(o) 1222770		1222770			
49	Sales		625611596				625611596		
50	Sales Discount	42757				42757			
51	Sales Ret. & Allowances	441516				441516			
52	Purchases	34612627				34612627			
53	Purchases Discount		1742232				1742232		
54	Purchases Ret. & Allow.		2112117				2112117		
55	Advertising Expense	31944				31944			
56	Credit Card Fee Expense	672183				672183			
57	Depr. Exp.—Store Equip.	59400		(h) 830000		889400			
58	Misc. Expense—Sales	47630				47630			

2 REINFORCEMENT ACTIVITY (continued)

[3]

Line	Account Title	TB Debit	TB Credit	Adj Debit	Adj Credit	IS Debit	IS Credit	BS Debit	BS Credit
59	Salary Expense—Sales	8403300		(m) 323204		8726504			
60	Supplies Expense—Sales			(d) 195072		195072			
61	Depr. Expense—Building			(i) 150000		150000			
62	Depr. Exp.—Office Equip.	200000		(j) 115000		315000			
63	Insurance Expense			(f) 79400		79400			
64	Misc. Expense—Admin.	39000				39000			
65	Payroll Taxes Expense	966015		(n) 43825		1009840			
66	Property Tax Expense	4000000				4000000			
67	Salary Expense—Admin.	1355138		(m) 71650		1426788			
68	Supplies Expense—Admin.			(e) 121728		121728			
69	Uncollectible Accounts Expense			(b) 34347		34347			
70	Utilities Expense	3411187				3411187			
71	Gain on Plant Assets		24000				24000		
72	Interest Income		1611129		95570		1706699		
73	Rent Income		10800000	(o) 1200000			9600000		
74	Interest Expense	2413423		(l) 202500	9333	2606590			
75	Loss on Plant Assets	64000				64000			
76	Organization Expense			(k) 30000		30000			
77	Federal Income Tax Expense	2220000		(p) 239570		2459570			
78		111752283	111752283	3797969	3797969	55599853	64101744	57812096	49670205
79						8141891			8141891
80						64101744	64101744	57812096	57812096
81									
82									
83									
84									
85									
86									
87									
88									

2 REINFORCEMENT ACTIVITY (continued)

Income statement analysis

[5]

	Acceptable %	Actual %	Positive Result		Recommended Action If Needed
			Yes	No	
Cost of merchandise sold	Not more than 55.0%	57.1%		✓	Analyze purchases and inventory controls and correct any negative situations.
Gross profit on operations	Not less than 45.0%	42.9%		✓	Correcting cost of merchandise sold will correct gross profit.
Total selling expenses	Not more than 20.0%	17.0%	✓		None
Total administrative expenses	Not more than 8.0%	6.3%	✓		None
Total operating expenses	Not more than 28.0%	23.3%	✓		None
Income from operations	Not less than 17.0%	19.6%	✓		None
Net deduction from other revenue and expenses	Not more than 3.0%	2.5%	✓		None
Net income before federal income tax	Not less than 14.0%	17.1%	✓		None

[6]

Earnings per share:

Stock	Share of Net Income	÷	Shares Outstanding	=	Earnings per Share
Preferred	$ 4,440.00	÷	444	=	$10.00
Common	$76,978.91	÷	12,630 (12,680 – 50)	=	$ 6.09

2 **REINFORCEMENT ACTIVITY (continued)**

[4]

Whitehurst, Inc.

Income Statement

For Year Ended December 31, 20--

							% OF NET SALES
Operating Revenue:							
Sales				625 6 1 5 96			
Less: Sales Discount		4 2 7 57					
Sales Ret. & Allow.		4 4 1 5 16	4 8 4 2 73				
Net Sales					620 7 7 3 23	100.0	
Cost of Merchandise Sold:							
Mdse. Inventory, January 1, 20--				218 8 4 6 33			
Purchases		346 1 2 6 27					
Less: Purchases Discount	1 7 4 2 32						
Purch. Ret. & Allow.	2 1 1 2 17	3 8 5 4 49					
Net Purchases				342 2 7 1 78			
Total Cost of Mdse. Avail. for Sale				561 1 1 8 11			
Less Mdse. Inventory, Dec. 31, 20--				206 6 1 8 63			
Cost of Merchandise Sold					354 4 9 9 48	57.1	
Gross Profit on Operations					266 2 7 3 75	42.9	
Operating Expenses:							
Selling Expenses:							
Advertising Expense		3 1 9 44					
Credit Card Fee Expense		6 7 2 1 83					
Depr. Expense—Store Equip.		8 8 9 4 00					
Miscellaneous Expense—Sales		4 7 6 30					
Salary Expense—Sales		87 2 6 5 04					
Supplies Expense—Sales		1 9 5 0 72					
Total Selling Expenses				105 6 2 7 33		17.0	
Administrative Expenses:							
Depr. Expense—Building		1 5 0 0 00					
Depr. Expense—Office Equip.		3 1 5 0 00					
Insurance Expense		7 9 4 00					
Miscellaneous Expense—Admin.		3 9 0 00					
Payroll Taxes Expense		10 0 9 8 40					
Property Tax Expense		4 0 0 0 00					
Salary Expense—Admin.		14 2 6 7 88					

2 REINFORCEMENT ACTIVITY (continued)

[4]

Whitehurst, Inc.

Income Statement (continued)

For Year Ended December 31, 20--

		% OF NET SALES
Supplies Expense—Admin.	1 2 1 7 28	
Uncollectible Accounts Expense	3 4 3 47	
Utilities Expense	3 4 1 1 87	
Total Admin. Expense	39 1 7 2 90	6.3
Total Operating Expenses	144 8 0 0 23	23.3
Income from Operations	121 4 7 3 52	19.6
Other Revenue:		
Gain on Plant Assets	2 4 0 00	
Interest Income	1 7 0 6 99	
Rent Income	9 6 0 0 00	
Total Other Revenue	11 5 4 6 99	
Other Expenses:		
Interest Expense	26 0 6 5 90	
Loss on Plant Assets	6 4 0 00	
Organization Expense	3 0 0 00	
Total Other Expenses	27 0 0 5 90	
Net Deduction from Other Rev. & Exp.	15 4 5 8 91	2.5
Net Income before Fed. Income Tax	106 0 1 4 61	17.1
Less Federal Income Tax Expense	24 5 9 5 70	4.0
Net Income after Fed. Income Tax	81 4 1 8 91	13.1

2   REINFORCEMENT ACTIVITY (continued)

[7]

Whitehurst, Inc.

Statement of Stockholders' Equity

For Year Ended December 31, 20--

Paid-in Capital:																		
Common Stock, $10.00 Stated Value:																		
January 1, 20--, 11,780 Shares Issued	117	8	0	0	00													
Issued during Current Year, 900 Shares	9	0	0	0	00													
Balance, Dec. 31, 20--, 12,680 Shares Issued						126	8	0	0	00								
Preferred Stock, 10.0%, $100.00 Par Value:																		
January 1, 20--, 404 Shares Issued	40	4	0	0	00													
Issued during Current Year, 40 Shares	4	0	0	0	00													
Balance, Dec. 31, 20--, 444 Shares Issued						44	4	0	0	00								
Total Value of Capital Stock Issued											171	2	0	0	00			
Additional Paid-in Capital:																		
Pd.-in-Cap. in Exc. of St. Value—Common						3	0	0	0	00								
Pd.-in-Cap. in Exc. of Par Value—Preferred						1	5	0	0	00								
Pd.-in-Cap. from Sale of Treasury Stock							4	0	00									
Total Additional Paid-in Capital											4	5	4	0	00			
Total Paid-in Capital											175	7	4	0	00			
Retained Earnings:																		
Balance, January 1, 20--						26	7	5	9	39								
Net Income after Federal Income Tax for 20--	81	4	1	8	91													
Less Dividends Declared during 20--	15	8	2	0	00													
Net Increase during 20--						65	5	9	8	91								
Balance, December 31, 20--											92	3	5	8	30			
Total Pd.-in Capital & Retained Earnings											268	0	9	8	30			
Less Treasury Stock, 50 Shares of																		
Common Stock, December 31, 20--											4	5	0	00				
Total Stockholders' Equity, Dec. 31, 20--											267	6	4	8	30			

2   REINFORCEMENT ACTIVITY (continued)

[8]

a. Equity per share:

Stock	Equity	÷	Shares Outstanding	=	Earnings per Share
Preferred	$ 44,400.00	÷	444	=	$100.00
Common	$223,248.30	÷	12,630	=	$ 17.68

b. Price-earnings ratio:

Stock	Market Price	÷	Earnings per Share	=	Price-earnings Ratio
Common	$13.50	÷	$6.09	=	2.2 times

[9]

Whitehurst, Inc.

Balance Sheet

December 31, 20--

ASSETS					
Current Assets:					
Cash		24 8 6 1 59			
Petty Cash		3 0 0 00			
Notes Receivable		5 0 0 00			
Interest Receivable		9 5 70			
Accounts Receivable	40 9 5 7 65				
Less Allow. for Uncoll. Accounts	7 6 2 75	40 1 9 4 90			
Merchandise Inventory		206 6 1 8 63			
Supplies—Sales		1 4 5 6 06			
Supplies—Administrative		7 3 0 00			
Prepaid Insurance		9 7 0 00			
Prepaid Interest		9 3 33			
Total Current Assets			275 8 2 0 21		
Long-Term Investment:					
Bond Sinking Fund			60 0 0 0 00		
Plant Assets:					
Store Equipment	93 4 0 0 00				
Less Accum. Depr.—Store Equip.	36 3 2 0 00	57 0 8 0 00			
Building	80 0 0 0 00				
Less Accum. Depr.—Building	6 0 0 0 00	74 0 0 0 00			
Office Equipment	31 5 6 8 00				
Less Accum. Depr.—Office Equip.	10 6 2 0 40	20 9 4 7 60			

2 **REINFORCEMENT ACTIVITY (continued)**

[9]

Whitehurst, Inc.

Balance Sheet (continued)

December 31, 20--

Land		20 0 0 0 00		
Total Plant Assets			172 0 2 7 60	
Intangible Asset:				
Organization Costs			3 0 0 00	
Total Assets			508 1 4 7 81	
LIABILITIES				
Current Liabilities:				
Notes Payable		15 0 0 0 00		
Interest Payable		2 0 2 5 00		
Accounts Payable		12 4 2 0 00		
Employee Income Tax Payable		1 6 3 4 40		
Federal Income Tax Payable		2 3 9 5 70		
Social Security Tax Payable		4 0 9 17		
Medicare Tax Payable		9 4 43		
Salaries Payable		3 9 4 8 54		
Sales Tax Payable		9 5 1 42		
Unearned Rent		1 2 0 0 00		
Unemploy. Tax Payable—Federal		2 6 51		
Unemploy. Tax Payable—State		1 7 8 94		
Health Insurance Premiums Payable		2 1 5 40		
Total Current Liabilities			40 4 9 9 51	
Long-Term Liability:				
Bonds Payable			200 0 0 0 00	
Total Liabilities			240 4 9 9 51	
STOCKHOLDERS' EQUITY				
Total Stockholders' Equity			267 6 4 8 30	
Total Liabilities & Stockholders' Equity			508 1 4 7 81	

2   REINFORCEMENT ACTIVITY (continued)

[10a]

Accounts receivable turnover ratio:

(January 1 Book Value	+	December 31 Book Value)	÷	2	=	Average
($36,087.10	+	$40,194.90)	÷	2	=	$38,141.00

Net Sales on Account	÷	Average Book Value	=	Ratio
$343,472.60	÷	$38,141.00	=	9.0 times

[10b]

Rate earned on average stockholders' equity:

(January 1 Equity	+	December 31 Equity)	÷	2	=	Average
($186,459.39	+	$267,648.30)	÷	2	=	$227,053.85

Net Income	÷	Average Equity	=	Rate
$81,418.91	÷	$227,053.85	=	35.9%

[10c]

Rate earned on average total assets:

(January 1 Assets	+	December 31 Assets)	÷	2	=	Average
($458,204.24	+	$508,147.81)	÷	2	=	$483,176.03

Net Income	÷	Average Assets	=	Rate
$81,418.91	÷	$483,176.03	=	16.9%

2 REINFORCEMENT ACTIVITY (continued)

[11]

GENERAL JOURNAL   PAGE 13

	DATE		ACCOUNT TITLE	DOC. NO.	POST. REF.	DEBIT	CREDIT	
1			*Adjusting Entries*					1
2	20-- Dec.	31	Interest Receivable			9570		2
3			Interest Income				9570	3
4		31	Uncollectible Accounts Expense			34347		4
5			Allowance for Uncollectible Accounts				34347	5
6		31	Income Summary			122270		6
7			Merchandise Inventory				122270	7
8		31	Supplies Expense—Sales			195072		8
9			Supplies—Sales				195072	9
10		31	Supplies Expense—Administrative			121728		10
11			Supplies—Administrative				121728	11
12		31	Insurance Expense			79400		12
13			Prepaid Insurance				79400	13
14		31	Prepaid Interest			9333		14
15			Interest Expense				9333	15
16		31	Depreciation Expense—Store Equipment			830000		16
17			Accum. Depr.—Store Equipment				830000	17
18		31	Depreciation Expense—Building			150000		18
19			Accum. Depr.—Building				150000	19
20		31	Depreciation Expense—Office Equipment			115000		20
21			Accum. Depr.—Office Equipment				115000	21
22		31	Organization Expense			30000		22
23			Organization Costs				30000	23
24		31	Interest Expense			202500		24
25			Interest Payable				202500	25
26		31	Salary Expense—Sales			323204		26
27			Salary Expense—Administrative			71650		27
28			Salaries Payable				394854	28
29		31	Payroll Taxes Expense			43825		29
30			Social Security Tax Payable				25665	30
31			Medicare Tax Payable				5923	31
32			Unemployment Tax Payable—Federal				1579	32
33			Unemployment Tax Payable—State				10658	33

2 REINFORCEMENT ACTIVITY (continued)

[11, 12]

GENERAL JOURNAL   PAGE 14

	DATE		ACCOUNT TITLE	DOC. NO.	POST. REF.	DEBIT	CREDIT	
1	20-- Dec.	31	Rent Income			1 20 0 00		1
2			Unearned Rent				1 20 0 00	2
3		31	Federal Income Tax Expense			2 39 5 70		3
4			Federal Income Tax Payable				2 39 5 70	4
5			Closing Entries					5
6		31	Sales			625 6 1 5 96		6
7			Purchases Discount			1 7 4 2 32		7
8			Purchases Returns and Allowances			2 1 1 2 17		8
9			Gain on Plant Assets			2 4 0 00		9
10			Interest Income			1 7 0 6 99		10
11			Rent Income			9 6 0 0 00		11
12			Income Summary				641 0 1 7 44	12
13		31	Income Summary			547 3 7 0 83		13
14			Sales Discount				4 2 7 57	14
15			Sales Returns and Allowances				4 4 1 5 16	15
16			Purchases				346 1 2 6 27	16
17			Advertising Expense				3 1 9 44	17
18			Credit Card Fee Expense				6 7 2 1 83	18
19			Depreciation Expense—Store Equip.				8 8 9 4 00	19
20			Miscellaneous Expense—Sales				4 7 6 30	20
21			Salary Expense—Sales				87 2 6 5 04	21
22			Supplies Expense—Sales				1 9 5 0 72	22
23			Depreciation Expense—Building				1 5 0 0 00	23
24			Depreciation Expense—Office Equip.				3 1 5 0 00	24
25			Insurance Expense				7 9 4 00	25
26			Miscellaneous Expense—Admin.				3 9 0 00	26
27			Payroll Taxes Expense				10 0 9 8 40	27
28			Property Tax Expense				4 0 0 0 00	28
29			Salary Expense—Administrative				14 2 6 7 88	29
30			Supplies Expense—Administrative				1 2 1 7 28	30
31			Uncollectible Accounts Expense				3 4 3 47	31
32			Utilities Expense				3 4 1 1 87	32

2 REINFORCEMENT ACTIVITY (concluded)

[12]

GENERAL JOURNAL   PAGE 15

	DATE		ACCOUNT TITLE	DOC. NO.	POST. REF.	DEBIT	CREDIT	
1	20-- Dec.	31	*Interest Expense*				2 6 0 6 5 90	1
2			*Loss on Plant Assets*				6 4 0 00	2
3			*Organization Expense*				3 0 0 00	3
4			*Federal Income Tax Expense*				2 4 5 9 5 70	4
5		31	*Income Summary*			8 1 4 1 8 91		5
6			*Retained Earnings*				8 1 4 1 8 91	6
7		31	*Retained Earnings*			1 5 8 2 0 00		7
8			*Dividends—Common*				1 1 7 8 0 00	8
9			*Dividends—Preferred*				4 0 4 0 00	9
10								10

[13]

GENERAL JOURNAL   PAGE 1

	DATE		ACCOUNT TITLE	DOC. NO.	POST. REF.	DEBIT	CREDIT	
1			*Reversing Entries*					1
2	20-- Jan.	1	*Interest Income*			9 5 70		2
3			*Interest Receivable*				9 5 70	3
4		1	*Interest Expense*			9 3 33		4
5			*Prepaid Interest*				9 3 33	5
6		1	*Interest Payable*			2 0 2 5 00		6
7			*Interest Expense*				2 0 2 5 00	7
8		1	*Salaries Payable*			3 9 4 8 54		8
9			*Salary Expense—Sales*				3 2 3 2 04	9
10			*Salary Expense—Administrative*				7 1 6 50	10
11		1	*Social Security Tax Payable*			2 5 6 65		11
12			*Medicare Tax Payable*			5 9 23		12
13			*Unemployment Tax Payable—Federal*			1 5 79		13
14			*Unemployment Tax Payable—State*			1 0 6 58		14
15			*Payroll Taxes Expense*				4 3 8 25	15
16		1	*Unearned Rent*			1 2 0 0 00		16
17			*Rent Income*				1 2 0 0 00	17

14-1 WORK TOGETHER, p. 392

Analyzing a comparative income statement [4]

Cost/Expense Item	Percentage of Increase (Decrease)	Favorable/Unfavorable
Cost of Merchandise Sold	11.0%	*favorable*
Advertising Expense	15.1%	*unfavorable*
Salary Expense	12.5%	*favorable*
Utilities Expense	(1.2%)	*favorable*

14-1 ON YOUR OWN, p. 392

Analyzing a comparative income statement [5]

Cost/Expense Item	Percentage of Increase (Decrease)	Favorable/Unfavorable
Cost of Merchandise Sold	11.0%	*unfavorable*
Advertising Expense	7.3%	*favorable*
Insurance Expense	(4.5%)	*favorable*
Rent Expense	2.0%	*favorable*

14-1 WORK TOGETHER ON YOUR OWN

Extra form

	Budget 1st Qtr.	Actual 1st Qtr.	Increase (Decrease)	
			Amount	Percentage
Unit Sales.				
Operating Revenue:				
Net Sales.				
Cost of Merchandise Sold.				
Gross Profit on Operations.				
Operating Expenses:				
Selling Expenses:				
Advertising Expense.				
Delivery Expense				
Depr. Expense—Delivery Equipment				
Depr. Expense—Warehouse Equipment.				
Miscellaneous Expense—Sales.				
Salary Expense—Commissions				
Salary Expense—Regular				
Supplies Expense—Sales				
Total Selling Expenses				
Administrative Expenses:				
Depr. Expense—Office Equipment				
Insurance Expense				
Miscellaneous Expense—Adminstrative.				
Payroll Taxes Expense				
Rent Expense				
Salary Expense—Administrative				
Supplies Expense—Administrative				
Uncollectible Accounts Expense.				
Utilities Expense.				
Total Administrative Expenses				
Total Operating Expenses				
Income from Operations				
Other Expenses:				
Interest Expense.				
Net Income before Federal Income Tax.				
Federal Income Tax Expense.				
Net Income after Federal Income Tax				

14-2 WORK TOGETHER, p. 401

Planning for a budgeted income statement   [3–6]

3. **Units projected to be sold during first quarter of 20X2:**   _45,900 units_

   230,000 units × 10.8% = 24,840 + 230,000 = 254,840, rounded to 254,800 units

   254,800 units × 18% = 45,864, rounded to 45,900 units

   Projected sales for first quarter of 20X2:   _$344,250.00_

   45,900 units × $7.50 = $344,250.00

4. **Number of units needed for first quarter:**   _57,000 units_

   11,100 ending inventory + 45,900 quarter sales = 57,000 units

5. **Units purchased during first quarter:**   _47,600 units_

   57,000 units needed – 9,400 beginning inventory units = 47,600 units

6. **Projected cost of purchases:**   _$195,160.00_

   47,600 units purchased × $4.10 = $195,160.00

14-2 WORK TOGETHER

Extra space for calculations

14-2 ON YOUR OWN, p. 401

Planning for a budgeted income statement   [7–10]

7. **Units projected to be sold during first quarter of 20X2:**   *19,100 units*

   90,000 units × 6.1% = 5,490 units + 90,000 units = 94,490, rounded to 95,500 units

   95,500 units × 20% = 19,100 units

   Projected sales for first quarter of 20X2:   *$305,600.00*

   19,100 units × $16.00 = $305,600.00

8. **Number of units needed for first quarter:**   *23,800 units*

   4,700 ending inventory + 19,100 quarter sales = 23,800 units

9. **Units purchased during first quarter:**   *20,400 units*

   23,800 units needed – 3,400 beginning inventory units = 20,400 units

10. **Projected cost of purchases:**   *$159,120.00*

    20,400 units purchased × $7.80 = $159,120.00

14-2 ON YOUR OWN

Extra space for calculations

14-3 WORK TOGETHER, p. 408

Planning for a cash budget [4–6]

4. Total amount of cash received during second quarter: $364,900.00

$360,500.00 \times 50\% = \$180,250.00$
$360,500.00 \times 30\% = 108,150.00$
$425,000.00 \times 18\% = 76,500.00$
$\overline{} \$364,900.00$

5. Total cash payments for second quarter: $403,290.00

$289,000.00 + \$97,840.00 + \$9,210.00 + \$7,240.00 = \$403,290.00$

6. Ending cash balance for second quarter: $23,170.00

$61,560.00 beginning cash + $364,900.00 cash received –
$403,290.00 cash payments = $23,170.00

14-3 WORK TOGETHER

Extra space for calculations

14-3 ON YOUR OWN, p. 408

Planning for a cash budget   [7-9]

7. **Total amount of cash received during second quarter:** $642,230.00

$670,250.00 × 45% = $301,612.50, rounded to $301,610.00
$670,250.00 × 40% =   268,100.00
$518,000.00 × 14% =   72,520.00
                                                $642,230.00

8. **Total cash payments for second quarter:** $603,410.00

$410,000.00 + $101,630.00 + $11,780.00 + $80,000.00 = $603,410.00

9. **Ending cash balance for second quarter:** $63,680.00

$24,860.00 beginning cash + $642,230.00 cash received −
$603,410.00 cash payments = $63,680.00

14-3 ON YOUR OWN

Extra space for calculations

14-1 APPLICATION PROBLEM, p. 410

Preparing a sales budget schedule and a purchase budget schedule   [1]

PhotoMax, Inc. Sales Budget Schedule For Year Ended December 31, 20X3		Quarter				Schedule 1
	Annual Budget	**1st**	**2d**	**3d**	**4th**	
Actual Unit Sales, 20X2	234,000	58,500	62,700	68,900	43,900	
Sales Percentage by Quarter		25.0%	26.8%	29.4%	18.8%	
Projected Unit Sales, 20X3.	250,000	62,500	67,000	73,500	47,000	
Times Unit Sales Price		$14.00	$14.00	$14.00	$14.00	
Net Sales	$3,500,000	$875,000	$938,000	$1,029,000	$658,000	

[2]

PhotoMax, Inc. Purchases Budget Schedule For Year Ended December 31, 20X3	Quarter				Schedule 2
	1st	**2d**	**3d**	**4th**	
Ending Inventory	20,100	22,100	14,100	19,500	
Unit Sales for Quarter	62,500	67,000	73,500	47,000	
Total Units Needed	82,600	89,100	87,600	66,500	
Less Beginning Inventory	27,700	20,100	22,100	14,100	
Purchases	54,900	69,000	65,500	52,400	
Times Unit Cost.	$7.50	$7.50	$7.50	$7.50	
Cost of Purchases.	$411,750	$517,500	$491,250	$393,000	

Extra space for calculations

14-1 APPLICATION PROBLEM

Extra forms

		Schedule 1			
	Annual Budget	Quarter			
		1st	2d	3d	4th
Actual Unit Sales, 20X2					
Sales Percentage by Quarter					
Projected Unit Sales, 20X3					
Times Unit Sales Price					
Net Sales					

	Schedule 2			
	Quarter			
	1st	2d	3d	4th
Ending Inventory				
Unit Sales for Quarter				
Total Units Needed				
Less Beginning Inventory				
Purchases				
Times Unit Cost				
Cost of Purchases				

Extra space for calculations

14-2 APPLICATION PROBLEM, p. 410

Preparing a budgeted income statement

[1]

Coffee Oasis Selling Expenses Budget Schedule For Year Ended December 31, 20X3					Schedule 3
	Annual Budget	**Quarter**			
		1st	**2d**	**3d**	**4th**
Advertising Expense...........	$21,000	$4,200	$5,250	$5,250	$6,300
Delivery Expense	37,800	7,560	9,450	9,450	11,340
Depr. Expense—Del. Equip. ..	3,400	850	850	850	850
Depr. Expense—Store Equipment .	4,200	1,050	1,050	1,050	1,050
Miscellaneous Expense—Sales....	15,800	3,950	3,950	3,950	3,950
Salary Expense—Sales...........	84,000	16,800	21,000	21,000	25,200
Supplies Expense—Sales	28,000	5,600	7,000	7,000	8,400
Total Selling Expenses	$194,200	$40,010	$48,550	$48,550	$57,090

[2]

Coffee Oasis Administrative Expenses Budget Schedule For Year Ended December 31, 20X3					Schedule 4
	Annual Budget	**Quarter**			
		1st	**2d**	**3d**	**4th**
Depr. Expense—Office Equipment..	$4,800	$1,200	$1,200	$1,200	$1,200
Insurance Expense..............	6,000	1,500	1,500	1,500	1,500
Miscellaneous Expense—Admin....	5,600	1,400	1,400	1,400	1,400
Payroll Taxes Expense	17,160	3,740	4,290	4,290	4,840
Rent Expense	12,800	3,200	3,200	3,200	3,200
Salary Expense—Administrative....	46,000	11,500	11,500	11,500	11,500
Supplies Expense—Administrative..	4,240	1,060	1,060	1,060	1,060
Uncollectible Accounts Expense....	11,200	2,240	2,800	2,800	3,360
Utilities Expense	18,400	4,600	4,600	4,600	4,600
Total Administrative Expenses	$126,200	$30,440	$31,550	$31,550	$32,660

Name _____ Date _____ Class _____

14-2 APPLICATION PROBLEM (concluded)

		Quarter			
Coffee Oasis Budgeted Income Statement For Year Ended December 31, 20X3	Annual Budget	1st	2d	3d	4th
Operating Revenue: Net Sales (Schedule 1)	$1,400,000	$280,000	$350,000	$350,000	$420,000
Cost of Merchandise Sold: Beginning Inventory.	$88,250	$88,250	$111,500	$110,500	$132,500
Purchases (Schedule 2).	972,750	201,000	242,500	283,000	246,250
Total Merchandise Available.	$1,061,000	$289,250	$354,000	$393,500	$378,750
Less Ending Inventory.	99,250	111,500	110,500	132,500	99,250
Cost of Merchandise Sold	$961,750	$177,750	$243,500	$261,000	$279,500
Gross Profit on Operations	$438,250	$102,250	$106,500	$89,000	$140,500
Operating Expenses: Selling Expenses (Schedule 3)	$194,200	$40,010	$48,550	$48,550	$57,090
Administrative Expenses (Schedule 4)	126,200	30,440	31,550	31,550	32,660
Total Operating Expenses	$320,400	$70,450	$80,100	$80,100	$89,750
Net Income before Federal Income Tax	$117,850	$31,800	$26,400	$8,900	$50,750
Federal Income Tax Expense.	29,210	7,300	7,300	7,300	7,310
Net Income after Federal Income Tax	$88,640	$24,500	$19,100	$1,600	$43,440

Space for calculations:

14-3 APPLICATION PROBLEM, p. 411

Preparing a cash budget with supporting schedules

[1]

SeaWest Fabrication
Cash Receipts Budget Schedule
For Year Ended December 31, 20X3

Schedule A

	Quarter			
	1st	2d	3d	4th
From Sales:				
Prior Year's 4th Quarter ($639,200)	$252,480			
1st Quarter Sales ($646,300)	387,780	$255,290		
2d Quarter Sales ($674,900)		404,940	$266,590	
3d Quarter Sales ($661,800)			397,080	$261,410
4th Quarter Sales ($681,600)				408,960
Total Receipts from Sales	$640,260	$660,230	$663,670	$670,370
From Other Sources:				
Note Payable to Bank		35,000		
Total Cash Receipts.	$640,260	$695,230	$663,670	$670,370

[2]

SeaWest Fabrication
Cash Payments Budget Schedule
For Year Ended December 31, 20X3

Schedule B

	Quarter			
	1st	2d	3d	4th
For Merchandise:				
Prior Year's 4th Quarter Purchases ($548,240) . . .	$328,940			
1st Quarter Purchases ($558,300)	223,320	$334,980		
2d Quarter Purchases ($571,600)		228,640	$342,960	
3d Quarter Purchases ($561,200)			224,480	$336,720
4th Quarter Purchases ($582,300)				232,920
Total Cash Payments for Purchases	$552,260	$563,620	$567,440	$569,640
From Operating Expenses:				
Cash Selling Expenses	$32,100	$36,200	$42,400	$36,800
Cash Administrative Expenses	38,600	38,900	39,700	39,800
Total Cash Operating Expenses	$70,700	$75,100	$82,100	$76,600
For Other Cash Payments:				
Federal Income Tax Expense	$1,930	$1,930	$1,930	$1,930
Equipment Purchases		31,600		
Cash Dividend.			30,000	
Note Payable and Interest.				37,500
Total Other Cash Payments	$1,930	$33,530	$31,930	$39,430
Total Cash Payments	$624,890	$672,250	$681,470	$685,670

14-3 APPLICATION PROBLEM (concluded)

[3]

	SeaWest Fabrication Cash Budget For Year Ended December 31, 20X3			
	Quarter			
	1st	**2d**	**3d**	**4th**
Cash Balance—Beginning......................	$35,720	$51,090	$74,070	$56,270
Cash Receipts (Schedule A).....................	640,260	695,230	663,670	670,370
Cash Available.................................	$675,980	$746,320	$737,740	$726,640
Less Cash Payments (Schedule B).............	624,890	672,250	681,470	685,670
Cash Balance—Ending	$51,090	$74,070	$56,270	$40,970

Space for calculations:

14-4 MASTERY PROBLEM, p. 412

Preparing a budgeted income statement and a cash budget   [a]
with supporting budget schedules

Zylar, Inc. Sales Budget Schedule For Year Ended December 31, 20X3	Annual Budget	Quarter			Schedule 1
		1st	2d	3d	4th
Actual Unit Sales, 20X2	120,000	22,000	34,400	34,800	28,800
Sales Percentage by Quarter		18.3%	28.7%	29.0%	24.0%
Projected Unit Sales, 20X3	130,000	23,800	37,300	37,700	31,200
Times Unit Sales Price		$6.00	$6.00	$6.00	$6.00
Net Sales	$780,000	$142,800	$223,800	$226,200	$187,200

[b]

Zylar, Inc. Purchases Budget Schedule For Year Ended December 31, 20X3	Quarter			Schedule 2
	1st	2d	3d	4th
Ending Inventory	14,900	15,100	12,500	9,600
Unit Sales for Quarter	23,800	37,300	37,700	31,200
Total Units Needed	38,700	52,400	50,200	40,800
Less Beginning Inventory	12,500	14,900	15,100	12,500
Purchases	26,200	37,500	35,100	28,300
Times Unit Cost	$4.25	$4.25	$4.25	$4.25
Cost of Purchases	$111,350	$159,380	$149,180	$120,280

Space for calculations:

14-4 MASTERY PROBLEM (continued)

[c]

<table>
<tr><td colspan="6">Zylar, Inc.
Selling Expenses Budget Schedule
For Year Ended December 31, 20X3   Schedule 3</td></tr>
<tr><td rowspan="2"></td><td rowspan="2">Annual Budget</td><td colspan="4">Quarter</td></tr>
<tr><td>1st</td><td>2d</td><td>3d</td><td>4th</td></tr>
<tr><td>Advertising Expense............</td><td>$9,360</td><td>$1,710</td><td>$2,690</td><td>$2,710</td><td>$2,250</td></tr>
<tr><td>Delivery Expense ....</td><td>4,680</td><td>860</td><td>1,340</td><td>1,360</td><td>1,120</td></tr>
<tr><td>Depr. Expense—Del. Equipment..</td><td>2,400</td><td>600</td><td>600</td><td>600</td><td>600</td></tr>
<tr><td>Depr. Expense—Store Equipment.</td><td>6,680</td><td>1,670</td><td>1,670</td><td>1,670</td><td>1,670</td></tr>
<tr><td>Miscellaneous Expense—Sales....</td><td>3,120</td><td>570</td><td>900</td><td>900</td><td>750</td></tr>
<tr><td>Salary Expense—Sales..........</td><td>39,000</td><td>7,140</td><td>11,190</td><td>11,310</td><td>9,360</td></tr>
<tr><td>Supplies Expense—Sales ....</td><td>6,240</td><td>1,140</td><td>1,790</td><td>1,810</td><td>1,500</td></tr>
<tr><td>Total Selling Expenses ....</td><td>$71,480</td><td>$13,690</td><td>$20,180</td><td>$20,360</td><td>$17,250</td></tr>
</table>

[d]

<table>
<tr><td colspan="6">Zylar, Inc.
Administrative Expenses Budget Schedule
For Year Ended December 31, 20X3   Schedule 4</td></tr>
<tr><td rowspan="2"></td><td rowspan="2">Annual Budget</td><td colspan="4">Quarter</td></tr>
<tr><td>1st</td><td>2d</td><td>3d</td><td>4th</td></tr>
<tr><td>Depr. Expense—Office Equipment..</td><td>$3,600</td><td>$900</td><td>$900</td><td>$900</td><td>$900</td></tr>
<tr><td>Insurance Expense..............</td><td>4,200</td><td>1,050</td><td>1,050</td><td>1,050</td><td>1,050</td></tr>
<tr><td>Miscellaneous Expense—Admin....</td><td>3,000</td><td>750</td><td>750</td><td>750</td><td>750</td></tr>
<tr><td>Payroll Taxes Expense ....</td><td>7,700</td><td>1,610</td><td>2,100</td><td>2,110</td><td>1,880</td></tr>
<tr><td>Rent Expense ....</td><td>9,600</td><td>2,400</td><td>2,400</td><td>2,400</td><td>2,400</td></tr>
<tr><td>Salary Expense—Administrative....</td><td>25,200</td><td>6,300</td><td>6,300</td><td>6,300</td><td>6,300</td></tr>
<tr><td>Supplies Expense—Administrative..</td><td>2,800</td><td>700</td><td>700</td><td>700</td><td>700</td></tr>
<tr><td>Uncollectible Accounts Expense....</td><td>4,680</td><td>860</td><td>1,340</td><td>1,360</td><td>1,120</td></tr>
<tr><td>Utilities Expense ....</td><td>14,040</td><td>2,570</td><td>4,030</td><td>4,070</td><td>3,370</td></tr>
<tr><td>Total Administrative Expenses.....</td><td>$74,820</td><td>$17,140</td><td>$19,570</td><td>$19,640</td><td>$18,470</td></tr>
</table>

[e]

<table>
<tr><td colspan="6">Zylar, Inc.
Other Revenue and Expenses Budget Schedule
For Year Ended December 31, 20X3   Schedule 5</td></tr>
<tr><td rowspan="2"></td><td rowspan="2">Annual Budget</td><td colspan="4">Quarter</td></tr>
<tr><td>1st</td><td>2d</td><td>3d</td><td>4th</td></tr>
<tr><td>Other Expenses
  Interest Expense ....</td><td>5,000</td><td>$1,250</td><td>$1,250</td><td>$1,250</td><td>$1,250</td></tr>
</table>

14-4 MASTERY PROBLEM (continued)

[f]

Zylar, Inc.
Budgeted Income Statement
For Year Ended December 31, 20X3

	Annual Budget	Quarter			
		1st	2d	3d	4th
Operating Revenue: Net Sales (Schedule 1)	$780,000	$142,800	$223,800	$226,200	$187,200
Cost of Merchandise Sold: Beginning Inventory.	$50,000	$50,000	$63,330	$64,180	$53,130
Purchases (Schedule 2).	540,190	111,350	159,380	149,180	120,280
Total Merchandise Available.	$590,190	$161,350	$222,710	$213,360	$173,410
Less Ending Inventory	40,800	63,330	64,180	53,130	40,800
Cost of Merchandise Sold	$549,390	$98,020	$158,530	$160,230	$132,610
Gross Profit on Operations	$230,610	$44,780	$65,270	$65,970	$54,590
Operating Expenses: Selling Expenses (Schedule 3)	$71,480	$13,690	$20,180	$20,360	$17,250
Administrative Expenses (Schedule 4)	74,820	17,140	19,570	19,640	18,470
Total Operating Expenses	$146,300	$30,830	$39,750	$40,000	$35,720
Income from Operations	$84,310	$13,950	$25,520	$25,970	$18,870
Other Expense Deduction (Schedule 5)	$5,000	$1,250	$1,250	$1,250	$1,250
Net Income before Federal Income Tax	$79,310	$12,700	$24,270	$24,720	$17,620
Federal Income Tax Expense	15,220	3,810	3,810	3,810	3,790
Net Income after Federal Income Tax	$64,090	$8,890	$20,460	$20,910	$13,830

[g]

Zylar, Inc.
Cash Receipts Budget Schedule
For Year Ended December 31, 20X3   Schedule A

	Quarter			
	1st	2d	3d	4th
From Sales: Prior Year's 4th Quarter ($161,280)	$79,670			
1st Quarter Sales ($142,800)	71,400	$70,540		
2d Quarter Sales ($223,800)		111,900	$110,560	
3d Quarter Sales ($226,200)			113,100	$111,740
4th Quarter Sales ($187,200)				93,600
Total Receipts from Sales	$151,070	$182,440	$223,660	$205,340
From Other Sources: Note Payable to Bank	40,000			
Total Cash Receipts	$191,070	$182,440	$223,660	$205,340

14-4 MASTERY PROBLEM (concluded)

[h]

Zylar, Inc.
Cash Payments Budget Schedule
For Year Ended December 31, 20X3   Schedule B

	Quarter			
	1st	2d	3d	4th
For Merchandise:				
Prior Year's 4th Quarter Purchases ($105,600) ...	$36,960			
1st Quarter Purchases ($111,350).............	72,380	$38,970		
2d Quarter Purchases ($159,380).............		103,600	$55,780	
3d Quarter Purchases ($149,180).............			96,970	$52,210
4th Quarter Purchases ($120,280).............				78,180
Total Cash Payments for Purchases	$109,340	$142,570	$152,750	$130,390
For Operating Expenses:				
Cash Selling Expenses.......................	$11,420	$17,910	$18,090	$14,980
Cash Administrative Expenses	15,380	17,330	17,380	16,450
Total Cash Operating Expenses	$26,800	$35,240	$35,470	$31,430
For Other Cash Payments:				
Federal Income Tax Expense	$3,810	$3,810	$3,810	$3,790
Equipment Purchases	30,000			
Cash Dividend	10,000	10,000	10,000	10,000
Note Payable and Interest...................				45,000
Total Other Cash Payments	$43,810	$13,810	$13,810	$58,790
Total Cash Payments	$179,950	$191,620	$202,030	$220,610

[i]

Zylar, Inc.
Cash Budget
For Year Ended December 31, 20X3

	Quarter			
	1st	2d	3d	4th
Cash Balance—Beginning......................	$41,600	$52,720	$43,540	$65,170
Cash Receipts (Schedule A)...................	191,070	182,440	223,660	205,340
Cash Available.............................	$232,670	$235,160	$267,200	$270,510
Less Cash Payments (Schedule B).............	179,950	191,620	202,030	220,610
Cash Balance—Ending	$52,720	$43,540	$65,170	$49,900

14-5 CHALLENGE PROBLEM, p. 413

Preparing a performance report

[1, 2]

Quasar Robotics, Inc.
Performance Report
For Quarter Ended March 31, 20X3

	Budget 1st Qtr.	Actual 1st Qtr.	Increase (Decrease) Amount	Percentage
Unit Sales	80,000	82,400	2,400	3.0
Operating Revenue:				
Net Sales	$336,000	$346,080	$10,080	3.0
Cost of Merchandise Sold	184,000	192,520	8,520	4.6
Gross Profit on Operations	$152,000	$153,560	$1,560	1.0
Operating Expenses:				
Selling Expenses:				
Advertising Expense	$2,500	$2,650	$150	6.0*
Delivery Expense	4,320	4,380	60	1.4
Depr. Expense—Delivery Equipment	4,260	4,260		
Depr. Expense—Warehouse Equipment	3,450	3,450		
Miscellaneous Expense—Sales	1,670	1,650	(20)	(1.2)
Salary Expense—Commissions	10,080	10,382	302	3.0
Salary Expense—Regular	25,680	25,680		
Supplies Expense—Sales	2,450	2,630	180	7.3*
Total Selling Expenses	$54,410	$55,082	$672	1.2
Administrative Expenses:				
Depr. Expense—Office Equipment	$4,200	$4,200		
Insurance Expense	900	900		
Miscellaneous Expense—Adminstrative	6,500	6,580	$80	1.2
Payroll Taxes Expense	8,470	8,500	30	0.4
Rent Expense	2,500	2,500		
Salary Expense—Administrative	34,800	34,800		
Supplies Expense—Administrative	4,400	4,160	(240)	(5.5)*
Uncollectible Accounts Expense	3,360	3,380	20	0.6
Utilities Expense	5,400	5,490	90	1.7
Total Administrative Expenses	$70,530	$70,510	($20)	0.0
Total Operating Expenses	$124,940	$125,592	$652	0.5
Income from Operations	$27,060	$27,968	$908	3.4
Other Expenses:				
Interest Expense	$1,200	$1,200		
Net Income before Federal Income Tax	$25,860	$26,768	$908	3.5
Federal Income Tax Expense	5,170	5,350	180	3.5
Net Income after Federal Income Tax	$20,690	$21,418	$728	3.5

14-5 CHALLENGE PROBLEM

Extra form

	Budget 1st Qtr.	Actual 1st Qtr.	Increase (Decrease)	
			Amount	Percentage
Unit Sales.................................				
Operating Revenue:				
Net Sales.................................				
Cost of Merchandise Sold....................				
Gross Profit on Operations....................				
Operating Expenses:				
Selling Expenses:				
Advertising Expense......................				
Delivery Expense........................				
Depr. Expense—Delivery Equipment.........				
Depr. Expense—Warehouse Equipment.......				
Miscellaneous Expense—Sales..............				
Salary Expense—Commissions..............				
Salary Expense—Regular..................				
Supplies Expense—Sales..................				
Total Selling Expenses....................				
Administrative Expenses:				
Depr. Expense—Office Equipment...........				
Insurance Expense.......................				
Miscellaneous Expense—Adminstrative.......				
Payroll Taxes Expense....................				
Rent Expense...........................				
Salary Expense—Administrative.............				
Supplies Expense—Administrative...........				
Uncollectible Accounts Expense.............				
Utilities Expense........................				
Total Administrative Expenses.............				
Total Operating Expenses....................				
Income from Operations.....................				
Other Expenses:				
Interest Expense.........................				
Net Income before Federal Income Tax..........				
Federal Income Tax Expense.................				
Net Income after Federal Income Tax...........				

Name _____ Date _____ Class _____

15-1 WORK TOGETHER, p. 422

Preparing an income statement with contribution margin [3]

Wightman's Lumber

Income Statement

For Month Ended January 31, 20--

Operating Revenue:				
Net Sales (52,000 sq. ft. @ $7.50)		390 0 0 0 00	
Variable Costs:				
Cost of Merchandise Sold (52,000 sq. ft. @ $4.60)	239 2 0 0 00		
Sales Commission (52,000 sq. ft. @ $.32)	16 6 4 0 00		
Delivery Costs (52,000 sq. ft. @ $.50)	26 0 0 0 00		
Other Selling Costs (52,000 sq. ft. @ $.35)	18 2 0 0 00		
Other Administrative Costs (52,000 sq. ft. @ $.30)	15 6 0 0 00		
Total Variable Costs		315 6 4 0 00	
Contribution Margin		74 3 6 0 00	
Fixed Costs:				
Rent	3 8 0 0 00		
Insurance	4 5 0 00		
Other Selling Costs	7 1 2 0 00		
Other Administrative Costs	12 5 4 0 00		
Total Fixed Costs		23 9 1 0 00	
Net Income		50 4 5 0 00	

Chapter 15 Accounting Information for Management Decisions • 143

15-1 WORK TOGETHER

Extra form

15-1 ON YOUR OWN, p. 422

Preparing an income statement with contribution margin [4]

Wightman's Lumber

Income Statement

For Month Ended February 28, 20--

Operating Revenue:			
Net Sales (47,000 sq. ft. @ $7.50)			352 5 0 0 00
Variable Costs:			
Cost of Merchandise Sold (47,000 sq. ft. @ $4.80)	225 6 0 0 00		
Sales Commission (47,000 sq. ft. @ $.32)	15 0 4 0 00		
Delivery Costs (47,000 sq. ft. @ $.55)	25 8 5 0 00		
Other Selling Costs (47,000 sq. ft. @ $.35)	16 4 5 0 00		
Other Administrative Costs (47,000 sq. ft. @ $.33)	15 5 1 0 00		
Total Variable Costs		298 4 5 0 00	
Contribution Margin		54 0 5 0 00	
Fixed Costs:			
Rent	3 8 0 0 00		
Insurance	4 5 0 00		
Other Selling Costs	7 1 2 0 00		
Other Administrative Costs	12 5 4 0 00		
Total Fixed Costs		23 9 1 0 00	
Net Income		30 1 4 0 00	

15-1 ON YOUR OWN

Extra form

15-2 WORK TOGETHER, p. 426

Calculating breakeven in sales dollars and unit sales and [4]
preparing a breakeven income statement

Breakeven point in sales dollars:

Contribution Margin	÷	Net Sales	=	Contribution Margin Rate
$12,000.00	÷	$60,000.00	=	20%

Total Fixed Costs	÷	Contribution Margin Rate	=	Sales Dollars Breakeven Point
$8,000.00	÷	20%	=	$40,000.00

Unit sales breakeven point for July:

Sales Dollars Breakeven Point	÷	Unit Sales Price	=	Unit Sales Breakeven Point
$40,000.00	÷	$8.00	=	5,000 units

[5]

Cherie's Pizza

Breakeven Income Statement

For Month Ended July 31, 20--

Operating Revenue:										
Net Sales (5,000 units @ $8.00)	40	0	0	0	00					
Variable Costs (5,000 units @ $6.40)	32	0	0	0	00					
Contribution Margin	8	0	0	0	00					
Fixed Costs	8	0	0	0	00					
Net Income			0	00						

Name _____ Date _____ Class _____

Extra form

Name _____ Date _____ Class _____

15-2 ON YOUR OWN, p. 426

Calculating breakeven in sales dollars and unit sales and [6]
preparing a breakeven income statement

Breakeven point in sales dollars:

Contribution Margin	÷	Net Sales	=	Contribution Margin Rate
$10,000.00	÷	$80,000.00	=	12.5%

Total Fixed Costs	÷	Contribution Margin Rate	=	Sales Dollars Breakeven Point
$8,000.00	÷	12.5%	=	$64,000.00

Unit sales breakeven point for August:

Sales Dollars Breakeven Point	÷	Unit Sales Price	=	Unit Sales Breakeven Point
$64,000.00	÷	$8.00	=	8,000 units

[7]

Cherie's Pizza

Breakeven Income Statement

For Month Ended August 31, 20--

Operating Revenue:		
Net Sales (8,000 units @ $8.00)	64 0 0 0 00	
Variable Costs (8,000 units @ $7.00)	56 0 0 0 00	
Contribution Margin	8 0 0 0 00	
Fixed Costs	8 0 0 0 00	
Net Income		0 00

15-2 ON YOUR OWN

Extra form

15-3 WORK TOGETHER, p. 434

Calculating sales to earn a planned net income, calculating the effect of volume changes on net income, and calculating the effect of changes in selling price [3]

Sales dollars needed to achieve $3,000 planned net income for July:

Total Fixed Costs	+	Planned Net Income	=	Required Contribution Margin
$8,000.00	+	$3,000.00	=	$11,000.00

Required Contribution Margin	÷	Contribution Margin Rate	=	Sales Dollars
$11,000.00	÷	20%	=	$55,000.00

[4]

	Per Unit	Number of Units		
		4,000	5,000	6,000
Net Sales	$8.00	$32,000.00	$40,000.00	$48,000.00
Variable Costs	6.40	25,600.00	32,000.00	38,400.00
Contribution Margin	$1.60	$ 6,400.00	$ 8,000.00	$ 9,600.00
Fixed Costs		8,000.00	8,000.00	8,000.00
Net Income (Loss).		$ (1,600.00)	$ –0–	$ 1,600.00

[5]

	Per Unit	Units at Normal Price 7,500	Per Unit	Units at Reduced Price 9,000
Net Sales.	$8.00	$60,000.00	$7.50	$67,500.00
Variable Costs.	6.40	48,000.00	6.40	57,600.00
Contribution Margin.	$1.60	$12,000.00	$1.10	$ 9,900.00
Fixed Costs.		8,000.00		8,000.00
Net Income (Loss)		$ 4,000.00		$ 1,900.00

15-3 WORK TOGETHER

Extra space for calculations

15-3 ON YOUR OWN, p. 434

Calculating sales to earn a planned net income, calculating the effect of volume changes on net income, and calculating the effect of changes in selling price [6]

Sales dollars needed to achieve $3,000 planned net income for August:

Total Fixed Costs	+	Planned Net Income	=	Required Contribution Margin
$8,000.00	+	$3,000.00	=	$11,000.00

Required Contribution Margin	÷	Contribution Margin Rate	=	Sales Dollars
$11,000.00	÷	12.5%	=	$88,000.00

[7]

	Per Unit	Number of Units		
		7,000	8,000	9,000
Net Sales	$8.00	$56,000.00	$64,000.00	$72,000.00
Variable Costs	7.00	49,000.00	56,000.00	63,000.00
Contribution Margin	$1.00	$ 7,000.00	$ 8,000.00	$ 9,000.00
Fixed Costs		8,000.00	8,000.00	8,000.00
Net Income (Loss)		$ (1,000.00)	$ –0–	$ 1,000.00

[8]

	Per Unit	Units at Normal Price	Per Unit	Units at Increased Price
		10,000		9,500
Net Sales	$8.00	$80,000.00	$8.50	$80,750.00
Variable Costs	7.00	70,000.00	7.00	66,500.00
Contribution Margin	$1.00	$10,000.00	$1.50	$14,250.00
Fixed Costs		8,000.00		8,000.00
Net Income (Loss)		$ 2,000.00		$ 6,250.00

15-3 ON YOUR OWN

Extra space for calculations

15-1 APPLICATION PROBLEM, p. 436

Preparing an income statement reporting contribution margin [1]

Milford Pump Company

Income Statement

For Month Ended November 30, 20--

Operating Revenue:													
Net Sales *(8,700 units @ $210.00)*									1827	0	0	0	00
Variable Costs:													
Cost of Merchandise Sold *(8,700 units @ $145.00)*	1261	5	0	0	00								
Sales Commissions *(8,700 units @ $6.00)*	52	2	0	0	00								
Delivery Costs *(8,700 units @ $4.80)*	41	7	6	0	00								
Other Selling Costs *(8,700 units @ $2.75)*	23	9	2	5	00								
Other Administrative Costs *(8,700 units @ $5.50)*	47	8	5	0	00								
Total Variable Costs									1427	2	3	5	00
Contribution Margin									399	7	6	5	00
Fixed Costs:													
Rent	15	0	0	0	00								
Insurance	9	7	5	0	00								
Other Selling Costs	76	5	1	0	00								
Other Administrative Costs	45	2	9	0	00								
Other Expenses	12	0	0	0	00								
Total Fixed Costs									158	5	5	0	00
Net Income									241	2	1	5	00

Extra space for calculations

15-1 APPLICATION PROBLEM (concluded)

[2]

Contribution margin per unit:

Contribution Margin per Unit   =   *Total Contribution Margin ÷ Units Sold*
          45.95   *($399,765/8700)*

[3]

Variable cost per unit:

Variable Cost per Unit   =   *Total Variable Costs/Units Sold*
          164.05   *($164.05/unit)*

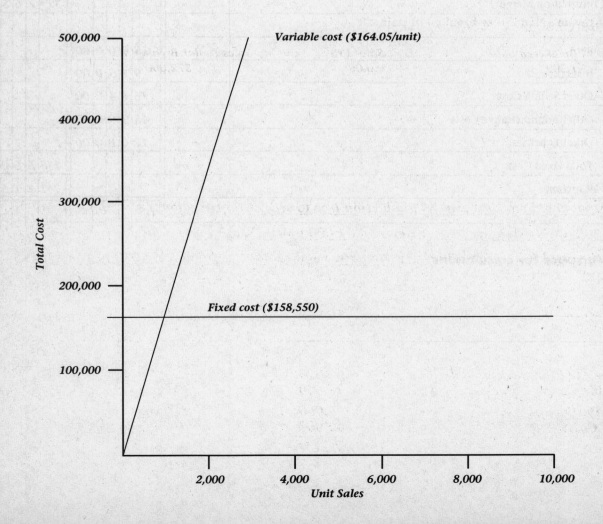

15-2 APPLICATION PROBLEM, p. 436

Calculating contribution margin and breakeven point [4]

Calculate the contribution margin per unit:

Unit Sales Price	–	Variable Cost per Unit	=	Contribution Margin per Unit
$60.00	–	$25.00	=	$35.00

Calculate the unit sales breakeven point:

Total Fixed Costs	÷	Contribution Margin per Unit	=	Unit Sales Breakeven Point
$42,000	÷	$35.00	=	1,200 units

Calculate the sales dollar breakeven point:

Unit Sales Breakeven Point	×	Unit Sales Price	=	Sales Dollar Breakeven Point
1,200	×	$60.00	=	$72,000

No, Farris should not expand its production line to sell portable radios. The company cannot sell
the 1,200 units necessary to break even. At 1,000 units, the company would sell 200 units less
than the breakeven point. Thus, the company would have a net loss of $7,000 (200 × $35.00).

Net Sales (1,000 units @ $60.00)	$60,000
Variable Costs (1,000 units @ $25.00)	25,000
Contribution Margin	$35,000
Fixed Costs	42,000
Net Loss	$ (7,000)

15-2 APPLICATION PROBLEM

Extra space for calculations

15-3 APPLICATION PROBLEM, p. 437

Calculating plans for net income [1]

Calculate the contribution margin per unit

Unit Sales Price	–	Variable Cost per Unit	=	Contribution Margin per Unit
$15.00	–	$10.00	=	$5.00

a. Calculate the unit sales breakeven point:

Total Fixed Costs	÷	Contribution Margin per Unit	=	Unit Sales Breakeven Point
$135,000	÷	$5.00	=	27,000 units

b. Calculate the sales dollar breakeven point:

Unit Sales Breakeven Point	×	Unit Sales Price	=	Sales Dollar Breakeven Point
27,000	×	$15.00	=	$405,000

[2]

Calculate the contribution margin per unit:

Unit Sales Price	–	Variable Cost per Unit	=	Contribution Margin per Unit
$15.00	–	$10.00	=	$5.00

Calculate the required contribution margin

Total Fixed Costs	+	Planned Net Income	=	Required Contribution Margin
$135,000	+	$50,000	=	$185,000

a. Calculate unit sales

Required Contribution Margin	÷	Contribution Margin per Unit	=	Unit Sales
$185,000	÷	$5.00	=	37,000 units

b. Calculate sales dollars

Unit Sales	×	Unit Sales Price	=	Sales Dollars
37,000	×	$15.00	=	$555,000

15-3 APPLICATION PROBLEM (concluded)

[3]

Calculate the contribution margin per unit:

Unit Sales Price	–	Variable Cost per Unit	=	Contribution Margin per Unit
$15.00	–	$9.50	=	$5.50

a. Calculate the unit sales breakeven point

Total Fixed Costs	÷	Contribution Margin per Unit	=	Unit Sales Breakeven Point
$187,000	÷	$5.50	=	34,000 units

b. Calculate the sales dollar breakeven point

Unit Sales Breakeven Point	×	Unit Sales Price	=	Sales Dollar Breakeven Point
34,000	×	$15.00	=	$510,000

Mr. Williams should purchase the mixing machine only if projected unit sales are estimated to
exceed 34,000 gallons. If sales are less than 34,000 gallons, the increase in fixed costs would be
greater than the decrease in variables costs, thus reducing net income. If unit sales exceed
34,000 gallons, the company will earn a higher net income than it would using its current
mixing method.

15-4 APPLICATION PROBLEM, p. 437

Calculating the effects on net income of changes in unit sales price, variable costs, fixed costs, and volume   [1]

	Per Unit	Number of Units		
		17,000	20,000	23,000
Net Sales.	$12.00	$204,000.00	$240,000.00	$276,000.00
Variable Costs.	9.60	$163,200.00	$192,000.00	$220,800.00
Contribution Margin	$ 2.40	$ 40,800.00	$ 48,000.00	$ 55,200.00
Fixed Costs.		$ 48,000.00	$ 48,000.00	$ 48,000.00
Net Income (Loss).		$ (7,200.00)	$ -0-	$ 7,200.00

[2a]

	Alternative 1			Alternative 2		
	Per Unit	Units Sold	Total	Per Unit	Units Sold	Total
Net Sales.	$12.00	20,000	$240,000	$12.00	20,000	$240,000
Variable Costs	$ 9.60	20,000	$192,000	$ 8.50	20,000	$170,000
Contribution Margin	$ 2.40	20,000	$ 48,000	$ 3.50	20,000	$ 70,000
Fixed Costs			$ 48,000			$ 58,000
Net Income (Loss)			$ -0-			$ 12,000

[2b]

	Alternative 1			Alternative 2		
	Per Unit	Units Sold	Total	Per Unit	Units Sold	Total
Net Sales.	$12.00	17,000	$204,000	$12.00	17,000	$204,000
Variable Costs	$ 9.60	17,000	$163,200	$ 8.50	17,000	$144,500
Contribution Margin	$ 2.40	17,000	$ 40,800	$ 3.50	17,000	$ 59,500
Fixed Costs			$ 48,000			$ 58,000
Net Income (Loss)			$ (7,200)			$ 1,500

Name _____ Date _____ Class _____

15-4 APPLICATION PROBLEM (concluded)

[3]

	Current Price			Price Reduction and Sales Volume Increase		
	Per Unit	Units Sold	Total	Per Unit	Units Sold	Total
Net Sales................	$12.00	20,000	$240,000	$10.80	26,000	$280,800
Variable Costs	$ 9.60	20,000	$192,000	$ 9.60	26,000	$249,600
Contribution Margin........	$ 2.40	20,000	$ 48,000	$ 1.20	26,000	$ 31,200
Fixed Costs..............			$ 48,000			$ 48,000
Net Income (Loss)..........			$ -0-			($16,800)

Extra forms

	Per Unit	Number of Units		
Net Sales.....................				
Variable Costs................				
Contribution Margin.............				
Fixed Costs...................				
Net Income (Loss)..............				

	Alternative 1			Alternative 2		
	Per Unit	Units Sold	Total	Per Unit	Units Sold	Total
Net Sales................						
Variable Costs						
Contribution Margin						
Fixed Costs						
Net Income (Loss)						

15-5 APPLICATION PROBLEM, p. 438

Calculating sales mix   **[a]**

Calculate the sales mix:

	Product Sales	÷	Net Sales	=	Sales Mix
Lamps	$40,000	÷	$100,000	=	40%
Desks	$60,000	÷	$100,000	=	60%

[b]

Calculate the contribution margin rate:

Contribution Margin	÷	Net Sales	=	Contribution Margin Rate
$40,000	÷	$100,000	=	40%

[c]

Calculate total sales dollars:

Total Fixed Costs	+	Planned Net Income	=	Required Contribution Margin
$38,000	+	$10,000	=	$48,000

Required Contribution Margin	÷	Contribution Margin Rate	=	Total Sales Dollars
$48,000	÷	40%	=	$120,000

15-5 APPLICATION PROBLEM (concluded)

[d]

Calculate product sales dollars:

	Sales Mix	×	Total Sales Dollars	=	Product Sales Dollars
Lamps	40%	×	$120,000	=	$48,000
Desks	60%	×	$120,000	=	$72,000

[e]

Calculate product unit sales:

	Product Sales Dollars	÷	Unit Sales Price	=	Product Unit Sales
Lamps	$48,000	÷	$ 40.00	=	1,200 units
Desks	$72,000	÷	$250.00	=	288 units

15-6 MASTERY PROBLEM, p. 438

Calculating contribution margins and breakeven point, calculating sales dollars and unit sales for planned net income   [1]

Ratliff Corporation
Income Statement
For Month Ended August 31, 20--

Operating Revenue:		
Net Sales *(3,000 units @ $25.00)*		75 0 0 0 00
Variable Costs:		
Cost of Merchandise Sold *(3,000 units @ $16.00)*	48 0 0 0 00	
Sales Commission *(3,000 units @ $0.60)*	1 8 0 0 00	
Delivery Costs *(3,000 units @ $0.75)*	2 2 5 0 00	
Other Selling Costs *(3,000 units @ $1.15)*	3 4 5 0 00	
Other Administrative Costs *(3,000 units @ $0.25)*	7 5 0 00	
Total Variable Costs		56 2 5 0 00
Contribution Margin		18 7 5 0 00
Fixed Costs:		
Rent	1 0 0 0 00	
Insurance	6 0 0 00	
Other Selling Costs	3 5 9 0 00	
Other Administrative Costs	5 6 1 0 00	
Other Expenses	8 0 0 00	
Total Fixed Costs		11 6 0 0 00
Net Income		7 1 5 0 00

[2]

Calculate the contribution margin rate:

Contribution Margin	÷	Net Sales	=	Contribution Margin Rate
$18,750	÷	$75,000	=	25%

[3]

Calculate the sales dollar breakeven point:

Total Fixed Costs	÷	Contribution Margin Rate	=	Sales Dollar Breakeven Point
$11,600	÷	25%	=	$46,400

15-6 MASTERY PROBLEM (concluded)

[4]

Calculate the unit sales breakeven point:

Sales Dollar Breakeven Point	÷	Unit Sales Price	=	Unit Sales Breakeven Point
$46,400	÷	$25.00	=	1,856 units

[5]

Calculate the required contribution margin:

Total Fixed Costs	+	Planned Net Income	=	Required Contribution Margin
$11,600	+	$15,000	=	$26,600

a. Calculate sales dollars:

Required Contribution Margin	÷	Contribution Margin Rate	=	Sales Dollars
$26,600	÷	25%	=	$106,400

b. Calculate unit sales:

Sales Dollars	÷	Unit Sales Price	=	Unit Sales
$106,400	÷	$25.00	=	4,256 units

[6]

	Alternative 1 Current Machines			Alternative 2 Computer-Based Machines		
	Per Unit	Units Sold	Total	Per Unit	Units Sold	Total
Net Sales	$25.00	3,000	$75,000	$25.00	3,000	$75,000
Variable Costs	18.75	3,000	56,250	14.55	3,000	43,650
Contribution Margin	$ 6.25	3,000	$18,750	$10.45	3,000	$31,350
Fixed Costs			11,600			21,600
Net Income (Loss)			$ 7,150			$ 9,750

Yes, Ratliff should purchase the computer-based machines. The new machines would increase net income by $2,600 ($9,750 – $7,150) if 3,000 units are sold.

15-7 CHALLENGE PROBLEM, p. 439

Calculating the effects on net income of changes in unit sales price, variable costs, and fixed costs   [1]

	Alternative 1 Current Unit Sales Price			Alternative 2 Decreased Unit Sales Price		
	Per Unit	Units Sold	Total	Per Unit	Units Sold	Total
Net Sales.................	$250.00	75,000	$18,750,000	$230.00	100,000	$23,000,000
Variable Costs	200.00	75,000	15,000,000	200.00	100,000	20,000,000
Contribution Margin	$ 50.00	75,000	$ 3,750,000	$ 30.00	100,000	$ 3,000,000
Fixed Costs			2,980,000			2,980,000
Net Income (Loss)			$ 770,000			$ 20,000

   No, Millard should not reduce the unit selling price to $230.00 since it results in a $750,000 decrease in net income ($770,000 – $20,000).

   To earn $770,000 of net income with the $230.00 unit sales price, Millard must have a contribution margin of $3,750,000. Unit sales to earn this amount of contribution margin are calculated as shown below.

Required Contribution Margin	÷	Contribution Margin per Unit	=	Unit Sales
$3,750.000	÷	$30,000	=	125,000 units

Space for calculations

15-7 CHALLENGE PROBLEM (concluded)

[2]

	Alternative 1 Purchase Power Cable			Alternative 2 Produce Power Cable		
	Per Unit	Units Sold	Total	Per Unit	Units Sold	Total
Net Sales..................	$250.00	75,000	$18,750,000	$250.00	75,000	$18,750,000
Variable Costs	200.00	75,000	15,000,000	195.00	75,000	14,625,000
Contribution Margin	$50.00	75,000	$3,750,000	$55.00	75,000	$4,125,000
Fixed Costs			2,980,000			3,220,000
Net Income (Loss)			$770,000			$905,000

<u>Yes, Millard should produce the power cables since net income is increased by $135,000</u>

<u>($905,000 – $770,000).</u>

_____

_____

_____

_____

Space for calculations

16-1 WORK TOGETHER ON YOUR OWN, p. 451

Analyzing comparative financial statements [5]

	Current Year	Prior Year	Increase (Decrease)	
			Amount	Percentage
Operating Revenue: Net Sales..........................	$865,000.00	$740,000.00	$125,000.00	16.9%
Cost of Merchandise Sold: Merchandise Inv., Jan. 1	145,800.00	147,600.00	(1,800.00)	(1.2%)
Net Purchases	372,000.00	358,300.00	13,700.00	3.8%
Total Cost of Mdse. Avail. for Sale......	$517,800.00	$505,900.00	$ 11,900.00	2.4%
Less Mdse. Inventory, Dec. 31	188,700.00	145,800.00	42,900.00	29.4%
Cost of Merchandise Sold	329,100.00	360,100.00	(31,000.00)	(8.6%)
Gross Profit on Operations	$535,900.00	$379,900.00	$156,000.00	41.1%

[6]

	Current Year		Prior Year	
	Amount	Percentage	Amount	Percentage
Operating Revenue: Net Sales..........................	$865,000.00	100.0%	$740,000.00	100.0%
Cost of Merchandise Sold: Merchandise Inv., Jan. 1	145,800.00	16.9%	147,600.00	19.9%
Net Purchases	372,000.00	43.0%	358,300.00	48.4%
Total Cost of Mdse. Avail. for Sale......	$517,800.00	59.9%	$505,900.00	68.4%
Less Mdse. Inventory, Dec. 31	188,700.00	21.8%	145,800.00	19.7%
Cost of Merchandise Sold	329,100.00	38.0%	360,100.00	48.7%
Gross Profit on Operations	$535,900.00	62.0%	$379,900.00	51.3%

16-1 WORK TOGETHER

Extra space for calculations

16-1 ON YOUR OWN, p. 451

Analyzing comparative financial statements

[7]

Baycom Corporation Comparative Balance Sheet December 31, 20-- and 20--				
	Current Year	Prior Year	Increase (Decrease)	
			Amount	Percentage
ASSETS				
Current Assets:				
Cash...	$ 246,300	$ 204,900	41,400	20.2
Accounts Receivable (net).........................	574,000	469,200	104,800	22.3
Merchandise Inventory......................	597,000	623,800	(26,800)	(4.3)
Other Current Assets......................	16,100	11,300	4,800	42.5
Total Current Assets......................	$1,433,400	$1,309,200	124,200	9.5
Total Plant Assets (net)......................	713,600	681,100	32,500	4.8
Total Assets.....................	$2,147,000	$1,990,300	156,700	7.9
LIABILITIES				
Current Liabilities:				
Notes Payable........................	$ 261,200	$ 281,600	(20,400)	(7.2)
Interest Payable	8,900	10,700	(1,800)	(16.8)
Accounts Payable........................	344,900	393,300	(48,400)	(12.3)
Federal Income Tax Payable	7,300	3,300	4,000	121.2
Other Current Liabilities........................	5,400	6,500	(1,100)	(16.9)
Total Current Liabilities	$ 627,700	$ 695,400	(67,700)	(9.7)
Long-Term Liability:				
Mortgage Payable	$ 480,000	$ 325,000	155,000	47.7
Total Liabilities........................	$1,107,700	$1,020,400	87,300	8.6
STOCKHOLDERS' EQUITY				
Capital Stock........................	$ 500,000	$ 450,000	50,000	11.1
Retained Earnings........................	539,300	519,900	19,400	3.7
Total Stockholders' Equity	$1,039,300	$ 969,900	69,400	7.2
Total Liabilities and Stockholders' Equity	$2,147,000	$1,990,300	156,700	7.9

16-1 ON YOUR OWN (concluded)

[8]

	Current Year		Prior Year	
Baycom Corporation **Comparative Balance Sheet** **December 31, 20-- and 20--**				
	Amount	Percentage	Amount	Percentage
ASSETS Current Assets:				
Cash	$ 246,300	11.5	$ 204,900	10.3
Accounts Receivable (book value)	574,000	26.7	469,200	23.6
Merchandise Inventory	597,000	27.8	623,800	31.3
Other Current Assets.	16,100	0.7	11,300	0.6
Total Current Assets	$1,433,400	66.8	$1,309,200	65.8
Total Plant Assets (book value)	713,600	33.2	681,100	34.2
Total Assets	$2,147,000	100.0	$1,990,300	100.0
LIABILITIES Current Liabilities:				
Notes Payable	$ 261,200	12.2	$ 281,600	14.1
Interest Payable.	8,900	0.4	10,700	0.5
Accounts Payable	344,900	16.1	393,300	19.8
Federal Income Tax Payable.	7,300	0.3	3,300	0.2
Other Current Liabilities.	5,400	0.3	6,500	0.3
Total Current Liabilities	$ 627,700	29.2	$ 695,400	34.9
Long-Term Liability:				
Mortgage Payable	$ 480,000	22.4	$ 325,000	16.3
Total Liabilities	$1,107,700	51.6	$1,020,400	51.3
STOCKHOLDERS' EQUITY Capital Stock.	$ 500,000	23.3	$ 450,000	22.6
Retained Earnings.	539,300	25.1	519,900	26.1
Total Stockholders' Equity.	$1,039,300	48.4	$ 969,900	48.7
Total Liabilities and Stockholders' Equity.	$2,147,000	100.0	$1,990,300	100.0

16-2 WORK TOGETHER, p. 460

Calculating earnings performance efficiency and analysis ratios   [4]

	January 1	December 31
Total Assets	$4,600,000.00	$5,300,000.00
Book Value of Accounts Receivable	630,000.00	710,000.00
Merchandise Inventory	500,000.00	550,000.00
Stockholders' Equity	$2,500,000.00	$2,900,000.00
Net Sales (all sales on account)		5,760,000.00
Cost of Merchandise Sold		3,810,000.00
Net Income after Federal Income Tax		530,000.00
Shares of Capital Stock Outstanding		100,000
Market Price per Share		$ 52.50

[4a]

Rate earned on average total assets:

(January 1 Total Assets   +   December 31 Total Assets)   ÷   2   =   Average Total Assets
    ($4,600,000.00   + $5,300,000.00)   ÷   2   = $4,950,000.00

Net Income after Federal Income Tax   ÷   Average Total Assets   =   Rate Earned on Average Total Assets
        $530,000.00   ÷ $4,950,000.00   =   10.7%

[4b]

Rate earned on average stockholders' equity:

(January 1 Stockholders' Equity   +   December 31 Stockholders' Equity)   ÷   2   =   Average Stockholders' Equity
    ($2,500,000.00   + $2,900,000.00)   ÷   2   = $2,700,000.00

Net Income after   Average   Rate Earned on
Federal Income Tax   ÷   Stockholders' Equity   =   Average Stockholders' Equity
    $530,000.00   ÷ $2,700,000.00   =   19.6%

[4c]

Rate earned on net sales:

Net Income after Federal Income Tax   ÷   Net Sales   =   Rate Earned on Net Sales
        $530,000.00   ÷ $5,760,000.00   =   9.2%

[4d]

Earnings per share:

Net Income after Federal Income Tax   ÷   Shares of Capital Stock Outstanding   =   Earnings per Share
        $530,000.00   ÷   100,000   = $5.30

16-2 WORK TOGETHER (concluded)

[4e]

Price earnings ratio:

Market Price per Share	÷	Earnings per Share	=	Price Earnings Ratio
$52.50	÷	$5.30	=	9.9 times

[4f]

Accounts receivable turnover ratio:

(January 1 Accounts Receivable	+	December 31 Accounts Receivable)	÷	2	=	Average Book Value of Accounts Receivable
($630,000.00	+	$710,000.00)	÷	2	=	$670,000.00

Net Sales on Account	÷	Average Book Value of Accounts Receivable	=	Accounts Receivable Turnover Ratio
$5,760,000.00	÷	$670,000.00	=	8.6 times

[4g]

Average number of days for accounts receivable payment:

Days in Year	÷	Accounts Receivable Turnover Ratio	=	Average Number of Days for Payment
365	÷	8.6	=	42 days

[4h]

Merchandise inventory turnover ratio:

(January 1 Merchandise Inventory	+	December 31 Merchandise Inventory)	÷	2	=	Average Merchandise Inventory
($500,000.00	+	$550,000.00)	÷	2	=	$525,000.00

Cost of Merchandise Sold	÷	Average Merchandise Inventory	=	Merchandise Inventory Turnover Ratio
$3,810,000.00	÷	$525,000.00	=	7.3 times

[4i]

Average number of days' sales in merchandise inventory:

Days in Year	÷	Merchandise Inventory Turnover Ratio	=	Average Number of Days' Sales in Merchandise Inventory
365	÷	7.3	=	50 days

Name _____ Date _____ Class _____

16-2 ON YOUR OWN, p. 460

Calculating earnings performance and efficiency analysis ratios [5]

	January 1	December 31
Total Assets	$3,400,000.00	$4,000,000.00
Book Value of Accounts Receivable	475,000.00	525,000.00
Merchandise Inventory	300,000.00	280,000.00
Stockholders' Equity	$1,900,000.00	$3,000,000.00
Net Sales (all sales on account)		4,320,000.00
Cost of Merchandise Sold		2,800,000.00
Net Income after Federal Income Tax		392,000.00
Shares of Capital Stock Outstanding		100,000
Market Price per Share		$ 48.00

[5a]

Rate earned on average total assets:

(January 1 Total Assets + December 31 Total Assets) ÷ 2 = Average Total Assets
($3,400,000.00 + $4,000,000.00) ÷ 2 = $3,700,000.00

Net Income after Federal Income Tax ÷ Average Total Assets = Rate Earned on Average Total Assets
$392,000.00 ÷ $3,700,000.00 = 10.6%

[5b]

Rate earned on average stockholders' equity:

(January 1 Stockholders' Equity + December 31 Stockholders' Equity) ÷ 2 = Average Stockholders' Equity
($1,900,000.00 + $3,000,000.00) ÷ 2 = $2,450,000.00

Net Income after Federal Income Tax	÷	*Average Stockholders' Equity*	=	*Rate Earned on Average Stockholders' Equity*
$392,000.00	÷	*$2,450,000.00*	=	*16%*

[5c]

Rate earned on net sales:

Net Income after Federal Income Tax ÷ Net Sales = Rate Earned on Net Sales
$392,000.00 ÷ $4,320,000.00 = 9.1%

[5d]

Earnings per share:

Net Income after Federal Income Tax ÷ Shares of Capital Stock Outstanding = Earnings per Share
$392,000.00 ÷ 100,000 = $3.92

16-2 ON YOUR OWN (concluded)

[5e]

Price earnings ratio:

Market Price per Share	÷	Earnings per Share	=	Price Earnings Ratio
$48.00	÷	$3.92	=	12.2 times

[5f]

Accounts receivable turnover ratio:

(January 1 Accounts Receivable	+	December 31 Accounts Receivable)	÷	2	=	Average Book Value of Accounts Receivable
($475,000.00	+	$525,000.00)	÷	2	=	$500,000.00

Net Sales on Account	÷	Average Book Value of Accounts Receivable	=	Accounts Receivable Turnover Ratio
$4,320,000.00	÷	$500,000.00	=	8.6 times

[5g]

Average number of days for accounts receivable payment:

Days in Year	÷	Accounts Receivable Turnover Ratio	=	Average Number of Days for Payment
365	÷	8.6	=	42 days

[5h]

Merchandise inventory turnover ratio:

(January 1 Merchandise Inventory	+	December 31 Merchandise Inventory)	÷	2	=	Average Merchandise Inventory
($300,000.00	+	$280,000.00)	÷	2	=	$290,000.00

Cost of Merchandise Sold	÷	Average Merchandise Inventory	=	Merchandise Inventory Turnover Ratio
$2,800,000.00	÷	$290,000.00	=	9.7 times

[5i]

Average number of days' sales in merchandise inventory:

Days in Year	÷	Merchandise Inventory Turnover Ratio	=	Average Number of Days' Sales in Merchandise Inventory
365	÷	9.7	=	38 days

16-3 WORK TOGETHER, p. 465

Analyzing short-term and long-term financial strength [8]

	Current Year	Prior Year
Total Current Assets	$2,150,000.00	$1,900,000.00
Total Quick Assets (cash + accounts receivable)	664,000.00	1,176,500.00
Total Assets	3,210,000.00	2,960,000.00
Total Current Liabilities	830,000.00	905,000.00
Total Liabilities	1,340,000.00	1,325,000.00
Total Stockholders' Equity	1,870,000.00	1,635,000.00
Shares of Capital Stock Outstanding	120,000	113,000

[8a]

Working capital:

	Total Current Assets	−	Total Current Liabilities	=	Working Capital
Current Year	$2,150,000.00	−	$830,000.00	=	$1,320,000.00
Prior Year	1,900,000.00	−	905,000.00	=	995,000.00

[8b]

Current ratio:

	Total Current Assets	÷	Total Current Liabilities	=	Current Ratio
Current Year	$2,150,000.00	÷	$830,000.00	=	2.6 times
Prior Year	1,900,000.00	÷	905,000.00	=	2.1 times

[8c]

Acid-test ratio:

	Total Quick Assets	÷	Total Current Liabilities	=	Acid-test Ratio
Current Year	$ 664,000.00	÷	$830,000.00	=	0.8 times
Prior Year	1,176,500.00	÷	905,000.00	=	1.3 times

16-3 WORK TOGETHER (concluded)

[8d]

Debt ratio:

	Total Liabilities	÷	Total Assets	=	Debt Ratio
Current Year	$1,340,000.00	÷	$3,210,000.00	=	41.7%
Prior Year	1,325,000.00	÷	2,960,000.00	=	44.7%

[8e]

Equity ratio:

	Total Stockholders' Equity	÷	Total Assets	=	Equity Ratio
Current Year	$1,870,000.00	÷	$3,210,000.00	=	58.3%
Prior Year	1,635,000.00	÷	2,960,000.00	=	55.2%

[8f]

Equity per share:

	Total Stockholders' Equity	÷	Shares of Capital Stock Outstanding	=	Equity per Share
Current Year	$1,870,000.00	÷	120,000	=	$15.58
Prior Year	1,635,000.00	÷	113,000	=	14.47

Extra space for calculations

16-3 ON YOUR OWN, p. 465

Analyzing short-term and long-term financial strength   [9]

	Current Year	Prior Year
Total Current Assets	$1,612,000.00	$1,400,000.00
Total Quick Assets (cash + accounts receivable)	805,000.00	725,000.00
Total Assets	2,450,000.00	2,050,000.00
Total Current Liabilities	620,000.00	410,000.00
Total Liabilities	1,580,000.00	975,000.00
Total Stockholders' Equity	870,000.00	1,075,000.00
Shares of Capital Stock Outstanding	70,000	65,000

[9a]

Working capital:

	Total Current Assets	–	Total Current Liabilities	=	Working Capital
Current Year	$1,612,000.00	–	$620,000.00	=	$992,000.00
Prior Year	1,400,000.00	–	410,000.00	=	990,000.00

[9b]

Current ratio:

	Total Current Assets	÷	Total Current Liabilities	=	Current Ratio
Current Year	$1,612,000.00	÷	$620,000.00	=	2.6 times
Prior Year	1,400,000.00	÷	410,000.00	=	3.4 times

[9c]

Acid-test ratio:

	Total Quick Assets	÷	Total Current Liabilities	=	Acid-test Ratio
Current Year	$805,000.00	÷	$620,000.00	=	1.3 times
Prior Year	725,000.00	÷	410,000.00	=	1.8 times

16-3 ON YOUR OWN (concluded)

[9d]

Debt ratio:

	Total Liabilities	÷	Total Assets	=	Debt Ratio
Current Year	$1,580,000.00	÷	$2,450,000.00	=	64.5%
Prior Year	975,000.00	÷	2,050,000.00	=	47.6%

[9e]

Equity ratio:

	Total Stockholders' Equity	÷	Total Assets	=	Equity Ratio
Current Year	$ 870,000.00	÷	$2,450,000.00	=	35.5%
Prior Year	1,075,000.00	÷	2,050,000.00	=	52.4%

[9f]

Equity per share:

	Total Stockholders' Equity	÷	Shares of Capital Stock Outstanding	=	Equity per Share
Current Year	$ 870,000.00	÷	70,000	=	$12.43
Prior Year	1,075,000.00	÷	65,000	=	16.54

Extra space for calculations

Name _____ Date _____ Class _____

16-1 APPLICATION PROBLEM, p. 467

Analyzing comparative financial statements using trend analysis [1]

The comparative statements prepared in this problem are needed to complete Application Problems 16-3, 16-4, 16-5, and 16-6.

CyberOptic Corporation

Comparative Income Statement

For Years Ended December 31, 20-- and 20--

	CURRENT YEAR	PRIOR YEAR	INCREASE (DECREASE) AMOUNT	%
Operating Revenue:				
Net Sales	1041 9 8 0 00	914 5 6 0 00	127 4 2 0 00	13.9
Cost of Merchandise Sold:				
Merchandise Inventory, Jan. 1	220 3 8 0 00	125 0 1 0 00	95 3 7 0 00	76.3
Net Purchases	827 4 5 0 00	789 4 8 0 00	37 9 7 0 00	4.8
Total Cost of Merchandise Available for Sale	1047 8 3 0 00	914 4 9 0 00	133 3 4 0 00	14.6
Less Merchandise Inventory, Dec. 31	318 8 4 0 00	220 3 8 0 00	98 4 6 0 00	44.7
Cost of Merchandise Sold	728 9 9 0 00	694 1 1 0 00	34 8 8 0 00	5.0
Gross Profit on Operations	312 9 9 0 00	220 4 5 0 00	92 5 4 0 00	42.0
Operating Expenses:				
Selling Expenses:				
Advertising Expense	7 3 6 0 00	5 8 0 0 00	1 5 6 0 00	26.9
Delivery Expense	13 8 0 0 00	12 4 3 0 00	1 3 7 0 00	11.0
Salary Expense—Sales	59 8 0 0 00	49 7 3 0 00	10 0 7 0 00	20.2
Supplies Expense	2 7 6 0 00	2 4 9 0 00	2 7 0 00	10.8
Other Selling Expenses	3 6 8 0 00	3 3 1 0 00	3 7 0 00	11.2
Total Selling Expenses	87 4 0 0 00	73 7 6 0 00	13 6 4 0 00	18.5
Administrative Expenses:				
Salary Expense—Administrative	22 0 8 0 00	20 7 2 0 00	1 3 6 0 00	6.6
Uncollectible Accounts Expense	9 2 0 0 00	4 1 4 0 00	5 0 6 0 00	122.2
Other Administrative Expenses	11 0 4 0 00	9 9 5 0 00	1 0 9 0 00	11.0
Total Administrative Expenses	42 3 2 0 00	34 8 1 0 00	7 5 1 0 00	21.6
Total Operating Expenses	129 7 2 0 00	108 5 7 0 00	21 1 5 0 00	19.5
Income from Operations	183 2 7 0 00	111 8 8 0 00	71 3 9 0 00	63.8
Other Expenses:				
Interest Expense	18 4 0 0 00	15 7 5 0 00	2 6 5 0 00	16.8
Net Income before Federal Income Tax	164 8 7 0 00	96 1 3 0 00	68 7 4 0 00	71.5
Less Federal Income Tax Expense	47 5 5 0 00	20 9 3 0 00	26 6 2 0 00	127.2
Net Income after Federal Income Tax	117 3 2 0 00	75 2 0 0 00	42 1 2 0 00	56.0

16-1 APPLICATION PROBLEM (continued)

[1]

CyberOptic Corporation

Comparative Balance Sheet

December 31, 20-- and 20--

	CURRENT YEAR	PRIOR YEAR	INCREASE (DECREASE) AMOUNT	%
ASSETS				
Current Assets:				
Cash	137 4 9 0 00	138 5 3 0 00	(1 0 4 0 00)	(0.8)
Accounts Receivable (book value)	78 8 2 0 00	76 8 2 0 00	2 0 0 0 00	2.6
Merchandise Inventory	318 8 4 0 00	220 3 8 0 00	98 4 6 0 00	44.7
Other Current Assets	10 8 0 0 00	10 5 7 0 00	2 3 0 00	2.2
Total Current Assets	545 9 5 0 00	446 3 0 0 00	99 6 5 0 00	22.3
Plant Assets (book value)	252 9 8 0 00	224 3 7 0 00	28 6 1 0 00	12.8
Total Assets	798 9 3 0 00	670 6 7 0 00	128 2 6 0 00	19.1
LIABILITIES				
Current Liabilities:				
Notes Payable	86 2 5 0 00	57 5 3 0 00	28 7 2 0 00	49.9
Interest Payable	5 4 6 0 00	4 7 2 0 00	7 4 0 00	15.7
Accounts Payable	143 5 6 0 00	139 9 8 0 00	3 5 8 0 00	2.6
Federal Income Tax Payable	4 2 2 0 00	1 1 3 0 00	3 0 9 0 00	273.5
Other Current Liabilities	22 0 8 0 00	17 2 7 0 00	4 8 1 0 00	27.9
Total Current Liabilities	261 5 7 0 00	220 6 3 0 00	40 9 4 0 00	18.6
Long-Term Liability:				
Mortgage Payable	80 0 0 0 00	100 0 0 0 00	(20 0 0 0 00)	(20.0)
Total Liabilities	341 5 7 0 00	320 6 3 0 00	20 9 4 0 00	6.5
STOCKHOLDERS' EQUITY				
Capital Stock	250 0 0 0 00	200 0 0 0 00	50 0 0 0 00	25.0
Retained Earnings	207 3 6 0 00	150 0 4 0 00	57 3 2 0 00	38.2
Total Stockholders' Equity	457 3 6 0 00	350 0 4 0 00	107 3 2 0 00	30.7
Total Liabilities and Stockholders' Equity	798 9 3 0 00	670 6 7 0 00	128 2 6 0 00	19.1

16-1 APPLICATION PROBLEM (continued)

[1]

CyberOptic Corporation
Comparative Statement of Stockholders' Equity
For Years Ended December 31, 20-- and 20--

	CURRENT YEAR	PRIOR YEAR	INCREASE (DECREASE) AMOUNT	%
Capital Stock:				
$5 Per Share				
Balance, January 1	200 0 0 0 00	200 0 0 0 00	- 0 -	—
Additional Capital Stock Issued	50 0 0 0 00	- 0 -	50 0 0 0 00	—
Balance, December 31	250 0 0 0 00	200 0 0 0 00	50 0 0 0 00	25.0
Retained Earnings:				
Balance, January 1	150 0 4 0 00	114 8 4 0 00	35 2 0 0 00	30.7
Net Income after Federal Income Tax	117 3 2 0 00	75 2 0 0 00	42 1 2 0 00	56.0
Total	267 3 6 0 00	190 0 4 0 00	77 3 2 0 00	40.7
Less Dividends Declared	60 0 0 0 00	40 0 0 0 00	20 0 0 0 00	50.0
Balance, December 31	207 3 6 0 00	150 0 4 0 00	57 3 2 0 00	38.2
Total Stockholders' Equity, December 31	457 3 6 0 00	350 0 4 0 00	107 3 2 0 00	30.7
Capital Stock Shares Outstanding	50 0 0 0	40 0 0 0 00	10 0 0 0	25.0

16-1 APPLICATION PROBLEM (concluded)

[2]

[a] Net sales: *+13.9%*	Trend: *Favorable* Reason: *Possible causes are:* 　*1) The increase in advertising* 　　*expense increased demand.* 　*2) The increase in salary expense* 　　*for sales personnel provided more* 　　*or better sales.*
[b] Net income: *+56.0%*	Trend: *Favorable* Reason: *The percentage increase in net sales is much larger than the percentage increase in cost of merchandise sold.*
[c] Net stockholders' equity: *+30.7%*	Trend: *Favorable* Reason: *Retained earnings and net income have increased. Also, additional capital stock was issued.*
[d] Total assets: *+19.1%*	Trend: *Favorable* Reason: *Although current liabilities increased significantly, total stockholders' equity increased more than total liabilities. However, most of the increase in assets is due to the significant increase in merchandise inventory, which may account for the increase in sales, but could be unfavorable.*

16-2 APPLICATION PROBLEM, p. 467

Analyzing comparative financial statements using component percentage analysis   [1]

CyberOptic Corporation

Comparative Income Statement

For Years Ended December 31, 20-- and 20--

	CURRENT YEAR		PRIOR YEAR	
	AMOUNT	%	AMOUNT	%
Operating Revenue:				
Net Sales	1041 9 8 0 00	100.0	914 5 6 0 00	100.0
Cost of Merchandise Sold:				
Merchandise Inventory, Jan. 1	220 3 8 0 00	21.2	125 0 1 0 00	13.7
Net Purchases	827 4 5 0 00	79.4	789 4 8 0 00	86.3
Total Cost of Merchandise Available for Sale	1047 8 3 0 00	100.6	914 4 9 0 00	100.0
Less Merchandise Inventory, Dec. 31	318 8 4 0 00	30.6	220 3 8 0 00	24.1
Cost of Merchandise Sold	728 9 9 0 00	70.0	694 1 1 0 00	75.9
Gross Profit on Operations	312 9 9 0 00	30.0	220 4 5 0 00	24.1
Operating Expenses:				
Selling Expenses:				
Advertising Expense	7 3 6 0 00	0.7	5 8 0 0 00	0.6
Delivery Expense	13 8 0 0 00	1.3	12 4 3 0 00	1.4
Salary Expense—Sales	59 8 0 0 00	5.7	49 7 3 0 00	5.4
Supplies Expense	2 7 6 0 00	0.3	2 4 9 0 00	0.3
Other Selling Expenses	3 6 8 0 00	0.4	3 3 1 0 00	0.4
Total Selling Expenses	87 4 0 0 00	8.4	73 7 6 0 00	8.1
Administrative Expenses:				
Salary Expense—Administrative	22 0 8 0 00	2.1	20 7 2 0 00	2.3
Uncollectible Accounts Expense	9 2 0 0 00	0.9	4 1 4 0 00	0.5
Other Administrative Expenses	11 0 4 0 00	1.1	9 9 5 0 00	1.1
Total Administrative Expenses	42 3 2 0 00	4.1	34 8 1 0 00	3.8
Total Operating Expenses	129 7 2 0 00	12.4	108 5 7 0 00	11.9
Income from Operations	183 2 7 0 00	17.6	111 8 8 0 00	12.2
Other Expenses:				
Interest Expense	18 4 0 0 00	1.8	15 7 5 0 00	1.7
Net Income before Federal Income Tax	164 8 7 0 00	15.8	96 1 3 0 00	10.5
Less Federal Income Tax	47 5 5 0 00	4.6	20 9 3 0 00	2.3
Net Income after Federal Income Tax	117 3 2 0 00	11.3	75 2 0 0 00	8.2

16-2 APPLICATION PROBLEM (continued)

[1]

CyberOptic Corporation

Comparative Statement of Stockholders' Equity

For Years Ended December 31, 20-- and 20--

	CURRENT YEAR		PRIOR YEAR	
	AMOUNT	%	AMOUNT	%
Capital Stock:				
$5 Per Share				
Balance, January 1	200 0 0 0 00	43.7	200 0 0 0 00	57.1
Additional Capital Stock Issued	50 0 0 0 00	10.9	- 0 -	0.0
Balance, December 31	250 0 0 0 00	54.7	200 0 0 0 00	57.1
Retained Earnings:				
Balance, January 1	150 0 4 0 00	32.8	114 8 4 0 00	32.8
Net Income after Federal Income Tax	117 3 2 0 00	25.7	75 2 0 0 00	21.5
Total	267 3 6 0 00	58.5	190 0 4 0 00	54.3
Less Dividends Declared	60 0 0 0 00	13.1	40 0 0 0 00	11.4
Balance, December 31	207 3 6 0 00	45.3	150 0 4 0 00	42.9
Total Stockholders' Equity, December 31	457 3 6 0 00	100.0	350 0 4 0 00	100.0
Capital Stock Shares Outstanding	50 0 0 0		40 0 0 0	

16-2 APPLICATION PROBLEM (continued)

[1]

CyberOptic Corporation
Comparative Balance Sheet
December 31, 20-- and 20--

	CURRENT YEAR		PRIOR YEAR	
	AMOUNT	%	AMOUNT	%
ASSETS				
Current Assets:				
Cash	137 4 9 0 00	17.2	138 5 3 0 00	20.7
Accounts Receivable (book value)	78 8 2 0 00	9.9	76 8 2 0 00	11.5
Merchandise Inventory	318 8 4 0 00	39.9	220 3 8 0 00	32.9
Other Current Assets	10 8 0 0 00	1.4	10 5 7 0 00	1.6
Total Current Assets	545 9 5 0 00	68.3	446 3 0 0 00	66.5
Plant Assets (book value)	252 9 8 0 00	31.7	224 3 7 0 00	33.5
Total Assets	798 9 3 0 00	100.0	670 6 7 0 00	100.0
LIABILITIES				
Current Liabilities:				
Notes Payable	86 2 5 0 00	10.8	57 5 3 0 00	8.6
Interest Payable	5 4 6 0 00	0.7	4 7 2 0 00	0.7
Accounts Payable	143 5 6 0 00	18.0	139 9 8 0 00	20.9
Federal Income Tax Payable	4 2 2 0 00	0.5	1 1 3 0 00	0.2
Other Current Liabilities	22 0 8 0 00	2.8	17 2 7 0 00	2.6
Total Current Liabilities	261 5 7 0 00	32.7	220 6 3 0 00	32.9
Long-Term Liability:				
Mortgage Payable	80 0 0 0 00	10.0	100 0 0 0 00	14.9
Total Liabilities	341 5 7 0 00	42.8	320 6 3 0 00	47.8
STOCKHOLDERS' EQUITY				
Capital Stock	250 0 0 0 00	31.3	200 0 0 0 00	29.8
Retained Earnings	207 3 6 0 00	26.0	150 0 4 0 00	22.4
Total Stockholders' Equity	457 3 6 0 00	57.2	350 0 4 0 00	52.2
Total Liabilities and Stockholders' Equity	798 9 3 0 00	100.0	670 6 7 0 00	100.0

16-2 APPLICATION PROBLEM (continued)

[2]

[a]	As a Percentage of Net Sales:	Trend: *Favorable*
(1)	Cost of merchandise sold: Current year: *70.0%* Prior year: *75.9%*	Reason: *Cost of merchandise sold as a percentage of net sales has decreased. A decreasing percentage of the revenue from sales is being used to pay for merchandise sold.*
(2)	Gross profit on operations: Current year: *30.0%* Prior year: *24.1%*	Trend: *Favorable* Reason: *The decreased percentage of cost of merchandise sold has resulted in a higher gross profit percentage.*
(3)	Total operating expenses: Current year: *12.4%* Prior year: *11.9%*	Trend: *Unfavorable* Reason: *The percentage of operating expenses to net sales has increased. The cost of operating the business has increased so the business is operating less economically.*
(4)	Net income after federal income tax: Current year: *11.3%* Prior year: *8.2%*	Trend: *Favorable* Reason: *Cost of merchandise sold decreased more than the percentage increase in total operating expenses. Thus a larger percentage of sales revenue is retained as net income.*

16-2 APPLICATION PROBLEM (concluded)

[2]

[b]	As a Percentage of Total Stockholders' Equity:	Trend: *Favorable*
(1)	Retained earnings:	Reason: *Net income increased by more than the increase in dividends.*
	Current year: *45.3%*	
	Prior year: *42.9%*	
(2)	Capital stock:	Trend: *Favorable*
	Current year: *54.7%*	Reason: *A larger portion of the business is being financed through increased earnings and less from invested capital.*
	Prior year: *57.1%*	
[c]	As a Percentage of Total Assets or Total Liabilities and Stockholders' Equity:	Trend: *Favorable*
(1)	Current assets:	Reason: *Current assets provide the company's working capital—the capital used to operate the business. A higher portion of current assets means more assets are available for the daily profit making activities of the business.*
	Current year: *68.3%*	
	Prior year: *66.5%*	
(2)	Current liabilities:	Trend: *Favorable*
	Current year: *32.7%*	Reason: *Slightly decreased current liabilities strengthen CyberOptic's cash position.*
	Prior year: *32.9%*	

16-2 APPLICATION PROBLEM

Extra form

	CURRENT YEAR	PRIOR YEAR	INCREASE (DECREASE)	
			AMOUNT	%

16-3 APPLICATION PROBLEM, p. 468

Analyzing earnings performance from comparative financial statements   **[1, 2]**

The comparative statements from Application Problem 16-1 are needed to complete this problem.

[a]	Rate earned on average total assets: Current year: $\$117,320 \div \dfrac{670,670 + 798,930}{2} = 16.0\%$ Prior year: $\$75,200 \div \dfrac{544,200 + 670,670}{2} = 12.4\%$	Trend: *Favorable* Reason: ***For each dollar in company assets, the net income has increased from 12.4¢ to 16.0¢.***
[b]	Rate earned on average stockholders' equity: Current year: $\$117,320 \div \dfrac{350,040 + 457,360}{2} = 29.1\%$ Prior year: $\$75,200 \div \dfrac{314,840 + 350,040}{2} = 22.6\%$	Trend: *Favorable* Reason: ***For each dollar of stockholders' equity, the net income increased from 22.6¢ to 29.1¢.***
[c]	Rate earned on net sales: Current year: $\$117,320 \div 1,041,980 = 11.3\%$ Prior year: $\$75,200 \div 914,560 = 8.2\%$	Trend: *Favorable* Reason: ***For each dollar of sales, the net income increased from 8.2¢ to 11.3¢.***
[d]	Earnings per share: Current year: $\$117,320 \div 50,000 = \$2.35$ Prior year: $\$75,200 \div 40,000 = \$1.88$	Trend: *Favorable* Reason: ***The net income earned for each share of capital stock increased from \$1.88 to \$2.35.***
[e]	Price earnings ratio: Current year: $\$23.50 \div 2.35 = 10.0$ *times* Prior year: $\$16.50 \div 1.88 = 8.8$ *times*	Trend: *Favorable* Reason: ***The increase shows that stock market investors have increased confidence in the profitability of CyberOptic.***

16-3 APPLICATION PROBLEM

Extra form

	CURRENT YEAR	PRIOR YEAR	INCREASE (DECREASE)	
			AMOUNT	%

16-4 APPLICATION PROBLEM, p. 468

Analyzing efficiency from comparative financial statements [1, 2]

The comparative statements from Application Problem 16-1 are needed to complete this problem.

[a]	Accounts receivable turnover ratio: Current year: $\$1,041,980 \div \dfrac{76,820 + 78,820}{2} = 13.4 \text{ times}$ Prior year: $\$914,560 \div \dfrac{69,450 + 76,820}{2} = 12.5 \text{ times}$	Trend: *Favorable* Reason: *There is increasing collection efficiency of accounts receivable by reduction of the average collection period.*
[b]	Average number of days for payment: Current year: *365 ÷ 13.4 = 27 days* Prior year: *365 ÷ 12.5 = 29 days*	Trend: *Favorable* Reason: *There is increasing efficiency of collection of accounts receivable. Accounts are collected, on average, in 2 fewer days.*
[c]	Merchandise inventory turnover ratio: Current year: $\$728,990 \div \dfrac{220,380 + 318,840}{2} = 2.7 \text{ times}$ Prior year: $\$694,110 \div \dfrac{125,010 + 220,380}{2} = 4.0 \text{ times}$	Trend: *Unfavorable* Reason: *The number of times the average amount of inventory is sold each year has decreased from 4.0 to 2.7. The amount of sales relative to inventory on hand has decreased—an indication of inefficiency.*
[d]	Number of days' sales in merchandise inventory: Current year: *365 ÷ 2.7 = 135 days* Prior year: *365 ÷ 4.0 = 91 days*	Trend: *Unfavorable* Reason: *It is taking longer to sell merchandise items—an increase from 91 days to 135 days to sell the average level of inventory.*

16-4 APPLICATION PROBLEM

Extra form

	CURRENT YEAR	PRIOR YEAR	INCREASE (DECREASE)	
			AMOUNT	%

16-5 APPLICATION PROBLEM, p. 468

The comparative balance sheet from Application Problem 16-1 is needed to complete this problem.

Analyzing short-term financial strength from a comparative balance sheet [1, 2]

[a]	Working capital:	Trend: *Favorable*
	Current year: *$545,950 − 261,570 = $284,380*	Reason: *The amount of working capital is increasing.*
	Prior year: *$446,300 − 220,630 = $225,670*	
[b]	Current ratio:	Trend: *Favorable*
	Current year: *$545,950 ÷ 261,570 = 2.1 times*	Reason: *The amount of current assets in relation to current liabilities has increased and is still at a satisfactory level.*
	Prior year: *$446,300 ÷ 220,630 = 2.0 times*	
[c]	Acid-test ratio:	Trend: *Unfavorable*
	Current year: *$216,310 ÷ 261,570 = .8 times* ($137,490 + 78,820 = $216,310)	Reason: *Current liabilities have increased more than quick assets. All current liabilities could not be paid immediately if necessary.*
	Prior year: *$215,350 ÷ 220,630 = 1.0 times* ($138,530 + 76,820 = $215,350)	

16-6 APPLICATION PROBLEM, p. 469

The comparative balance sheet from Application Problem 16-1 is needed to complete this problem.

Analyzing long-term financial strength from a comparative balance sheet [1, 2]

[a]	Debt ratio:	Trend: *Favorable*
	Current year: *$341,570 ÷ 798,930 = 42.8%*	Reason: *The per dollar assets owned that are financed with borrowed capital decreased from 47.8¢ to 42.7¢.*
	Prior year: *$320,630 ÷ 670,670 = 47.8%*	
[b]	Equity ratio:	Trend: *Favorable*
	Current year: *$457,360 ÷ 798,930 = 57.2%*	Reason: *The per dollar assets owned that are provided by stockholders' equity have increased from 52.2¢ to 57.2¢.*
	Prior year: *$350,040 ÷ 670,670 = 52.2%*	
[c]	Equity per share:	Trend: *Favorable*
	Current year: *$457,360 ÷ 50,000 = $9.15*	Reason: *The ownership of the total equity per share of stock has increased from $8.75 to $9.15.*
	Prior year: *$350,040 ÷ 40,000 = $8.75*	

16-6 APPLICATION PROBLEM

Extra form

	CURRENT YEAR				PRIOR YEAR				INCREASE (DECREASE)				
									AMOUNT				%

16-7 MASTERY PROBLEM, p. 469

Analyzing comparative financial statements [1]

Advanced Auto Technology, Inc.

Comparative Income Statement

For Years Ended December 31, 20-- and 20--

	CURRENT YEAR	PRIOR YEAR	INCREASE (DECREASE) AMOUNT	%
Operating Revenue:				
Net Sales	2064 0 0 0 00	1563 9 0 0 00	500 1 0 0 00	32.0
Cost of Merchandise Sold:				
Merchandise Inventory, Jan. 1	172 8 9 0 00	53 7 6 0 00	119 1 3 0 00	221.6
Net Purchases	1255 6 0 0 00	1109 6 6 0 00	145 9 4 0 00	13.2
Total Cost of Merchandise Available for Sale	1428 4 9 0 00	1163 4 2 0 00	265 0 7 0 00	22.8
Less Merchandise Inventory, Dec. 31	194 2 3 0 00	172 8 9 0 00	21 3 4 0 00	12.3
Cost of Merchandise Sold	1234 2 6 0 00	990 5 3 0 00	243 7 3 0 00	24.6
Gross Profit on Operations	829 7 4 0 00	573 3 7 0 00	256 3 7 0 00	44.7
Operating Expenses:				
Selling Expenses:				
Advertising Expense	15 2 6 0 00	10 1 7 0 00	5 0 9 0 00	50.0
Delivery Expense	22 8 8 0 00	17 4 4 0 00	5 4 4 0 00	31.2
Salary Expense—Sales	286 0 5 0 00	216 5 0 0 00	69 5 5 0 00	32.1
Supplies Expense	13 3 5 0 00	10 1 7 0 00	3 1 8 0 00	31.3
Other Selling Expenses	38 1 4 0 00	30 5 1 0 00	7 6 3 0 00	25.0
Total Selling Expenses	375 6 8 0 00	284 7 9 0 00	90 8 9 0 00	31.9
Administrative Expenses:				
Salary Expense—Administrative	80 0 9 0 00	63 9 3 0 00	16 1 6 0 00	25.3
Uncollectible Accounts Expense	11 4 4 0 00	7 2 7 0 00	4 1 7 0 00	57.4
Other Administrative Expenses	57 2 1 0 00	47 9 5 0 00	9 2 6 0 00	19.3
Total Administrative Expenses	148 7 4 0 00	119 1 5 0 00	29 5 9 0 00	24.8
Total Operating Expenses	524 4 2 0 00	403 9 4 0 00	120 4 8 0 00	29.8
Income from Operations	305 3 2 0 00	169 4 3 0 00	135 8 9 0 00	80.2
Other Expenses:				
Interest Expense	25 5 6 0 00	22 5 0 0 00	3 0 6 0 00	13.6
Net Income before Federal Income Tax	279 7 6 0 00	146 9 3 0 00	132 8 3 0 00	90.4
Less Federal Income Tax Expense	92 3 6 0 00	40 5 5 0 00	51 8 1 0 00	127.8
Net Income after Federal Income Tax	187 4 0 0 00	106 3 8 0 00	81 0 2 0 00	76.2

16-7 MASTERY PROBLEM (continued)

[1]

Advanced Auto Technology, Inc.

Comparative Statement of Stockholders' Equity

For Years Ended December 31, 20-- and 20--

	CURRENT YEAR	PRIOR YEAR	INCREASE (DECREASE) AMOUNT	%
Capital Stock:				
$5 Per Share				
Balance, January 1	200 0 0 0 00	200 0 0 0 00	- 0 -	—
Additional Capital Stock Issued	40 0 0 0 00	- 0 -	40 0 0 0 00	—
Balance, December 31	240 0 0 0 00	200 0 0 0 00	40 0 0 0 00	20.0
Retained Earnings:				
Balance, January 1	173 1 6 0 00	106 7 8 0 00	66 3 8 0 00	62.2
Net Income after Federal Income Tax	187 4 0 0 00	106 3 8 0 00	81 0 2 0 00	76.2
Total	360 5 6 0 00	213 1 6 0 00	147 4 0 0 00	69.1
Less Dividends Declared	62 5 0 0 00	40 0 0 0 00	22 5 0 0 00	56.3
Balance, December 31	298 0 6 0 00	173 1 6 0 00	124 9 0 0 00	72.1
Total Stockholders' Equity, December 31	538 0 6 0 00	373 1 6 0 00	164 9 0 0 00	44.2
Capital Stock Shares Outstanding	48 0 0 0	40 0 0 0	8 0 0 0	20.0

16-7 **MASTERY PROBLEM (continued)**

[1]

Advanced Auto Technology, Inc.

Comparative Balance Sheet

December 31, 20-- and 20--

	CURRENT YEAR	PRIOR YEAR	INCREASE (DECREASE) AMOUNT	%
ASSETS				
Current Assets:				
Cash	75 4 0 0 00	32 5 6 0 00	42 8 4 0 00	131.6
Accounts Receivable (book value)	201 6 4 0 00	242 8 9 0 00	(41 2 5 0 00)	(17.0)
Merchandise Inventory	194 2 3 0 00	172 8 9 0 00	21 3 4 0 00	12.3
Other Current Assets	10 9 2 0 00	8 5 2 0 00	2 4 0 0 00	28.2
Total Current Assets	482 1 9 0 00	456 8 6 0 00	25 3 3 0 00	5.5
Plant Assets (book value)	422 0 0 0 00	306 0 0 0 00	116 0 0 0 00	37.9
Total Assets	904 1 9 0 00	762 8 6 0 00	141 3 3 0 00	18.5
LIABILITIES				
Current Liabilities:				
Notes Payable	64 8 6 0 00	83 4 1 0 00	(18 5 5 0 00)	(22.2)
Interest Payable	5 1 6 0 00	8 0 4 0 00	(2 8 8 0 00)	(35.8)
Accounts Payable	113 4 5 0 00	154 4 7 0 00	(41 0 2 0 00)	(26.6)
Federal Income Tax Payable	5 5 0 0 00	1 2 8 0 00	4 2 2 0 00	329.7
Other Current Liabilities	2 1 6 0 00	2 5 0 0 00	(3 4 0 00)	(13.6)
Total Current Liabilities	191 1 3 0 00	249 7 0 0 00	(58 5 7 0 00)	(23.5)
Long-Term Liability:				
Mortgage Payable	175 0 0 0 00	140 0 0 0 00	35 0 0 0 00	25.0
Total Liabilities	366 1 3 0 00	389 7 0 0 00	(23 5 7 0 00)	(6.0)
STOCKHOLDERS' EQUITY				
Capital Stock	240 0 0 0 00	200 0 0 0 00	40 0 0 0 00	20.0
Retained Earnings	298 0 6 0 00	173 1 6 0 00	124 9 0 0 00	72.1
Total Stockholders' Equity	538 0 6 0 00	373 1 6 0 00	164 9 0 0 00	44.2
Total Liabilities and Stockholders' Equity	904 1 9 0 00	762 8 6 0 00	141 3 3 0 00	18.5

16-7 MASTERY PROBLEM (continued)

[2]

[a] Net sales: *+32.0%*	Trend: *Favorable*
	
	Reason: *Possible causes are:*
	    1) Increased advertising efforts.
	    2) Increased sales efforts as shown by increased spending for advertising and sales salaries.

[b] Net income: *+76.2%*	Trend: *Favorable* Reason: *The percentage increase in net sales is larger than the percentage increase in cost of merchandise sold.*
[c] Net stockholders' equity: *+44.2%*	Trend: *Favorable* Reason: *Retained earnings and net income have increased. Additional capital stock was issued.*
[d] Total assets: *+18.5%*	Trend: *Favorable* Reason: *Significant increases in cash and plant assets resulting from an increase in long-term liabilities and stockholders' equity.*

16-7 MASTERY PROBLEM (continued)

[3]

Advanced Auto Technology, Inc.

Comparative Income Statement

For Years Ended December 31, 20-- and 20--

	CURRENT YEAR		PRIOR YEAR	
	AMOUNT	%	AMOUNT	%
Operating Revenue:				
Net Sales	2064 0 0 0 00	100.0	1563 9 0 0 00	100.0
Cost of Merchandise Sold:				
Merchandise Inventory, Jan. 1	172 8 9 0 00	8.4	53 7 6 0 00	3.4
Net Purchases	1255 6 0 0 00	60.8	1109 6 6 0 00	71.0
Total Cost of Merchandise Available for Sale	1428 4 9 0 00	69.2	1163 4 2 0 00	74.4
Less Merchandise Inventory, Dec. 31	194 2 3 0 00	9.4	172 8 9 0 00	11.1
Cost of Merchandise Sold	1234 2 6 0 00	59.8	990 5 3 0 00	63.3
Gross Profit on Operations	829 7 4 0 00	40.2	573 3 7 0 00	36.7
Operating Expenses:				
Selling Expenses:				
Advertising Expense	15 2 6 0 00	0.7	10 1 7 0 00	0.7
Delivery Expense	22 8 8 0 00	1.1	17 4 4 0 00	1.1
Salary Expense—Sales	286 0 5 0 00	13.9	216 5 0 0 00	13.8
Supplies Expense	13 3 5 0 00	0.6	10 1 7 0 00	0.7
Other Selling Expenses	38 1 4 0 00	1.8	30 5 1 0 00	2.0
Total Selling Expenses	375 6 8 0 00	18.2	284 7 9 0 00	18.2
Administrative Expenses:				
Salary Expense—Administrative	80 0 9 0 00	3.9	63 9 3 0 00	4.1
Uncollectible Accounts Expense	11 4 4 0 00	0.6	7 2 7 0 00	0.5
Other Administrative Expenses	57 2 1 0 00	2.8	47 9 5 0 00	3.1
Total Administrative Expenses	148 7 4 0 00	7.2	119 1 5 0 00	7.6
Total Operating Expenses	524 4 2 0 00	25.4	403 9 4 0 00	25.8
Income from Operations	305 3 2 0 00	14.8	169 4 3 0 00	10.8
Other Expenses:				
Interest Expense	25 5 6 0 00	1.2	22 5 0 0 00	1.4
Net Income before Federal Income Tax	279 7 6 0 00	13.6	146 9 3 0 00	9.4
Less Federal Income Tax Expense	92 3 6 0 00	4.5	40 5 5 0 00	2.6
Net Income after Federal Income Tax	187 4 0 0 00	9.1	106 3 8 0 00	6.8

16-7 MASTERY PROBLEM (continued)

[4]

[a] (1)	As a Percentage of Net Sales: Cost of merchandise sold: Current year: **59.8%** Prior year: **63.3%**	Trend: *Favorable* Reason: *A decreasing percentage of the revenue from sales is being used to pay for merchandise sold.*
(2)	Gross profit on operations: Current year: **40.2%** Prior year: **36.7%**	Trend: *Favorable* Reason: *The decreased percentage of cost of merchandise sold has resulted in a higher gross profit percentage.*
(3)	Total operating expenses: Current year: **25.4%** Prior year: **25.8%**	Trend: *Favorable* Reason: *The cost of operating the business has decreased so the business is operating more economically.*
(4)	Net income after federal income tax: Current year: **9.1%** Prior year: **6.8%**	Trend: *Favorable* Reason: *Cost of merchandise sold and operating expenses decreased.*

16-7 MASTERY PROBLEM (continued)

[4]

[b] **(1)**	As a Percentage of Total Stockholders' Equity: Retained earnings: Current year: *$298,060 ÷ 538,060 = 55.4%* Prior year: *$173,160 ÷ 373,160 = 46.4%*	Trend: *Favorable* Reason: *Net income increased and more was retained in the business.*
(2)	Capital stock: Current year: *$240,000 ÷ 538,060 = 44.6%* Prior year: *$200,000 ÷ 373,160 = 53.6%*	Trend: *Favorable* Reason: *A larger portion of the business is being financed through increased earnings and less from invested capital.*
[c] **(1)**	As a Percentage of Total Assets or Total Liabilities and Stockholders' Equity: Current assets: Current year: *$482,190 ÷ 904,190 = 53.3%* Prior year: *$456,860 ÷ 762,860 = 59.9%*	Trend: *Unfavorable* Reason: *Plant assets increased over 35%. Although current assets increased, the increase was only 5.5%, compared to the 37.9% plant asset increase.*
(2)	Current liabilities: Current year: *$191,130 ÷ 904,190 = 21.1%* Prior year: *$249,700 ÷ 762,860 = 32.7%*	Trend: *Favorable* Reason: *Current liabilities declined 23.5% while long-term liabilities increased 25% and total liabilities decreased 6.0%. The additional long-term liabilities probably were used to reduce current liabilities.*

16-7 MASTERY PROBLEM (continued)

[5, 6]

[a] **(1)**	Profitability ratios: Rate earned on average total assets: Current year: $\$187,400 \div \dfrac{762,860 + 904,190}{2} = 22.5\%$ Prior year: $\$106,380 \div \dfrac{693,200 + 762,860}{2} = 14.6\%$	Trend: *Favorable* Reason: *For each dollar in company assets, the net income has increased from 14.6¢ to 22.5¢.*
(2)	Rate earned on average stockholders' equity: Current year: $\$187,400 \div \dfrac{373,160 + 538,060}{2} = 41.1\%$ Prior year: $\$106,380 \div \dfrac{306,780 + 373,160}{2} = 31.3\%$	Trend: *Favorable* Reason: *For each dollar of stockholders' equity, the net income increased from 31.3¢ to 41.1¢.*
(3)	Rate earned on net sales: Current year: $\$187,400 \div 2,064,000 = 9.1\%$ Prior year: $\$106,380 \div 1,563,900 = 6.8\%$	Trend: *Favorable* Reason: *For each dollar of sales the net income increased from 6.8¢ to 9.1¢.*
(4)	Earnings per share: Current year: $\$187,400 \div 48,000 = \$3.90$ Prior year: $\$106,380 \div 40,000 = \$2.66$	Trend: *Favorable* Reason: *The net income earned for each share of capital stock increased from $2.66 to $3.90.*
(5)	Price earnings ratio: Current year: $\$42.50 \div 3.90 = 10.9$ times Prior year: $\$30.00 \div 2.66 = 11.3$ times	Trend: *Unfavorable* Reason: *The market price of the company's stock has not increased as much relatively as the earnings.*

16-7 MASTERY PROBLEM (continued)

[5, 6]

[b] **(1)**	Efficiency ratios: Accounts receivable turnover ratio: Current year: $\$2,064,000 \div \dfrac{242,890 + 201,640}{2} = 9.3 \text{ times}$ Prior year: $\$1,563,900 \div \dfrac{236,580 + 242,890}{2} = 6.5 \text{ times}$	Trend: *Favorable* Reason: *The number of times the average accounts receivable balance has been collected increased from 6.5 to 9.3. Thus accounts receivable are being collected more quickly than in the previous year.*
(2)	Merchandise inventory turnover ratio: Current year: $\$1,234,260 \div \dfrac{172,890 + 194,230}{2} = 6.7 \text{ times}$ Prior year: $\$990,530 \div \dfrac{53,760 + 172,890}{2} = 8.7 \text{ times}$	Trend: *Unfavorable* Reason: *The number of times the average amount of inventory is sold each year decreased from 8.7 to 6.7 times.*
[c] **(1)**	Short-term financial strength ratios: Working capital: Current year: $\$482,190 - 191,130 = \$291,060$ Prior year: $\$456,860 - 249,700 = \$207,160$	Trend: *Favorable* Reason: *The amount of working capital is increasing.*
(2)	Current ratio: Current year: $\$482,190 \div 191,130 = 2.5 \text{ times}$ Prior year: $\$456,860 \div 249,700 = 1.8 \text{ times}$	Trend: *Favorable* Reason: *The amount of current assets is increasing while current liabilities are decreasing.*
(3)	Acid-test ratio: Current year: $\$277,040 \div 191,130 = 1.4 \text{ times}$ ($\$75,400 + 201,640 = \$277,040$) Prior year: $\$275,450 \div 249,700 = 1.1 \text{ times}$ ($\$32,560 + 242,890 = \$275,450$)	Trend: *Favorable* Reason: *The amount of the most liquid current assets is increasing, while current liabilities are decreasing.*

16-7 MASTERY PROBLEM (concluded)

[5, 6]

[d]	Long-term financial strength ratios:	Trend: *Favorable*
(1)	Debt ratio:	Reason: *The per dollar assets owned that are financed with borrowed capital decreased from 51.1¢ to 40.5¢.*
	Current year: *$366,130 ÷ 904,190 = 40.5%*	
	Prior year: *$389,700 ÷ 762,860 = 51.1%*	
(2)	Equity ratio:	Trend: *Favorable*
	Current year: *$538,060 ÷ 904,190 = 59.5%*	Reason: *The per dollar assets owned that are provided by stockholders' equity have increased from 48.9¢ to 59.5¢.*
	Prior year: *$373,160 ÷ 762,860 = 48.9%*	
(3)	Equity per share:	Trend: *Favorable*
	Current year: *$538,060 ÷ 48,000 = $11.21*	Reason: *The ownership of the total equity per share of stock has increased from $9.33 to $11.21.*
	Prior year: *$373,160 ÷ 40,000 = $9.33*	

16-8 CHALLENGE PROBLEM, p. 470

Analyzing comparative financial statements [1]

CompuCircuit Corporation

Comparative Income Statement

For Years Ended December 31, 20-- and 20--

	CURRENT YEAR	PRIOR YEAR	INCREASE (DECREASE) AMOUNT	%
Operating Revenue:				
Net Sales	1287 9 0 0 00	1532 3 3 0 00	(244 4 3 0 00)	(16.0)
Cost of Merchandise Sold:				
Merchandise Inventory, Jan. 1	324 5 6 0 00	293 5 0 0 00	31 0 6 0 00	10.6
Net Purchases	924 3 5 0 00	1049 7 4 0 00	(125 3 9 0 00)	(11.9)
Total Cost of Merchandise Available for Sale	1248 9 1 0 00	1343 2 4 0 00	(94 3 3 0 00)	(7.0)
Less Merchandise Inventory, Dec. 31	335 7 8 0 00	324 5 6 0 00	11 2 2 0 00	3.5
Cost of Merchandise Sold	913 1 3 0 00	1018 6 8 0 00	(105 5 5 0 00)	(10.4)
Gross Profit on Operations	374 7 7 0 00	513 6 5 0 00	(138 8 8 0 00)	(27.0)
Operating Expenses:				
Selling Expenses:				
Advertising Expense	20 3 3 0 00	26 4 0 0 00	(6 0 7 0 00)	(23.0)
Delivery Expense	33 1 7 0 00	40 9 2 0 00	(7 7 5 0 00)	(18.9)
Salary Expense—Sales	86 6 7 0 00	116 1 6 0 00	(29 4 9 0 00)	(25.4)
Supplies Expense	8 5 6 0 00	10 5 6 0 00	(2 0 0 0 00)	(18.9)
Other Selling Expenses	37 4 5 0 00	46 2 0 0 00	(8 7 5 0 00)	(18.9)
Total Selling Expenses	186 1 8 0 00	240 2 4 0 00	(54 0 6 0 00)	(22.5)
Administrative Expenses:				
Salary Expense—Administrative	64 2 0 0 00	77 8 8 0 00	(13 6 8 0 00)	(17.6)
Uncollectible Accounts Expense	4 2 8 0 00	9 2 4 0 00	(4 9 6 0 00)	(53.7)
Other Administrative Expenses	55 6 4 0 00	66 0 0 0 00	(10 3 6 0 00)	(15.7)
Total Administrative Expenses	124 1 2 0 00	153 1 2 0 00	(29 0 0 0 00)	(18.9)
Total Operating Expenses	310 3 0 0 00	393 3 6 0 00	(83 0 6 0 00)	(21.1)
Income from Operations	64 4 7 0 00	120 2 9 0 00	(55 8 2 0 00)	(46.4)
Other Expenses:				
Interest Expense	31 0 3 0 00	26 4 0 0 00	4 6 3 0 00	17.5
Net Income before Federal Income Tax	33 4 4 0 00	93 8 9 0 00	(60 4 5 0 00)	(64.4)
Less Federal Income Tax Expense	5 0 2 0 00	20 1 7 0 00	(15 1 5 0 00)	(75.1)
Net Income after Federal Income Tax	28 4 2 0 00	73 7 2 0 00	(45 3 0 0 00)	(61.4)

16-8 CHALLENGE PROBLEM (continued)

[1]

CompuCircuit Corporation

Comparative Statement of Stockholders' Equity

For Years Ended December 31, 20-- and 20--

	CURRENT YEAR	PRIOR YEAR	INCREASE (DECREASE) AMOUNT	%
Capital Stock:				
$5 Per Share				
Balance, January 1	400 0 0 0 00	400 0 0 0 00	- 0 -	0.0
Additional Capital Stock Issued	- 0 -	- 0 -	- 0 -	—
Balance, December 31	400 0 0 0 00	400 0 0 0 00	- 0 -	0.0
Retained Earnings:				
Balance, January 1	67 0 6 0 00	43 3 4 0 00	23 7 2 0 00	54.7
Net Income after Federal income Tax	28 4 2 0 00	73 7 2 0 00	(45 3 0 0 00)	(61.4)
Total	95 4 8 0 00	117 0 6 0 00	(21 5 8 0 00)	(18.4)
Less Dividends Declared	50 0 0 0 00	50 0 0 0 00	- 0 -	0.0
Balance, December 31	45 4 8 0 00	67 0 6 0 00	(21 5 8 0 00)	(32.2)
Total Stockholders' Equity, December 31	445 4 8 0 00	467 0 6 0 00	(21 5 8 0 00)	(4.6)
Capital Stock Shares Outstanding	20 0 0 0	20 0 0 0	- 0 -	0.0

16-8 CHALLENGE PROBLEM (continued)

[1]

CompuCircuit Corporation

Comparative Balance Sheet

December 31, 20-- and 20--

	CURRENT YEAR	PRIOR YEAR	INCREASE (DECREASE) AMOUNT	%
ASSETS				
Current Assets:				
Cash	33 6 5 0 00	98 7 7 0 00	(65 1 2 0 00)	(65.9)
Accounts Receivable (book value)	88 4 9 0 00	105 5 0 0 00	(17 0 1 0 00)	(16.1)
Merchandise Inventory	335 7 8 0 00	324 5 6 0 00	11 2 2 0 00	3.5
Other Current Assets	145 8 3 0 00	125 1 3 0 00	20 7 0 0 00	16.5
Total Current Assets	603 7 5 0 00	653 9 6 0 00	(50 2 1 0 00)	(7.7)
Plant Assets (book value)	312 7 0 0 00	325 7 0 0 00	(13 0 0 0 00)	(4.0)
Total Assets	916 4 5 0 00	979 6 6 0 00	(63 2 1 0 00)	(6.5)
LIABILITIES				
Current Liabilities:				
Notes Payable	142 0 0 0 00	112 2 0 0 00	29 8 0 0 00	26.6
Interest Payable	3 1 0 0 00	2 6 0 0 00	5 0 0 00	19.2
Accounts Payable	72 0 4 0 00	135 9 2 0 00	(63 8 8 0 00)	(47.0)
Federal Income Tax Payable	5 0 0 00	2 0 0 0 00	(1 5 0 0 00)	(75.0)
Other Current Liabilities	28 3 3 0 00	27 8 8 0 00	4 5 0 00	1.6
Total Current Liabilities	245 9 7 0 00	280 6 0 0 00	(34 6 3 0 00)	(12.3)
Long-Term Liability:				
Mortgage Payable	225 0 0 0 00	232 0 0 0 00	(7 0 0 0 00)	(3.0)
Total Liabilities	470 9 7 0 00	512 6 0 0 00	(41 6 3 0 00)	(8.1)
STOCKHOLDERS' EQUITY				
Capital Stock	400 0 0 0 00	400 0 0 0 00	- 0 -	0.0
Retained Earnings	45 4 8 0 00	67 0 6 0 00	(21 5 8 0 00)	(32.2)
Total Stockholders' Equity	445 4 8 0 00	467 0 6 0 00	(21 5 8 0 00)	(4.6)
Total Liabilities and Stockholders' Equity	916 4 5 0 00	979 6 6 0 00	(63 2 1 0 00)	(6.5)

16-8 CHALLENGE PROBLEM (continued)

[2]

[a] Net sales: –16.0%	Trend: *Unfavorable* Reason: *Sales are down 16.0% and most costs and expenses are down 15% to 20%. However, uncollectible accounts expense is down 53.7% and sales salary expense is down 25.4%. In an attempt to cut costs, the company may have decreased its sales efforts and become too restrictive on credit, thus decreasing sales.*
[b] Net income: –61.4%	Trend: *Unfavorable* Reason: *Net sales decreased 16.0%. Cost of merchandise sold also decreased, but at the lower rate of 10.4%. Gross profit on operations, therefore, decreased 27.0%. Total operating expenses also decreased, but at the lower rate of 21.1%.*
[c] Net stockholders' equity: –4.6%	Trend: *Unfavorable* Reason: *The company experienced a significant reduction in net income. The annual dividend, $50,000, exceeded the current year's net income, $28,420, thus reducing stockholders' equity.*
[d] Total assets: –6.5%	Trend: *Unfavorable* Reason: *A significant portion of the decrease was caused by a 16.1% decrease in accounts receivable. This result could be positive if it is an indication of more efficient collection efforts. However, this effect could be caused by reduced sales efforts and stricter credit practices (as noted in [a] above). Cash was reduced by over 65% to reduce outstanding accounts payable.*

16-8 CHALLENGE PROBLEM (continued)

[3]

CompuCircuit Corporation

Comparative Income Statement

For Years Ended December 31, 20-- and 20--

	CURRENT YEAR		PRIOR YEAR	
	AMOUNT	%	AMOUNT	%
Operating Revenue:				
Net Sales	1287 9 0 0 00	100.0	1532 3 3 0 00	100.0
Cost of Merchandise Sold:				
Merchandise Inventory, Jan. 1	324 5 6 0 00	25.2	293 5 0 0 00	19.2
Net Purchases	924 3 5 0 00	71.8	1049 7 4 0 00	68.5
Total Cost of Merchandise Available for Sale	1248 9 1 0 00	97.0	1343 2 4 0 00	87.7
Less Merchandise Inventory, Dec. 31	335 7 8 0 00	26.1	324 5 6 0 00	21.2
Cost of Merchandise Sold	913 1 3 0 00	70.9	1018 6 8 0 00	66.5
Gross Profit on Operations	374 7 7 0 00	29.1	513 6 5 0 00	33.5
Operating Expenses:				
Selling Expenses:				
Advertising Expense	20 3 3 0 00	1.6	26 4 0 0 00	1.7
Delivery Expense	33 1 7 0 00	2.6	40 9 2 0 00	2.7
Salary Expense—Sales	86 6 7 0 00	6.7	116 1 6 0 00	7.6
Supplies Expense	8 5 6 0 00	0.7	10 5 6 0 00	0.7
Other Selling Expenses	37 4 5 0 00	2.9	46 2 0 0 00	3.0
Total Selling Expenses	186 1 8 0 00	14.5	240 2 4 0 00	15.7
Administrative Expenses:				
Salary Expense—Administrative	64 2 0 0 00	5.0	77 8 8 0 00	5.1
Uncollectible Accounts Expense	4 2 8 0 00	0.3	9 2 4 0 00	0.6
Other Administrative Expenses	55 6 4 0 00	4.3	66 0 0 0 00	4.3
Total Administrative Expenses	124 1 2 0 00	9.6	153 1 2 0 00	10.0
Total Operating Expenses	310 3 0 0 00	24.1	393 3 6 0 00	25.7
Income from Operations	64 4 7 0 00	5.0	120 2 9 0 00	7.9
Other Expenses:				
Interest Expense	31 0 3 0 00	2.4	26 4 0 0 00	1.7
Net Income before Federal Income Tax	33 4 4 0 00	2.6	93 8 9 0 00	6.1
Less Federal Income Tax	5 0 2 0 00	0.4	20 1 7 0 00	1.3
Net Income after Federal Income Tax	28 4 2 0 00	2.2	73 7 2 0 00	4.8

16-8 CHALLENGE PROBLEM (continued)

[4]

[a] (1)	As a Percentage of Net Sales: Cost of merchandise sold: Current year: *70.9%* Prior year: *66.5%*	Trend: *Unfavorable* Reason: *The cost of merchandise sold has increased from 66.5¢ to 70.9¢ per dollar of net sales. Therefore, there is 4.4¢ less per sales dollar that is available for net income in the current year.*
(2)	Gross profit on operations: Current year: *29.1%* Prior year: *33.5%*	Trend: *Unfavorable* Reason: *Cost of merchandise sold increased 4.4¢ per sales dollar. Therefore, the company has 4.4¢ less per sales dollar available for net income and operating expenses.*
(3)	Total operating expenses: Current year: *24.1%* Prior year: *25.7%*	Trend: *Favorable* Reason: *Increased efficiency decreased the operating expenses from 25.7¢ per sales dollar to 24.1¢, a 1.6¢ decrease.*
(4)	Net income after federal income tax: Current year: *2.2%* Prior year: *4.8%*	Trend: *Unfavorable* Reason: *Net income decreased from 4.8¢ per sales dollar to 2.2¢, a 2.6¢ reduction. This decrease per sales dollar was caused by the following changes in costs:* *Cost of merchandise . . . . 4.4¢ increase* *Operating expenses . . . . 1.6¢ decrease* *Interest Expense . . . . 0.7¢ increase* *Federal Income Tax Expense . 0.9¢ decrease* *Net increase in costs and* *decrease in net income . . . . 2.6¢*

Name _____ Date _____ Class _____

16-8 CHALLENGE PROBLEM (continued)

[4]

[b] **(1)**	As a Percentage of Total Stockholders' Equity: Retained earnings: Current year: $45,480 ÷ 445,480 = 10.2% Prior year: $67,060 ÷ 467,060 = 14.4%	Trend: *Unfavorable* Reason: *Net Income decreased below the amount of dividends, decreasing retained earnings.*
(2)	Capital stock: Current year: $400,000 ÷ 445,480 = 89.8% Prior year: $400,000 ÷ 467,060 = 85.6%	Trend: *Unfavorable* Reason: *The company has decreased its proportion of retained earnings and, as a result, the proportion of capital stock has increased.*
[c] **(1)**	As a Percentage of Total Assets or Total Liabilities and Stockholders' Equity: Current assets: Current year: $603,750 ÷ 916,450 = 65.9% Prior year: $653,960 ÷ 979,660 = 66.8%	Trend: *Unfavorable* Reason: *Cash decreased by $65,120. See also response to (2)[d].*
(2)	Current liabilities: Current year: $245,970 ÷ 916,450 = 26.8% Prior year: $280,600 ÷ 979,660 = 28.6%	Trend: *Favorable* Reason: *Accounts payable decreased by $63,880. Decreased liabilities strengthen the cash position.*

16-8 CHALLENGE PROBLEM (continued)

[5, 6]

[a] **(1)**	Profitability ratios: Rate earned on average total assets: Current year: $$\$28,420 \div \frac{\$979,660 + \$916,450}{2} = 3.0\%$$ Prior year: $$\$73,720 \div \frac{\$1,052,400 + \$979,660}{2} = 7.3\%$$	Trend: *Unfavorable* Reason: *The net income for each dollar in company assets has decreased from 7.3¢ to 3.0¢.*
(2)	Rate earned on average stockholders' equity: Current year: $$\$28,420 \div \frac{\$467,060 + \$445,480}{2} = 6.2\%$$ Prior year: $$\$73,720 \div \frac{\$443,340 + \$467,060}{2} = 16.2\%$$	Trend: *Unfavorable* Reason: *The net income for each dollar of stockholders' equity decreased from 16.2¢ to 6.2¢.*
(3)	Rate earned on net sales: Current year: *$28,420 ÷ $1,287,900 = 2.2%* Prior year: *$73,720 ÷ $1,532,330 = 4.8%*	Trend: *Unfavorable* Reason: *The amount earned per sales dollar decreased from 4.8¢ to 2.2¢.*
(4)	Earnings per share: Current year: *$28,420 ÷ 20,000 = $1.42* Prior year: *$73,720 ÷ 20,000 = $3.69*	Trend: *Unfavorable* Reason: *Annual net income per share decreased from $3.69 to $1.42.*
(5)	Price earnings ratio: Current year: *$7.50 ÷ $1.42 = 5.3 times* Prior year: *$29.50 ÷ $3.69 = 8.0 times*	Trend: *Unfavorable* Reason: *Investors considered the stock less valuable and were not willing to pay as much for the stock per dollar earned by the corporation.*
[b] **(1)**	Efficiency ratios: Accounts receivable turnover ratio: Current year: $$\$1,287,700 \div \frac{\$105,500 + \$88,490}{2} = 13.3 \text{ times}$$ Prior year: $$\$1,532,330 \div \frac{\$126,400 + \$105,500}{2} = 13.2 \text{ times}$$	Trend: *Favorable* Reason: *Collection efficiency was increased by reducing the collection period slightly.*

16-8 CHALLENGE PROBLEM (continued)

[5, 6]

[b] **(2)**	Efficiency ratios: Merchandise inventory turnover ratio: Current year: $\$913,130 \div \dfrac{\$324,560 + 335,780}{2} = 2.8$ times Prior year: $\$1,018,680 \div \dfrac{\$293,500 + 324,560}{2} = 3.3$ times	Trend: *Unfavorable* Reason: *The number of times the average amount of inventory is sold in a year has decreased from 3.3 to 2.8.*
[c] **(1)**	Short-term financial strength ratios: Working capital: Current year: $\$603,750 - 245,970 = \$357,780$ Prior year: $\$653,960 - 280,600 = \$373,360$	Trend: *Unfavorable* Reason: *The amount of working capital is decreasing.*
(2)	Current ratio: Current year: $\$603,750 \div 245,970 = 2.5$ times Prior year: $\$653,960 \div \$280,600 = 2.3$ times	Trend: *Favorable* Reason: *The amount of current liabilities in relation to current assets is decreasing.*
(3)	Acid-test ratio: Current year: $\$122,140 \div \$245,970 = 0.5$ times ($\$33,650 + \$88,490 = \$122,140$) Prior year: $\$204,270 \div \$280,600 = 0.7$ times ($\$98,770 + \$105,500 = \$204,270$)	Trend: *Unfavorable* Reason: *Many businesses consider an acid-test ratio of 1.0 times as satisfactory. The company's ratio is declining below this. It is probably having difficulty paying current liabilities without borrowing.*
[d] **(1)**	Long-term financial strength ratios: Debt ratio: Current year: $\$470,970 \div 916,450 = 51.4\%$ Prior year: $\$512,600 \div 979,660 = 52.3\%$	Trend: *Favorable* Reason: *The per dollar assets owned that are financed with borrowed capital decreased from 52.3¢ to 51.4¢.*
(2)	Equity ratio: Current year: $\$445,480 \div \$916,450 = 48.6\%$ Prior year: $\$467,060 \div \$979,660 = 47.7\%$	Trend: *Favorable* Reason: *The per dollar assets owned that are provided by stockholders' equity have increased from 47.7¢ to 48.6¢.*
(3)	Equity per share: Current year: $\$445,480 \div 20,000 = \$22.27$ Prior year: $\$467,060 \div 20,000 = \$23.25$	Trend: *Unfavorable* Reason: *The ownership of the total equity per share of stock has decreased from $23.35 to $22.27.*

16-8 CHALLENGE PROBLEM

Extra form

	CURRENT YEAR	PRIOR YEAR	INCREASE (DECREASE)	
			AMOUNT	%

Name _____ Date _____ Class _____

17-1 WORK TOGETHER, p. 481

Classifying cash flows [4]

Transaction	Cash Inflow	Cash Outflow	Operating Activity	Investing Activity	Financing Activity
a. Receipts from the issue of capital stock	✓				✓
b. Cash purchase of office furniture		✓		✓	
c. Dividend payment		✓			✓
d. Advertising expense		✓	✓		
e. Receipts from the sale of merchandise	✓		✓		
f. Cash received from the issue of a mortgage	✓				✓
g. Repayment of loan principal		✓			✓
h. Purchase of another company's stock		✓		✓	

17-1 ON YOUR OWN, p. 481

Classifying cash flows [5]

Transaction	Cash Inflow	Cash Outflow	Operating Activity	Investing Activity	Financing Activity
a. Receipts from the issue of bonds	✓				✓
b. Cash purchase of office furniture		✓		✓	
c. Salary expense		✓	✓		
d. Receipts from tuxedo rentals	✓		✓		
e. Receipts from the issue of a mortgage	✓				✓
f. Cash receipt from sale of equipment	✓			✓	
g. Cash purchase of treasury stock		✓			✓
h. Payment of property taxes		✓	✓		

17-1 WORK TOGETHER
ON YOUR OWN

Extra form

17-2 WORK TOGETHER, p. 487

Preparing the operating activity section for a statement of cash flows

Zephyr Corporation Comparative Balance Sheet December 31, 20X1 and 20X2			
	Current Year	Prior Year	Increase (Decrease)
ASSETS			
Current Assets:			
Cash	$ 98,760.00	$ 41,000.00	$ 57,760.00
Accounts Receivable (book value)............	155,000.00	160,000.00	(5,000.00)
Supplies	6,000.00	5,500.00	500.00
Merchandise Inventory...............	98,000.00	92,000.00	6,000.00
Total Current Assets............	$357,760.00	$298,500.00	$ 59,260.00
Plant Assets:			
Office Equipment.................	$ 45,000.00	$ 39,000.00	$ 6,000.00
Store Furniture..................	98,000.00	92,000.00	6,000.00
Building........................	140,000.00	140,000.00	0.00
Land...........................	0.00	25,000.00	(25,000.00)
Less Accum. Depr.—Equipment, Furniture & Bldg...	40,900.00	13,600.00	27,300.00
Total Plant Assets (book value)............	$242,100.00	$282,400.00	$ (40,300.00)
Total Assets	$599,860.00	$580,900.00	$ 18,960.00
LIABILITIES			
Current Liabilities:			
Notes Payable....................	$ 23,000.00	$ 21,000.00	$ 2,000.00
Accounts Payable..................	47,000.00	45,000.00	2,000.00
Sales Tax Payable.................	600.00	800.00	(200.00)
Total Current Liabilities	$ 70,600.00	$ 66,800.00	$ 3,800.00
Long-Term Liabilities:			
Mortgage Payable.................	$125,000.00	$140,000.00	$ (15,000.00)
Bonds Payable	80,000.00	70,000.00	10,000.00
Total Long-Term Liabilities...........	$205,000.00	$210,000.00	$ (5,000.00)
Total Liabilities	$275,600.00	$276,800.00	$ (1,200.00)
STOCKHOLDERS' EQUITY			
Total Stockholders' Equity	324,260.00	304,100.00	20,160.00
Total Liabilities and Stockholders' Equity	$599,860.00	$580,900.00	$ 18,960.00

[5–8]

Account	Current Year	Prior Year	Current Asset Current Liability	Increase (Decrease)	Source of Cash Use of Cash
Accounts Receivable (book value)	$155,000.00	$160,000.00	current asset	$(5,000)	source of cash
Notes Payable	23,000.00	21,000.00	current liability	2,000	source of cash
Merchandise Inventory	98,000.00	92,000.00	current asset	6,000	use of cash
Supplies	6,000.00	5,500.00	current asset	500	use of cash
Accounts Payable	47,000.00	45,000.00	current liability	2,000	source of cash
Sales Tax Payable	600.00	800.00	current liability	(200)	use of cash

17-2/17-3 WORK TOGETHER (concluded)

Zephyr Corporation

Statement of Cash Flows

For Year Ended December 31, 20--

Cash Flows from Operating Activities:			
Net Income		10 1 6 0 00	
Adjustments to Net Income:			
Depreciation Expense	27 3 0 0 00		
Changes in current assets and liabilities:			
Decrease in accounts receivable	5 0 0 0 00		
Increase in supplies	(5 0 0 00)		
Increase in merchandise inventory	(6 0 0 0 00)		
Increase in notes payable	2 0 0 0 00		
Increase in accounts payable	2 0 0 0 00		
Decrease in sales tax payable	(2 0 0 00)		
Total adjustments to net income		29 6 0 0 00	
Cash provided by operating activities			39 7 6 0 00
Cash Flows from Investing Activities:			
Addition to office equipment		(6 0 0 0 00)	
Addition to store furniture		(6 0 0 0 00)	
Proceeds from sale of land		25 0 0 0 00	
Cash provided by investing activities			13 0 0 0 00
Cash Flows from Financing Activities:			
Repayment of mortgage		(15 0 0 0 00)	
Proceeds from issuance of bonds		10 0 0 0 00	
Proceeds from issuance of common stock		20 0 0 0 00	
Dividend payment		(10 0 0 0 00)	
Cash provided by financing activities			5 0 0 0 00
Net Increase in Cash			57 7 6 0 00
Cash Balance, Beginning of Period			41 0 0 0 00
Cash Balance, End of Period			98 7 6 0 00

17-2 ON YOUR OWN, p. 487

Preparing the operating activity section for a statement of cash flows

Cirrus Corporation Comparative Balance Sheet December 31, 20X1 and 20X2			
	Current Year	Prior Year	Increase (Decrease)
ASSETS			
Current Assets:			
Cash	$ 66,300.00	$ 70,000.00	$ (3,700.00)
Accounts Receivable (book value).	94,000.00	90,000.00	4,000.00
Prepaid Insurance	2,000.00	3,000.00	(1,000.00)
Merchandise Inventory.	92,000.00	110,000.00	(18,000.00)
Total Current Assets.	$ 254,300.00	$ 273,000.00	$(18,700.00)
Plant Assets:			
Office Equipment.	$ 46,000.00	$ 26,000.00	$ 20,000.00
Office Furniture	18,000.00	12,000.00	6,000.00
Building.	235,000.00	210,000.00	25,000.00
Land	0.00	12,000.00	(12,000.00)
Less Accum. Depr.—Equipment, Furniture & Bldg. .	24,500.00	19,600.00	4,900.00
Total Plant Assets (book value).	$ 274,500.00	$ 240,400.00	$ 34,100.00
Total Assets	$ 528,800.00	$ 513,400.00	$ 15,400.00
LIABILITIES			
Current Liabilities:			
Notes Payable.	$ 16,500.00	$ 18,000.00	$ (1,500.00)
Accounts Payable.	38,000.00	34,000.00	4,000.00
Total Current Liabilities	$ 54,500.00	$ 52,000.00	$ 2,500.00
Long-Term Liabilities:			
Mortgage Payable.	$ 178,000.00	$ 186,000.00	$ (8,000.00)
Bonds Payable	40,000.00	50,000.00	(10,000.00)
Total Long-Term Liabilities.	$ 218,000.00	$ 236,000.00	$(18,000.00)
Total Liabilities	$ 272,500.00	$ 288,000.00	$(15,500.00)
STOCKHOLDERS' EQUITY			
Total Stockholders' Equity	$ 256,300.00	$ 225,400.00	$ 30,900.00
Total Liabilities and Stockholders' Equity	$ 528,800.00	$ 513,400.00	$ 15,400.00

[10–13]

Account	Current Year	Prior Year	Current Asset Current Liability	Increase (Decrease)	Source of Cash Use of Cash
Accounts Receivable (book value)	$94,000.00	$ 90,000.00	current asset	$4,000	use of cash
Prepaid Insurance	2,000.00	3,000.00	current asset	(1,000)	source of cash
Merchandise Inventory	92,000.00	110,000.00	current asset	(18,000)	source of cash
Notes Payable	16,500.00	18,000.00	current liability	(1,500)	use of cash
Accounts Payable	38,000.00	34,000.00	current liability	4,000	source of cash

17-2/17-3 ON YOUR OWN (continued)

Cirrus Corporation

Statement of Cash Flows

For Year Ended December 31, 20--

Cash Flows from Operating Activities:					
Net Income			20 9 0 0 00		
Adjustments to Net Income:					
Depreciation Expense	4 9 0 0 00				
Changes in current assets and liabilities:					
Increase in accounts receivable	(4 0 0 0 00)				
Decrease in prepaid insurance	1 0 0 0 00				
Decrease in merchandise inventory	18 0 0 0 00				
Decrease in notes payable	(1 5 0 0 00)				
Increase in accounts payable	4 0 0 0 00				
Total adjustments to net income			22 4 0 0 00		
Cash provided by operating activities				43 3 0 0 00	
Cash Flows from Investing Activities:					
Addition to office equipment			(20 0 0 0 00)		
Addition to office furniture			(6 0 0 0 00)		
Addition to building			(25 0 0 0 00)		
Proceeds from sale of land			12 0 0 0 00		
Cash used for investing activities				(39 0 0 0 00)	
Cash Flows from Financing Activities:					
Repayment of mortgage			(8 0 0 0 00)		
Repayment of bonds			(10 0 0 0 00)		
Proceeds from issuance of common stock			20 0 0 0 00		
Dividend payment			(10 0 0 0 00)		
Cash used for financing activities				(8 0 0 0 00)	
Net Decrease in Cash				(3 7 0 0 00)	
Cash Balance, Beginning of Period				70 0 0 0 00	
Cash Balance, End of Period				66 3 0 0 00	

Name _____ Date _____ Class _____

17-3 WORK TOGETHER, p. 493

The comparative balance sheet from Work Together 17-2 is needed to complete this problem.

Preparing the investing and financing activities sections for the statement of cash flows; completing the statement of cash flows [5]

Account	Current Year	Prior Year	Long-Term Asset Long-Term Liability	Increase (Decrease)	Source of Cash Use of Cash
Mortgage Payable	$125,000.00	$140,000.00	long-term liability	$(15,000)	use of cash
Office Equipment	45,000.00	39,000.00	long-term asset	6,000	use of cash
Store Furniture	98,000.00	92,000.00	long-term asset	6,000	use of cash
Building	140,000.00	140,000.00	long-term asset	–	no impact
Bonds Payable	80,000.00	70,000.00	long-term liability	10,000	source of cash
Land (no gain on sale)	0.00	25,000.00	long-term asset	(25,000)	source of cash

[7]

Activity	Amount	Source of Cash Use of Cash
Sale of additional common stock	$20,000.00	source of cash
Payment of cash dividend	10,000.00	use of cash

17-3 ON YOUR OWN, p. 493

The comparative balance sheet from On Your Own 17-2 is needed to complete this problem.

Preparing the investing and financing activities sections for the statement of cash flows; completing the statement of cash flows [10]

Account	Current Year	Prior Year	Long-Term Asset Long-Term Liability	Increase (Decrease)	Source of Cash Use of Cash
Office Equipment	$ 46,000.00	$ 26,000.00	long-term asset	$20,000	use of cash
Office Furniture	18,000.00	12,000.00	long-term asset	6,000	use of cash
Building	235,000.00	210,000.00	long-term asset	25,000	use of cash
Land (no gain on sale)	0.00	12,000.00	long-term asset	(12,000)	source of cash
Mortgage Payable	178,000.00	186,000.00	long-term liability	(8,000)	use of cash
Bonds Payable	40,000.00	50,000.00	long-term liability	(10,000)	use of cash

[12]

Activity	Amount	Source of Cash Use of Cash
Sale of additional common stock	$20,000.00	source of cash
Payment of cash dividend	10,000.00	use of cash

Chapter 17   Statement of Cash Flows • **223**

17-3 WORK TOGETHER
ON YOUR OWN

Extra form

17-1 APPLICATION PROBLEM, p. 495

Classifying cash flows   [a–g]

Transaction	Cash Inflow	Cash Outflow	Operating Activity	Investing Activity	Financing Activity
a. Dividend payment		✓			✓
b. Payment of insurance premium		✓	✓		
c. Receipts from signing of a note payable	✓				✓
d. Payment of payroll taxes		✓	✓		
e. Cash purchase of computer equipment		✓		✓	
f. Sale of treasury stock	✓				✓
g. Receipts from consulting services	✓		✓		

17-2 APPLICATION PROBLEM, p. 495

Calculating the cash flows from operating activities   [1]

Use the statement of cash flows on page 224.

Item	Amount	Source of Cash Use of Cash
Net income	$91,460	*source of cash*

[2]

Item	Amount	Source of Cash Use of Cash
Depreciation expense	$12,500	*source of cash*

[3]

Account	Current Year	Prior Year	Current Asset Current Liability	Increase (Decrease)	Source of Cash Use of Cash
Accounts Receivable (book value)	$ 55,515	$ 48,000	*current asset*	$7,515	*use of cash*
Merchandise Inventory	118,316	121,000	*current asset*	(2,684)	*source of cash*
Supplies	6,148	5,500	*current asset*	648	*use of cash*
Accounts Payable	49,762	44,000	*current liability*	5,762	*source of cash*

17-2/17-3/17-4 APPLICATION PROBLEM, pp. 495–496

Completing a statement of cash flows

Flexcor Corporation

Statement of Cash Flows

For Year Ended December 31, 20--

Cash Flows from Operating Activities:			
Net Income		91 4 6 0 00	
Adjustments to Net Income:			
Depreciation Expense	12 5 0 0 00		
Changes in current assets and liabilities:			
Increase in accounts receivable	(7 5 1 5 00)		
Decrease in merchandise inventory	2 6 8 4 00		
Increase in supplies	(6 4 8 00)		
Increase in accounts payable	5 7 6 2 00		
Total adjustments to net income		12 7 8 3 00	
Cash provided by operating activities			104 2 4 3 00
Cash Flows from Investing Activities:			
Addition to office equipment		(10 3 0 0 00)	
Addition to office furniture		(3 2 1 0 00)	
Proceeds from sale of land		40 0 0 0 00	
Cash provided by investing activities			26 4 9 0 00
Cash Flows from Financing Activities:			
Repayment of mortgage		(11 9 0 0 00)	
Proceeds from issuance of common stock		20 0 0 0 00	
Dividend payment		(50 0 0 0 00)	
Cash used for financing activities			(41 9 0 0 00)
Net Increase in Cash			88 8 3 3 00
Cash Balance, Beginning of Period			67 9 3 0 00
Cash Balance, End of Period			156 7 6 3 00

AP 17-2
AP 17-3
AP 17-4

17-3 APPLICATION PROBLEM, p. 496

Calculating the cash flows from investing activities

[1, 2]

Use the statement of cash flows on page 226.

Account	Current Year	Prior Year	Long-Term Asset Long-Term Liability	Increase (Decrease)	Source of Cash Use of Cash
Office Equipment	$ 22,800	$ 12,500	*long-term asset*	$ 10,300	*use of cash*
Office Furniture	12,210	9,000	*long-term asset*	3,210	*use of cash*
Land	100,000	140,000	*long-term asset*	(40,000)	*source of cash*

17-4 APPLICATION PROBLEM, p. 496

Calculating the cash flows from financing activities and completing a statement of cash flows

[1]

Use the statement of cash flows started on page 226.

Account	Current Year	Prior Year	Long-Term Asset Long-Term Liability	Increase (Decrease)	Source of Cash Use of Cash
Mortgage Payable	$80,100	$92,000	*long-term liability*	$(11,900)	*use of cash*

[2]

Activity	Amount	Source of Cash Use of Cash
Sale of additional common stock	$20,000.00	*source of cash*
Payment of cash dividend	50,000.00	*use of cash*

[4]

Item	Amount
Net increase in Cash	$88,833

[5]

Item	Amount
Cash balance, beginning of period	$67,930

[6]

Item	Amount
Cash balance, end of period	$156,763

Complete the statement of cash flows on page 226.

17-4 APPLICATION PROBLEM

Extra form

Name _____ Date _____ Class _____

MASTERY PROBLEM, p. 497

Preparing a statement of cash flows

<table>
<tr><td colspan="4" align="center">West Coast Construction, Inc.
Comparative Income Statement
For Years Ended December 31, 20-- and 20--</td></tr>
<tr><th></th><th>Current Year</th><th>Prior Year</th><th>Increase (Decrease)</th></tr>
<tr><td>Operating Revenue:</td><td></td><td></td><td></td></tr>
<tr><td>Net Sales . . . .</td><td>$ 712,655.00</td><td>$ 745,220.00</td><td>$(32,565.00)</td></tr>
<tr><td>Cost of Merchandise Sold . . . .</td><td>292,035.00</td><td>301,124.00</td><td>(9,089.00)</td></tr>
<tr><td>Gross Profit on Operations . . . .</td><td>$ 420,620.00</td><td>$ 444,096.00</td><td>$(23,476.00)</td></tr>
<tr><td>Operating Expenses:</td><td></td><td></td><td></td></tr>
<tr><td>Depreciation Expense—Equipment . . . .</td><td>$ 15,071.00</td><td>$ 14,261.00</td><td>$ 810.00</td></tr>
<tr><td>Other Operating Expenses . . . .</td><td>366,979.00</td><td>352,975.00</td><td>14,004.00</td></tr>
<tr><td>Total Operating Expenses . . . .</td><td>$ 382,050.00</td><td>$ 367,236.00</td><td>$ 14,814.00</td></tr>
<tr><td>Net Income before Federal Income Tax . . . .</td><td>$ 38,570.00</td><td>$ 76,860.00</td><td>$(38,290.00)</td></tr>
<tr><td>Less Federal Income Tax Expense . . . .</td><td>11,571.00</td><td>23,058.00</td><td>(11,487.00)</td></tr>
<tr><td>Net Income after Federal Income Tax . . . .</td><td>$ 26,999.00</td><td>$ 53,802.00</td><td>$(26,803.00)</td></tr>
</table>

<table>
<tr><td colspan="4" align="center">West Coast Construction, Inc.
Comparative Statement of Stockholders' Equity
For Years Ended December 31, 20-- and 20--</td></tr>
<tr><th></th><th>Current Year</th><th>Prior Year</th><th>Increase (Decrease)</th></tr>
<tr><td>Capital Stock:</td><td></td><td></td><td></td></tr>
<tr><td>$15.00 Per Share</td><td></td><td></td><td></td></tr>
<tr><td>Balance, January 1 . . . .</td><td>$ 150,000.00</td><td>$ 150,000.00</td><td>$ 0.00</td></tr>
<tr><td>Additional Capital Stock Issued . . . .</td><td>15,000.00</td><td>0.00</td><td>15,000.00</td></tr>
<tr><td>Balance, December 31 . . . .</td><td>$ 165,000.00</td><td>$ 150,000.00</td><td>$ 15,000.00</td></tr>
<tr><td>Retained Earnings:</td><td></td><td></td><td></td></tr>
<tr><td>Balance, January 1 . . . .</td><td>$ 92,986.00</td><td>$ 59,184.00</td><td>$ 33,802.00</td></tr>
<tr><td>Net Income after Federal Income Tax . . . .</td><td>26,999.00</td><td>53,802.00</td><td>(26,803.00)</td></tr>
<tr><td>Total . . . .</td><td>$ 119,985.00</td><td>$ 112,986.00</td><td>$ 6,999.00</td></tr>
<tr><td>Less Dividend Payment . . . .</td><td>$ 27,500.00</td><td>$ 20,000.00</td><td>7,500.00</td></tr>
<tr><td>Balance, December 31 . . . .</td><td>92,485.00</td><td>92,986.00</td><td>$ (501.00)</td></tr>
<tr><td>Total Stockholders' Equity, December 31 . . . .</td><td>$ 257,485.00</td><td>$ 242,986.00</td><td>$ 14,499.00</td></tr>
</table>

17-5 MASTERY PROBLEM (continued)

West Coast Construction, Inc.
Comparative Balance Sheet
December 31, 20-- and 20--

	Current Year	Prior Year	Increase (Decrease)
ASSETS			
Current Assets:			
Cash	$ 63,768.00	$ 31,524.00	$ 32,244.00
Accounts Receivable (book value)	258,967.00	288,763.00	(29,796.00)
Supplies	1,251.00	1,577.00	(326.00)
Merchandise Inventory	89,545.00	93,450.00	(3,905.00)
Total Current Assets	$413,531.00	$415,314.00	$ (1,783.00)
Plant Assets:			
Equipment	$ 72,320.00	$ 62,320.00	$ 10,000.00
Less Accumulated Depr.—Equipment	32,750.00	17,679.00	15,071.00
Total Plant Assets (book value)	$ 39,570.00	$ 44,641.00	$ (5,071.00)
Total Assets	$453,101.00	$459,955.00	$ (6,854.00)
LIABILITIES			
Current Liabilities:			
Notes Payable	$ 14,003.00	$ 15,575.00	$ (1,572.00)
Accounts Payable	111,624.00	129,064.00	(17,440.00)
Total Current Liabilities	$125,627.00	$144,639.00	$ (19,012.00)
Long-Term Liability:			
Mortgage Payable	$ 69,989.00	$ 72,330.00	$ (2,341.00)
Total Liabilities	$195,616.00	$216,969.00	$ (21,353.00)
STOCKHOLDERS' EQUITY			
Total Stockholders' Equity	$257,485.00	$242,986.00	$ 14,499.00
Total Liabilities and Stockholders' Equity	$453,101.00	$459,955.00	$ (6,854.00)

17-5 MASTERY PROBLEM (continued)

[1]

Item	Amount	Source of Cash Use of Cash
Net income	$26,999	source of cash
Depreciation expense	15,071	source of cash

[2]

Account	Current Year	Prior Year	Current Asset Current Liability	Increase (Decrease)	Source of Cash Use of Cash
Accounts Receivable	$258,967	$288,763	current asset	$(29,796)	source of cash
Supplies	1,251	1,577	current asset	(326)	source of cash
Merchandise Inventory	89,545	93,450	current asset	(3,905)	source of cash
Notes Payable	14,003	15,575	current liability	(1,572)	use of cash
Accounts Payable	111,624	129,064	current liability	(17,440)	use of cash

[3, 4]

Account	Current Year	Prior Year	Long-Term Asset Long-Term Liability	Increase (Decrease)	Source of Cash Use of Cash
Equipment	$72,320	$62,320	long-term asset	$ 10,000	use of cash
Mortgage Payable	69,989	72,330	long-term liability	(2,341)	use of cash

[5]

Activity	Amount	Source of Cash Use of Cash
Sale of additional common stock	$15,000.00	source of cash
Payment of cash dividend	27,500.00	use of cash

17-5 MASTERY PROBLEM (concluded)

[6–9]

West Coast Construction, Inc.

Statement of Cash Flows

For Year Ended December 31, 20--

Cash Flows from Operating Activities:				
Net Income		26 9 9 9 00		
Adjustments to Net Income:				
Depreciation Expense	15 0 7 1 00			
Changes in current assets and liabilities:				
Decrease in accounts receivable	29 7 9 6 00			
Decrease in supplies	3 2 6 00			
Decrease in merchandise inventory	3 9 0 5 00			
Decrease in notes payable	(1 5 7 2 00)			
Decrease in accounts payable	(17 4 4 0 00)			
Total adjustments to net income		30 0 8 6 00		
Cash provided by operating activities			57 0 8 5 00	
Cash Flows from Investing Activities:				
Addition to equipment		(10 0 0 0 00)		
Cash used for investing activities			(10 0 0 0 00)	
Cash Flows from Financing Activities:				
Repayment of mortgage		(2 3 4 1 00)		
Proceeds from issuance of common stock		15 0 0 0 00		
Dividend payment		(27 5 0 0 00)		
Cash used for financing activities			(14 8 4 1 00)	
Net Increase in Cash			32 2 4 4 00	
Cash Balance, Beginning of Period			31 5 2 4 00	
Cash Balance, End of Period			63 7 6 8 00	

17-6 CHALLENGE PROBLEM, p. 498

Preparing a statement of cash flows

Pacific Digital Corporation
Comparative Income Statement
For Years Ended December 31, 20-- and 20--

	Current Year	Prior Year	Increase (Decrease)
Operating Revenue:			
Net Sales	$ 673,194.00	$ 640,220.00	$ 32,974.00
Cost of Merchandise Sold	308,436.00	271,074.00	37,362.00
Gross Profit on Operations	$ 364,758.00	$ 369,146.00	$ (4,388.00)
Operating Expenses:			
Depr. Expense—Equipment, Furniture & Bldg.	$ 27,300.00	$ 9,400.00	$ 17,900.00
Other Operating Expenses	337,488.00	344,356.00	(6,868.00)
Amortized Patent	9,420.00	9,420.00	0.00
Total Expenses	$ 374,208.00	$ 363,176.00	$ 11,032.00
Net Income (Net Loss)	$ (9,450.00)	$ 5,970.00	$(15,420.00)

Pacific Digital Corporation
Comparative Statement of Stockholders' Equity
For Years Ended December 31, 20-- and 20--

	Current Year	Prior Year	Increase (Decrease)
Capital Stock:			
$10.00 Per Share			
Balance, January 1	$ 307,130.00	$ 307,130.00	$ 0.00
Additional Capital Stock Issued (1,400 shares)	14,000.00	0.00	14,000.00
Balance, December 31	$ 321,130.00	$ 307,130.00	$ 14,000.00
Retained Earnings:			
Balance, January 1	$ 15,970.00	$ 10,000.00	$ 5,970.00
Net Income (Net Loss)	(9,450.00)	5,970.00	(15,420.00)
Balance, December 31	$ 6,520.00	$ 15,970.00	$ (9,450.00)
Total Stockholders' Equity, December 31	$ 327,650.00	$ 323,100.00	$ 4,550.00

17-6 CHALLENGE PROBLEM (continued)

Pacific Digital Corporation
Comparative Balance Sheet
December 31, 20-- and 20--

	Current Year	Prior Year	Increase (Decrease)
ASSETS			
Current Assets:			
Cash	$ 46,710.00	$ 40,770.00	$ 5,940.00
Notes Receivable	20,260.00	12,650.00	7,610.00
Accounts Receivable (book value)	113,100.00	135,000.00	(21,900.00)
Supplies	5,000.00	1,600.00	3,400.00
Merchandise Inventory	182,100.00	93,200.00	88,900.00
Total Current Assets	$ 367,170.00	$ 283,220.00	$ 83,950.00
Plant Assets:			
Office Equipment	$ 55,620.00	$ 45,320.00	$ 10,300.00
Office Furniture	13,210.00	10,000.00	3,210.00
Building	65,000.00	0.00	65,000.00
Land	100,000.00	150,000.00	(50,000.00)
Less Accum. Depr.—Equipment, Furniture & Bldg.	40,900.00	13,600.00	27,300.00
Total Plant Assets (book value)	$ 192,930.00	$ 191,720.00	$ 1,210.00
Intangible Assets:			
Patents	28,260.00	37,680.00	(9,420.00)
Total Assets	$588,360.00	$512,620.00	$ 75,740.00
LIABILITIES			
Current Liabilities:			
Notes Payable	$ 15,560.00	$ 22,410.00	$ (6,850.00)
Accounts Payable	114,850.00	105,900.00	8,950.00
Salaries Payable	9,700.00	10,700.00	(1,000.00)
Total Current Liabilities	$ 140,110.00	$ 139,010.00	$ 1,100.00
Long-Term Liability:			
Mortgage Payable	120,600.00	50,510.00	70,090.00
Total Liabilities	$ 260,710.00	$ 189,520.00	$ 71,190.00
STOCKHOLDERS' EQUITY			
Total Stockholders' Equity	$ 327,650.00	$ 323,100.00	$ 4,550.00
Total Liabilities and Stockholders' Equity	$588,360.00	$512,620.00	$ 75,740.00

17-6 CHALLENGE PROBLEM (concluded)

Pacific Digital Corporation

Statement of Cash Flows

For Year Ended December 31, 20--

Cash Flows from Operating Activities:				
Net Loss		(9 4 5 0 00)		
Adjustments to Net Loss:				
Patents Amortized	9 4 2 0 00			
Depreciation Expense	27 3 0 0 00			
Changes in current assets and liabilities:				
Increase in notes receivable	(7 6 1 0 00)			
Decrease in accounts receivable	21 9 0 0 00			
Increase in supplies	(3 4 0 0 00)			
Increase in merchandise inventory	(88 9 0 0 00)			
Decrease in notes payable	(6 8 5 0 00)			
Increase in accounts payable	8 9 5 0 00			
Decrease in salaries payable	(1 0 0 0 00)			
Total adjustments to net loss		(40 1 9 0 00)		
Cash used for operating activities			(49 6 4 0 00)	
Cash Flows from Investing Activities:				
Addition to office equipment		(10 3 0 0 00)		
Addition to office furniture		(3 2 1 0 00)		
Addition to building		(65 0 0 0 00)		
Proceeds from sale of land		50 0 0 0 00		
Cash used for investing activities			(28 5 1 0 00)	
Cash Flows from Financing Activities:				
Proceeds from long-term mortgage		70 0 9 0 00		
Proceeds from issuance of common stock		14 0 0 0 00		
Cash provided by financing activities			84 0 9 0 00	
Net Increase in Cash			5 9 4 0 00	
Cash Balance, Beginning of Period			40 7 7 0 00	
Cash Balance, End of Period			46 7 1 0 00	

17-6 CHALLENGE PROBLEM

Extra form

18-1 WORK TOGETHER (concluded)

[4, 5]

Begin this problem on pages 238 and 239. Use this page with page 240.

Co. _____
(continued) _____
March 31, 20--

	Departmental Margin Statements				Income Statement		Balance Sheet		
	Books Debit	Books Credit	Music Debit	Music Credit	Debit	Credit	Debit	Credit	
40				3 6 92					40
41	2 3 1 0 80								41
42	4 5 0 00								42
43	9 0 80								43
44	3 9 5 60								44
45	13 5 6 2 30								45
46	4 2 0 00								46
47			1 5 3 8 20						47
48			1 6 0 4 90						48
49			3 7 8 0 00						49
50			1 3 6 00						50
51			4 3 5 30						51
52			11 9 2 6 10						52
53			2 0 5 00						53
54			2 5 5 00						54
55					1 5 8 6 30				55
56					1 4 0 0 00				56
57					8 8 00				57
58					1 2 4 5 20				58
59					5 3 7 10				59
60					4 5 6 0 00				60
61					12 8 4 5 60				61
62					3 4 8 50				62
63					1 8 3 3 30				63
64	44 9 5 1 30	77 6 2 6 30	42 6 4 2 10	70 9 0 1 60					64
65	32 6 7 5 00					32 6 7 5 00			65
66			28 2 5 9 50			28 2 5 9 50			66
67	77 6 2 6 30	77 6 2 6 30	70 9 0 1 60	70 9 0 1 60					67
68					3 0 0 0 00				68
69					27 4 4 4 00	60 9 3 4 50	245 2 5 0 90	211 7 6 0 40	69
70					33 4 9 0 50			33 4 9 0 50	70
71					60 9 3 4 50	60 9 3 4 50	245 2 5 0 90	245 2 5 0 90	71
72									72
73									73
74									74
75									75
76									76
77									77
78									78

18-1 WORK TOGETHER, p. 511

Prepare a work sheet with departmental margins   [4, 5]

Adjustment information is listed on page 241.

Callostay

Work

For Month Ended

	ACCOUNT TITLE	TRIAL BALANCE		ADJUSTMENTS		
		DEBIT	CREDIT	DEBIT	CREDIT	
1	Cash	46 2 1 3 30				1
2	Accounts Receivable	26 9 3 5 70				2
3	Allowance for Uncollectible Accounts		1 3 3 90		(a) 2 5 5 00	3
4	Merchandise Inventory—Books	52 3 6 0 80			(b) 1 1 6 0 00	4
5	Merchandise Inventory—Music	58 9 2 1 20		(c) 3 6 5 6 80		5
6	Supplies	2 4 0 0 00			(d) 9 7 3 50	6
7	Prepaid Insurance	5 2 8 40			(e) 3 1 4 80	7
8	Office Equipment	12 5 0 0 00				8
9	Accum. Depr.—Office Equipment		2 8 0 0 00		(f) 1 4 0 0 00	9
10	Store Equipment—Books	11 5 8 0 20				10
11	Accum. Depr.—Store Equip., Books		9 2 5 40		(g) 4 5 0 00	11
12	Store Equipment—Music	27 6 0 2 80				12
13	Accum. Depr.—Store Equip., Music		5 6 1 2 30		(h) 3 7 8 0 00	13
14	Accounts Payable		27 8 2 3 50			14
15	Employee Income Tax Payable		1 1 1 0 90			15
16	Federal Income Tax Payable				(i) 1 0 0 0 00	16
17	Social Security Tax Payable		1 6 0 3 14			17
18	Medicare Tax Payable		3 6 9 96			18
19	Salaries Payable					19
20	Unemployment Tax Payable—Federal		4 9 00			20
21	Unemployment Tax Payable—State		3 3 0 75			21
22	Dividends Payable					22
23	Capital Stock		115 0 0 0 00			23
24	Retained Earnings		49 1 1 6 55			24
25	Dividends	5 0 0 0 00				25
26	Income Summary—Books			(b) 1 1 6 0 00		26
27	Income Summary—Music				(c) 3 6 5 6 80	27
28	Income Summary—General					28
29	Sales—Books		77 2 5 3 40			29
30	Sales Discount—Books	2 0 1 52				30
31	Sales Returns and Allowances—Books	1 4 2 08				31
32	Sales—Music		66 9 5 2 50			32
33	Sales Discount—Music	1 8 6 92				33
34	Sales Returns and Allowances—Music	9 4 18				34
35	Purchases—Books	26 2 1 8 20				35
36	Purchases Discount—Books		1 5 8 30			36
37	Purchases Returns and Allowances—Books		2 1 4 60			37
38	Purchases—Music	22 4 8 0 50				38
39	Purchases Discounts—Music		2 5 5 38			39

[4, 5]

Co. _____
Sheet _____
March 31, 20--

#	Books Debit	Books Credit	Music Debit	Music Credit	IS Debit	IS Credit	BS Debit	BS Credit	#
1							46 2 1 3 30		1
2							26 9 3 5 70		2
3								3 8 8 90	3
4							51 2 0 0 80		4
5							62 5 7 8 00		5
6							1 4 2 6 50		6
7							2 1 3 60		7
8							12 5 0 0 00		8
9								4 2 0 0 00	9
10							11 5 8 0 20		10
11								1 3 7 5 40	11
12							27 6 0 2 80		12
13								9 3 9 2 30	13
14								27 8 2 3 50	14
15								1 1 1 0 90	15
16								1 0 0 0 00	16
17								1 6 0 3 14	17
18								3 6 9 96	18
19									19
20								4 9 00	20
21								3 3 0 75	21
22									22
23								115 0 0 0 00	23
24								49 1 1 6 55	24
25							5 0 0 0 00		25
26	1 1 6 0 00								26
27				3 6 5 6 80					27
28									28
29			77 2 5 3 40						29
30		2 0 1 52							30
31		1 4 2 08							31
32				66 9 5 2 50					32
33			1 8 6 92						33
34			9 4 18						34
35	26 2 1 8 20								35
36		1 5 8 30							36
37		2 1 4 60							37
38			22 4 8 0 50						38
39				2 5 5 38					39

18-1 WORK TOGETHER (continued)

[4, 5]

Callostay
Work Sheet
For Month Ended

	ACCOUNT TITLE	TRIAL BALANCE		ADJUSTMENTS		
		DEBIT (1)	CREDIT (2)	DEBIT (3)	CREDIT (4)	
40	Purchases Returns and Allow.—Music		3 6 92			40
41	Advertising Expense—Books	2 3 1 0 80				41
42	Depreciation Expense—Store Equip., Books			(g) 4 5 0 00		42
43	Insurance Expense—Books			(c) 9 0 80		43
44	Payroll Taxes Expense—Books	3 9 5 60				44
45	Salary Expense—Books	13 5 6 2 30				45
46	Supplies Expense—Books			(d) 4 2 0 00		46
47	Advertising Expense—Music	1 5 3 8 20				47
48	Delivery Expense—Music	1 6 0 4 90				48
49	Depr. Expense—Store Equip., Music			(h) 3 7 8 0 00		49
50	Insurance Expense—Music			(e) 1 3 6 00		50
51	Payroll Taxes Expense—Music	4 3 5 30				51
52	Salary Expense—Music	11 9 2 6 10				52
53	Supplies Expense—Music			(d) 2 0 5 00		53
54	Uncollectible Accounts Expense—Music			(a) 2 5 5 00		54
55	Credit Card Fee Expense	1 5 8 6 30				55
56	Depreciation Expense—Office Equipment			(f) 1 4 0 0 00		56
57	Insurance Expense—Administrative			(e) 8 8 00		57
58	Miscellaneous Expense	1 2 4 5 20				58
59	Payroll Taxes Expense—Administrative	5 3 7 10				59
60	Rent Expense	4 5 6 0 00				60
61	Salary Expense—Administrative	12 8 4 5 60				61
62	Supplies Expense—Administrative			(d) 3 4 8 50		62
63	Utilities Expense	1 8 3 3 30				63
64						64
65	*Departmental Margin—Books*					65
66	*Departmental Margin—Music*					66
67						67
68	Federal Income Tax Expense	2 0 0 0 00		(i) 1 0 0 0 00		68
69		349 7 4 6 50	349 7 4 6 50	12 9 9 0 10	12 9 9 0 10	69
70	*Net Income after Fed. Inc. Tax*					70
71						71
72						72
73						73
74						74
75						75
76						76
77						77
78						78

18-1 WORK TOGETHER (continued)

[4, 5]

Adjustment Information, March 31

Uncollectible Accounts Expense—Music Estimated at 1.0% of Sales on Account	
Sales on Account for the Month	$25,500.00
Merchandise Inventory—Books	51,200.80
Merchandise Inventory—Music	62,578.00
Supplies Used—Books	420.00
Supplies Used—Music	205.00
Supplies Used—Administrative	348.50
Insurance Expired—Books	90.80
Insurance Expired—Music	136.00
Insurance Expired—Administrative	88.00
Depreciation Expense—Office Equipment	1,400.00
Depreciation Expense—Store Equipment, Books	450.00
Depreciation Expense—Store Equipment, Music	3,780.00
Federal Income Tax for the Month	1,000.00

Extra form

							% OF NET SALES

Name _____ Date _____ Class _____

18-1 WORK TOGETHER

Extra form

													% OF NET SALES

18-1 ON YOUR OWN, p. 511

Journalizing direct and indirect expenses [6]

CASH PAYMENTS JOURNAL

PAGE 8

DATE		ACCOUNT TITLE	CK. NO.	POST. REF.	GENERAL DEBIT	GENERAL CREDIT	ACCOUNTS PAYABLE DEBIT	PURCHASES DISCOUNTS CREDIT CRAFTS	PURCHASES DISCOUNTS CREDIT FABRICS	CASH CREDIT	
20– Oct.	1	Utilities Expense	435		2 2 5 00					2 2 5 00	1
	8	Advertising Exp.—Crafts	485		1 5 0 00					1 5 0 00	2
	12	Delivery Exp.—Fabrics	491		3 5 00					3 5 00	3
	15	Salary Expense—Crafts	502		1 5 6 2 00					2 7 2 8 21	4
		Salary Expense—Fabrics			1 8 5 0 00						5
		Employee Income Tax Pay.				3 9 6 00					6
		Social Security Tax Pay.				2 3 8 34					7
		Medicare Tax Pay.				4 9 45					8
											9
											10
											11
											12
											13
											14
											15
											16
											17
											18
											19
											20
											21
											22
											23
											24
											25

18-1 ON YOUR OWN

Extra form

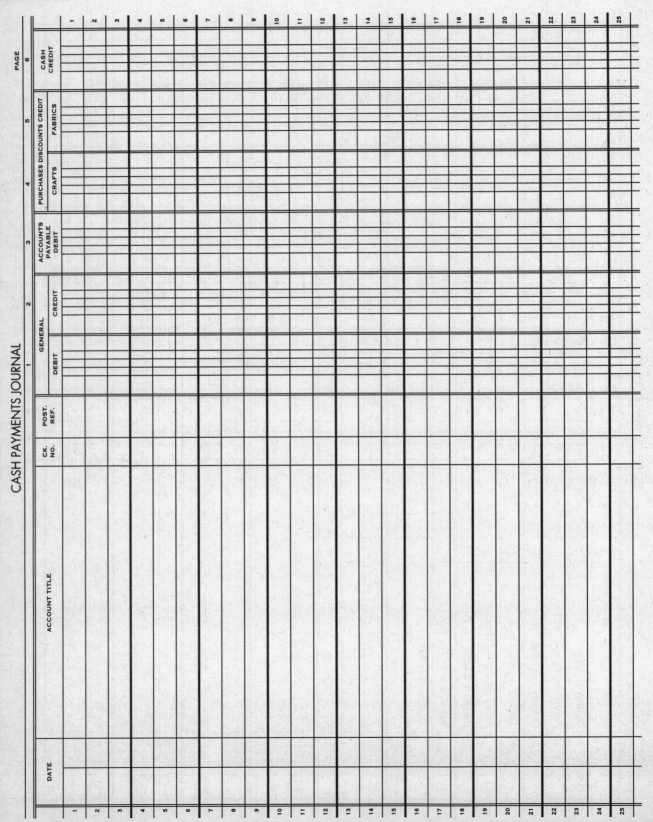

CASH PAYMENTS JOURNAL

| | | | | GENERAL | | ACCOUNTS PAYABLE DEBIT | PURCHASES DISCOUNTS CREDIT | | CASH CREDIT |
| DATE | ACCOUNT TITLE | CK. NO. | POST. REF. | DEBIT | CREDIT | | CRAFTS | FABRICS | |

PAGE

18-2 WORK TOGETHER, p. 516

Departmental margin statement   [5]

The work sheet from Work Together 18-1 is needed to complete this problem.

Callostay Co.

Departmental Margin Statement—Books

For Month Ended March 31, 20--

					% OF NET SALES
Operating Revenue:					
Sales			77 2 5 3 40		100.4
Less: Sales Discount		2 0 1 52			0.3
Sales Returns & Allow.		1 4 2 08	3 4 3 60		0.2
Net Sales				76 9 0 9 80	100.0
Cost of Merchandise Sold					
Mdse. Inv., Mar. 1, 20--			52 3 6 0 80		68.1
Purchases		26 2 1 8 20			34.1
Less: Purchases Discount	1 5 8 30				0.2
Purchases Returns & Allow.	2 1 4 60	3 7 2 90			0.3
Net Purchases			25 8 4 5 30		33.6
Total Cost of Mdse. Avail. for Sale			78 2 0 6 10		101.7
Less Mdse. Inv., Mar. 31, 20--			51 2 0 0 80		66.6
Cost of Merchandise Sold				27 0 0 5 30	35.1
Gross Profit on Operations				49 9 0 4 50	64.9
Direct Expenses:					
Advertising Expense			2 3 1 0 80		3.0
Depr. Exp.—Store Equipment			4 5 0 00		0.6
Insurance Expense			9 0 80		0.1
Payroll Taxes Expense			3 9 5 60		0.5
Salary Expense			13 5 6 2 30		17.6
Supplies Expense			4 2 0 00		0.5
Total Direct Expenses				17 2 2 9 50	22.4
Departmental Margin				32 6 7 5 00	42.5

18-2 ON YOUR OWN, p. 516

Departmental margin statement [6]

The work sheet from Work Together 18-1 is needed to complete this problem.

Callostay Co.

Departmental Margin Statement—Music

For Month Ended March 31, 20--

				% OF NET SALES
Operating Revenue:				
Sales			66 9 5 2 50	100.4
Less: Sales Discount		1 8 6 92		0.3
Sales Returns & Allow.		9 4 18	2 8 1 10	0.1
Net Sales			66 6 7 1 40	100.0
Cost of Merchandise Sold				
Mdse. Inv., Mar. 1, 20--		58 9 2 1 20		88.4
Purchases		22 4 8 0 50		33.7
Less: Purchases Discount	2 5 5 38			0.4
Purchases Returns & Allow.	3 6 92	2 9 2 30		0.1
Net Purchases		22 1 8 8 20		33.3
Total Cost of Mdse. Avail. for Sale		81 1 0 9 40		121.7
Less Mdse. Inv., Mar. 31, 20--		62 5 7 8 00		93.9
Cost of Merchandise Sold			18 5 3 1 40	27.8
Gross Profit on Operations			48 1 4 0 00	72.2
Direct Expenses:				
Advertising Expense		1 5 3 8 20		2.3
Delivery Expense		1 6 0 4 90		2.4
Depr. Exp.—Store Equipment		3 7 8 0 00		5.7
Insurance Expense		1 3 6 00		0.2
Payroll Taxes Expense		4 3 5 30		0.7
Salary Expense		11 9 2 6 10		17.9
Supplies Expense		2 0 5 00		0.3
Uncollectible Accounts Expense		2 5 5 00		0.4
Total Direct Expenses			19 8 8 0 50	29.8
Departmental Margin			28 2 5 9 50	42.4

18-1 APPLICATION PROBLEM, p. 518

Journalizing direct and indirect expenses

CASH PAYMENTS JOURNAL

PAGE 5

	DATE	CK. NO.	POST. REF.	GENERAL DEBIT	GENERAL CREDIT	ACCOUNTS PAYABLE DEBIT	PURCHASES DISCOUNTS CREDIT PAINT	PURCHASES DISCOUNTS CREDIT WALLPAPER	CASH CREDIT	
1	Mar. 1	234		500000					500000	1
2	4	262		5000					5000	2
3	11	316		8400					8400	3
4	16	331		12400					12400	4
5	23	394		7300					7300	5
6	30	437		284000					284000	6
7	31	486		480000					388800	7
8					52800					8
9					31392					9
10					7008					10
11										11
12										12
13										13
14										14
15										15
16										16
17										17
18										18
19										19
20										20
21										21
22										22
23										23
24										24
25										25

ACCOUNT TITLE column:
1. Rent Expense
2. Advertising Expense—Paint
3. Delivery Expense—Wallpaper
4. Miscellaneous Expense
5. Advertising Expense—Wallpaper
6. Utilities Expense
7. Salary Expense—Wallpaper
8. Employee Inc. Tax Pay.
9. Social Security Tax Payable
10. Medicare Tax Payable

18-1 APPLICATION PROBLEM

Extra form

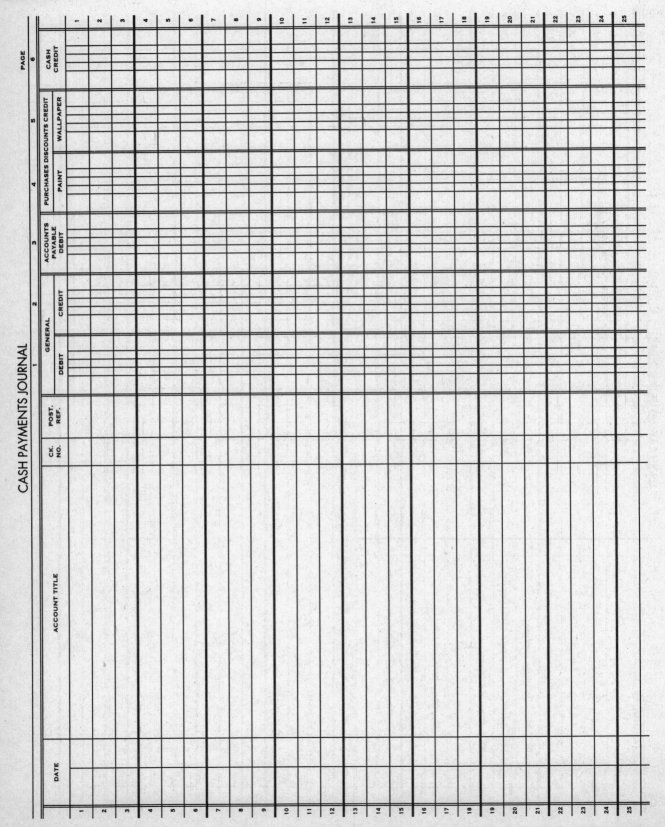

CASH PAYMENTS JOURNAL

PAGE

		CASH CREDIT 6	PURCHASES DISCOUNTS CREDIT		ACCOUNTS PAYABLE DEBIT 3	GENERAL		POST. REF.	CK. NO.	ACCOUNT TITLE	DATE
			WALLPAPER 5	PAINT 4		CREDIT 2	DEBIT 1				

18-2 APPLICATION PROBLEM (concluded)

[1, 2]

Begin this problem on pages 250 and 251. Use this page with page 252.

Center
(continued)
July 31, 20--

	CLOTHING DEBIT (5)	CLOTHING CREDIT (6)	EQUIPMENT DEBIT (7)	EQUIPMENT CREDIT (8)	INCOME STATEMENT DEBIT (9)	INCOME STATEMENT CREDIT (10)	BALANCE SHEET DEBIT (11)	BALANCE SHEET CREDIT (12)	
40		1 4 60							40
41			19 4 8 0 50						41
42				5 5 38					42
43				3 6 92					43
44	3 1 0 80								44
45	1 8 5 50								45
46	6 0 30								46
47	3 9 5 60								47
48	3 5 6 2 30								48
49	2 9 8 40								49
50			5 3 8 20						50
51			1 3 0 4 90						51
52			1 9 8 00						52
53			3 2 00						53
54			1 1 5 60						54
55			4 3 5 30						55
56			3 9 2 6 10						56
57			3 7 0 80						57
58			2 0 5 20						58
59					5 8 6 30				59
60					2 8 00				60
61					2 0 10				61
62					1 2 4 5 20				62
63					5 3 7 10				63
64					4 5 6 0 00				64
65					4 8 4 5 60				65
66					1 6 4 80				66
67					1 8 3 3 30				67
68	21 1 7 4 70	32 7 8 6 80	26 7 8 7 70	38 1 0 2 40					68
69	11 6 1 2 10					11 6 1 2 10			69
70			11 3 1 4 70			11 3 1 4 70			70
71	32 7 8 6 80	32 7 8 6 80	38 1 0 2 40	38 1 0 2 40					71
72					2 1 5 6 00				72
73					15 9 7 6 40	22 9 2 6 80	177 3 3 3 20	170 3 8 2 80	73
74					6 9 5 0 40			6 9 5 0 40	74
75					22 9 2 6 80	22 9 2 6 80	177 3 3 3 20	177 3 3 3 20	75
76									76
77									77
78									78

18-2 APPLICATION PROBLEM, p. 518

Preparing a work sheet with departmental margins   [1, 2]

The work sheet prepared in this problem is needed to complete Application Problems 18-3 and 18-4.

AllSports
Work
For Month Ended

	ACCOUNT TITLE	TRIAL BALANCE DEBIT	TRIAL BALANCE CREDIT	ADJUSTMENTS DEBIT	ADJUSTMENTS CREDIT	
1	Cash	38 2 1 3 30				1
2	Accounts Receivable	16 9 3 5 70				2
3	Allowance for Uncollectible Accounts		3 3 90		(a) 2 0 5 20	3
4	Merchandise Inventory—Clothing	32 3 6 0 80		(b) 5 4 6 0 50		4
5	Merchandise Inventory—Equip.	48 9 2 1 20		(c) 7 0 5 7 60		5
6	Supplies	1 6 4 9 00			(d) 8 3 4 00	6
7	Prepaid Insurance	6 2 4 30			(e) 1 9 6 00	7
8	Delivery Equipment—Equip.	11 5 3 1 80				8
9	Accum. Depr.—Deliver Equipment, Equip.		3 5 5 7 00		(f) 1 9 8 00	9
10	Office Equipment	1 4 2 6 00				10
11	Accum. Depr.—Office Equipment		1 8 4 90		(g) 2 8 00	11
12	Store Equipment—Clothing	1 5 8 0 20				12
13	Accum. Depr.—Store Equip., Clothing		5 2 5 40		(h) 1 8 5 50	13
14	Store Equipment—Equip.	7 6 0 2 80				14
15	Accum. Depr.—Store Equipment, Equip.		2 6 1 2 30		(i) 3 2 00	15
16	Accounts Payable		20 8 2 3 50			16
17	Employee Income Tax Payable		1 1 1 0 90			17
18	Federal Income Tax Payable				(j) 2 1 5 6 00	18
19	Social Security Tax Payable		1 6 0 3 14			19
20	Medicare Tax Payable		3 6 9 96			20
21	Salaries Payable					21
22	Sales Tax Payable		3 4 7 2 50			22
23	Unemployment Tax Payable—Federal		4 9 00			23
24	Unemployment Tax Payable—State		3 3 0 75			24
25	Dividends Payable					25
26	Capital Stock		85 0 0 0 00			26
27	Retained Earnings		47 9 0 4 85			27
28	Dividends	5 0 0 0 00				28
29	Income Summary—Clothing				(b) 5 4 6 0 50	29
30	Income Summary—Equip.				(c) 7 0 5 7 60	30
31	Income Summary—General					31
32	Sales—Clothing		27 2 5 3 40			32
33	Sales Discount—Clothing	1 0 1 52				33
34	Sales Returns and Allowances—Clothing	4 2 08				34
35	Sales—Equip.		30 9 5 2 50			35
36	Sales Discount—Equip.	8 6 92				36
37	Sales Returns and Allowances—Equip.	9 4 18				37
38	Purchases—Clothing	16 2 1 8 20				38
39	Purchases Discount—Clothing		5 8 30			39

18-2 APPLICATION PROBLEM (continued)

[1, 2]

Center
Sheet
July 31, 20--

	Departmental Margin Statements				Income Statement		Balance Sheet		
	Clothing		Equipment						
	Debit	Credit	Debit	Credit	Debit	Credit	Debit	Credit	
1							38213 30		1
2							16935 70		2
3								239 10	3
4							37821 30		4
5							55978 80		5
6							815 00		6
7							428 30		7
8							11531 80		8
9								3755 00	9
10							1426 00		10
11								2112 90	11
12							1580 20		12
13								710 90	13
14							7602 80		14
15								2644 30	15
16								20823 50	16
17								1110 90	17
18								2156 00	18
19								1603 14	19
20								369 96	20
21									21
22								3472 50	22
23								49 00	23
24								330 75	24
25									25
26								85000 00	26
27								47904 85	27
28							5000 00		28
29		5460 50							29
30				7057 60					30
31									31
32		27253 40							32
33	101 52								33
34	42 08								34
35				30952 50					35
36			86 92						36
37			94 18						37
38	16218 20								38
39		58 30							39

18-2 APPLICATION PROBLEM (continued)

[1, 2]

AllSports
Work Sheet
For Month Ended

#	ACCOUNT TITLE	TRIAL BALANCE DEBIT	TRIAL BALANCE CREDIT	ADJUSTMENTS DEBIT	ADJUSTMENTS CREDIT	#
40	Purchases Returns and Allowances—Clothing		1 4 60			40
41	Purchases—Equip.	19 4 8 0 50				41
42	Purchases Discount—Equip.		5 5 38			42
43	Purchases Returns and Allowances—Equip.		3 6 92			43
44	Advertising Expense—Clothing	3 1 0 80				44
45	Depreciation Expense—Store Equip., Clothing			(h) 1 8 5 50		45
46	Insurance Expense—Clothing			(e) 6 0 30		46
47	Payroll Taxes Expense—Clothing	3 9 5 60				47
48	Salary Expense—Clothing	3 5 6 2 30				48
49	Supplies Expense—Clothing			(d) 2 9 8 40		49
50	Advertising Expense—Equip.	5 3 8 20				50
51	Delivery Expense—Equip.	1 3 0 4 90				51
52	Depreciation Expense—Del. Equip., Equip.			(f) 1 9 8 00		52
53	Depreciation Expense—Store Equip., Equip.			(i) 3 2 00		53
54	Insurance Expense—Equip.			(e) 1 1 5 60		54
55	Payroll Taxes Expense—Equip.	4 3 5 30				55
56	Salary Expense—Equip.	3 9 2 6 10				56
57	Supplies Expense—Equip.			(d) 3 7 0 80		57
58	Uncollectible Accounts Expense—Equip.			(a) 2 0 5 20		58
59	Credit Card Fee Expense	5 8 6 30				59
60	Depreciation Expense—Office Equipment			(g) 2 8 00		60
61	Insurance Expense—Administrative			(e) 2 0 10		61
62	Miscellaneous Expense	1 2 4 5 20				62
63	Payroll Taxes Expense—Administrative	5 3 7 10				63
64	Rent Expense	4 5 6 0 00				64
65	Salary Expense—Administrative	4 8 4 5 60				65
66	Supplies Expense—Administrative			(d) 1 6 4 80		66
67	Utilities Expense	1 8 3 3 30				67
68						68
69	*Departmental Margin—Books*					69
70	*Departmental Margin—Music*					70
71						71
72	*Federal Income Tax Expense*			(f) 2 1 5 6 00		72
73		225 9 4 9 20	225 9 4 9 20	16 3 5 2 80	16 3 5 2 80	73
74	*Net Income after Fed. Inc. Tax*					74
75						75
76						76
77						77
78						78

18-3 APPLICATION PROBLEM, p. 519

Preparing departmental margin statements

The work sheet prepared in Application Problem 18-2 is needed to complete this problem. The statements prepared in this problem are needed to complete Application Problem 18-4.

AllSports Center

Departmental Margin Statement—Clothing

For Month Ended July 31, 20--

				% OF NET SALES
Operating Revenue:				
Sales		27 2 5 3 40		100.5
Less: Sales Discount	1 0 1 52			0.4
Sales Returns & Allow.	4 2 08	1 4 3 60		0.2
Net Sales			27 1 0 9 80	100.0
Cost of Merchandise Sold				
Mdse. Inv., July 1, 20--		32 3 6 0 80		119.4
Purchases	16 2 1 8 20			59.8
Less: Purchases Discount	5 8 30			0.2
Purchases Returns & Allow.	1 4 60	7 2 90		0.1
Net Purchases		16 1 4 5 30		59.6
Total Cost of Mdse. Avail. for Sale		48 5 0 6 10		178.9
Less Mdse. Inv., July 31, 20--		37 8 2 1 30		139.5
Cost of Merchandise Sold			10 6 8 4 80	39.4
Gross Profit on Operations			16 4 2 5 00	60.6
Direct Expenses:				
Advertising Expense		3 1 0 80		1.1
Depr. Exp.—Store Equipment		1 8 5 50		0.7
Insurance Expense		6 0 30		0.2
Payroll Taxes Expense		3 9 5 60		1.5
Salary Expense		3 5 6 2 30		13.1
Supplies Expense		2 9 8 40		1.1
Total Direct Expenses			4 8 1 2 90	17.8
Departmental Margin			11 6 1 2 10	42.8

18-3 APPLICATION PROBLEM (concluded)

The work sheet prepared in Application Problem 18-2 is needed to complete this problem. The statements prepared in this problem are needed to complete Application Problem 18-4.

AllSports Center

Departmental Margin Statement—Equipment

For Month Ended July 31, 20--

				% OF NET SALES
Operating Revenue:				
Sales		30 9 5 2 50		100.6
Less: Sales Discount	8 6 92			0.3
Sales Returns & Allow.	9 4 18	1 8 1 10		0.3
Net Sales			30 7 7 1 40	100.0
Cost of Merchandise Sold				
Mdse. Inv., July 1, 20--		48 9 2 1 20		159.0
Purchases	19 4 8 0 50			63.3
Less: Purchases Discount	5 5 38			0.2
Purchases Returns & Allow.	3 6 92	9 2 30		0.1
Net Purchases		19 3 8 8 20		63.0
Total Cost of Mdse. Avail. for Sale		68 3 0 9 40		222.0
Less Mdse. Inv., July 31, 20--		55 9 7 8 80		181.9
Cost of Merchandise Sold			12 3 3 0 60	40.1
Gross Profit on Operations			18 4 4 0 80	59.9
Direct Expenses:				
Advertising Expense		5 3 8 20		1.7
Delivery Expense		1 3 0 4 90		4.2
Depr. Exp.—Delivery Equipment		1 9 8 00		0.6
Depr. Exp.—Store Equipment		3 2 00		0.1
Insurance Expense		1 1 5 60		0.4
Payroll Taxes Expense		4 3 5 30		1.4
Salary Expense		3 9 2 6 10		12.8
Supplies Expense		3 7 0 80		1.2
Uncollectible Accounts Expense		2 0 5 20		0.7
Total Direct Expenses			7 1 2 6 10	23.2
Departmental Margin			11 3 1 4 70	36.8

18-4 APPLICATION PROBLEM, p. 519

Preparing an income statement with departmental margins

The work sheet prepared in Application Problem 18-2 and statements prepared in Application Problem 18-3 are needed to complete Application Problem 18-4.

AllSports Center

Income Statement

For Month Ended July 31, 20--

	DEPARTMENTAL		COMPANY		% OF NET SALES
	CLOTHING	EQUIPMENT	AMOUNTS		
Net Sales	27 1 0 9 80	30 7 7 1 40		57 8 8 1 20	100.0
Cost of Merchandise Sold	10 6 8 4 80	12 3 3 0 60		23 0 1 5 40	39.8
Gross Profit on Operations	16 4 2 5 00	18 4 4 0 80		34 8 6 5 80	60.2
Direct Expenses	4 8 1 2 90	7 1 2 6 10		11 9 3 9 00	20.6
Departmental Margin	11 6 1 2 10	11 3 1 4 70		22 9 2 6 80	39.6
Indirect Expenses:					
Credit Card Fee Expense			5 8 6 30		1.0
Depr. Exp.—Office Equip.			2 8 00		0.0
Insurance Expense—Admin.			2 0 10		0.0
Miscellaneous Expense			1 2 4 5 20		2.2
Payroll Taxes Expense—Admin.			5 3 7 10		0.9
Rent Expense			4 5 6 0 00		7.9
Salary Expense—Admin.			4 8 4 5 60		8.4
Supplies Expense—Admin.			1 6 4 80		0.3
Utilities Expense			1 8 3 3 30		3.2
Total Indirect Expenses				13 8 2 0 40	23.9
Net Income before Fed. Inc. Tax				9 1 0 6 40	15.7
Less Federal Income Tax Expense				2 1 5 6 00	3.7
Net Income after Fed. Inc. Tax				6 9 5 0 40	12.0

18-4 APPLICATION PROBLEM

Extra form

		DEPARTMENTAL		COMPANY	
		CLOTHING	EQUIPMENT	AMOUNTS	% OF NET SALES

18-5 MASTERY PROBLEM (continued)

[1, 2]

Begin this problem on pages 258 and 259. Use this page with page 260.

DeCor, Inc.
(continued)
December 31, 20--

#	Furniture Debit	Furniture Credit	Accessories Debit	Accessories Credit	Income Statement Debit	Income Statement Credit	Balance Sheet Debit	Balance Sheet Credit	#
40				277 40					40
41				118 90					41
42	2 838 40								42
43	2 131 30								43
44	1 395 00								44
45	5 568 00								45
46	56 240 00								46
47	1 409 00								47
48	101 60								48
49			715 60						49
50			981 70						50
51			1 395 00						51
52			2 365 00						52
53			23 890 00						53
54			896 30						54
55					6 255 30				55
56					529 50				56
57					325 00				57
58					8 076 80				58
59					1 873 00				59
60					15 000 00				60
61					18 920 00				61
62					422 70				62
63					4 016 20				63
64	304 939 40	368 794 50	112 455 30	123 742 70					64
65	63 855 10						63 855 10		65
66			11 287 40				11 287 40		66
67	368 794 50	368 794 50	123 742 70	123 742 70					67
68					2 958 60				68
69					58 377 10	75 142 50	256 556 20	239 790 80	69
70					16 765 40			16 765 40	70
71					75 142 50	75 142 50	256 556 20	256 556 20	71
72									72
73									73
74									74
75									75
76									76
77									77
78									78

18-5 MASTERY PROBLEM, p. 519
Begin Mastery Problem 18-5 on this page.

Completing end-of-fiscal period work for a merchandising business using departmental margins [1, 2]

Furniture
Work
For Year Ended

	ACCOUNT TITLE	TRIAL BALANCE DEBIT	TRIAL BALANCE CREDIT	ADJUSTMENTS DEBIT	ADJUSTMENTS CREDIT	
1	Cash	52 1 2 6 50				1
2	Accounts Receivable	2 7 6 8 40				2
3	Allowance for Uncollectible Accounts		5 4 20		(a) 1 0 1 60	3
4	Merchandise Inventory—Furniture	103 8 3 6 30		(b) 8 6 2 3 70		4
5	Merchandise Inventory—Accessories	35 3 9 4 70		(c) 11 1 4 9 10		5
6	Supplies	3 3 7 8 30			(d) 2 7 2 8 00	6
7	Prepaid Insurance	6 7 1 5 20			(e) 3 1 1 5 00	7
8	Office Equipment	5 4 5 7 00				8
9	Accum. Depr.—Office Equipment		8 6 0 60		(f) 5 2 9 50	9
10	Store Equipment—Furniture	19 0 4 0 00				10
11	Accum. Depr.—Store Equip., Furniture		5 8 3 2 10		(g) 2 1 3 1 30	11
12	Store Equipment—Accessories	8 9 1 0 00				12
13	Accum. Depr.—Store Equip., Accessories		2 5 6 8 30		(h) 9 8 1 70	13
14	Accounts Payable		26 1 3 1 60			14
15	Employee Income Tax Payable		9 3 6 90			15
16	Federal Income Tax Payable				(i) 1 5 8 60	16
17	Social Security Tax Payable		1 0 7 3 15			17
18	Medicare Tax Payable		2 4 7 65			18
19	Salaries Payable					19
20	Sales Tax Payable		2 1 5 6 10			20
21	Unemployment Tax Payable—Federal		6 80			21
22	Unemployment Tax Payable—State		4 5 90			22
23	Dividends Payable					23
24	Capital Stock		110 0 0 0 00			24
25	Retained Earnings		85 9 7 4 80			25
26	Dividends	5 0 0 0 00				26
27	Income Summary—Furniture				(b) 8 6 2 3 70	27
28	Income Summary—Accessories				(c) 11 1 4 9 10	28
29	Income Summary—General					29
30	Sales—Furniture		357 5 7 3 50			30
31	Sales Discount—Furniture	8 9 3 20				31
32	Sales Returns and Allowances—Furniture	8 4 1 30				32
33	Sales—Accessories		112 1 9 7 30			33
34	Sales Discount—Accessories	3 7 2 60				34
35	Sales Returns and Allowances—Accessories	1 5 9 80				35
36	Purchases—Furniture	233 5 2 1 60				36
37	Purchases Discount—Furniture		1 5 5 8 40			37
38	Purchases Returns and Allowances—Furniture		1 0 3 8 90			38
39	Purchases—Accessories	81 6 7 9 30				39

18-5 MASTERY PROBLEM (continued)

[1, 2]

DeCor, Inc.
Sheet
December 31, 20--

	DEPARTMENTAL MARGIN STATEMENTS				INCOME STATEMENT		BALANCE SHEET		
	FURNITURE		ACCESSORIES		DEBIT	CREDIT	DEBIT	CREDIT	
	DEBIT	CREDIT	DEBIT	CREDIT					
1							52 1 2 6 50		1
2							2 7 6 8 40		2
3								1 5 5 80	3
4							112 4 6 0 00		4
5							46 5 4 3 80		5
6							6 5 0 30		6
7							3 6 0 0 20		7
8							5 4 5 7 00		8
9								1 3 9 0 10	9
10							1 9 0 4 0 00		10
11								7 9 6 3 40	11
12							8 9 1 0 00		12
13								3 5 5 0 00	13
14								26 1 3 1 60	14
15								9 3 6 90	15
16								1 5 8 60	16
17								1 0 7 3 15	17
18								2 4 7 65	18
19									19
20								2 1 5 6 10	20
21								6 80	21
22								4 5 90	22
23									23
24								110 0 0 0 00	24
25								85 9 7 4 80	25
26							5 0 0 0 00		26
27		8 6 2 3 70							27
28				11 1 4 9 10					28
29									29
30		357 5 7 3 50							30
31	8 9 3 20								31
32	8 4 1 30								32
33				112 1 9 7 30					33
34			3 7 2 60						34
35			1 5 9 80						35
36	233 5 2 1 60								36
37		1 5 5 8 40							37
38		1 0 3 8 90							38
39			81 6 7 9 30						39

18-5 MASTERY PROBLEM (continued)

[1, 2]

Use this page with page 257.

Furniture
Work Sheet
For Year Ended

	ACCOUNT TITLE	TRIAL BALANCE DEBIT	TRIAL BALANCE CREDIT	ADJUSTMENTS DEBIT	ADJUSTMENTS CREDIT	
40	Purchases Discount—Accessories		2 7 7 40			40
41	Purchases Returns and Allow.—Accessories		1 1 8 90			41
42	Advertising Expense—Furniture	2 8 3 8 40				42
43	Depreciation Expense—Store Equip., Furniture			(g) 2 1 3 1 30		43
44	Insurance Expense—Furniture			(e) 1 3 9 5 00		44
45	Payroll Taxes Expense—Furniture	5 5 6 8 00				45
46	Salary Expense—Furniture	56 2 4 0 00				46
47	Supplies Expense—Furniture			(d) 1 4 0 9 00		47
48	Uncollectible Accounts Expense—Furniture			(a) 1 0 1 60		48
49	Advertising Expense—Accessories	7 1 5 60				49
50	Depr. Expense—Store Equip., Accessories			(h) 9 8 1 70		50
51	Insurance Expense—Accessories			(e) 1 3 9 5 00		51
52	Payroll Taxes Expense—Accessories	2 3 6 5 00				52
53	Salary Expense—Accessories	23 8 9 0 00				53
54	Supplies Expense—Accessories			(d) 8 9 6 30		54
55	Credit Card Fee Expense	6 2 5 5 30				55
56	Depreciation Expense—Office Equipment			(f) 5 2 9 50		56
57	Insurance Expense—Administrative			(e) 3 2 5 00		57
58	Miscellaneous Expense	8 0 7 6 80				58
59	Payroll Taxes Expense—Administrative	1 8 7 3 00				59
60	Rent Expense	15 0 0 0 00				60
61	Salary Expense—Administrative	18 9 2 0 00				61
62	Supplies Expense—Administrative			(d) 4 2 2 70		62
63	Utilities Expense	4 0 1 6 20				63
64						64
65	*Departmental Margin—Furniture*					65
66	*Departmental Margin—Accessories*					66
67						67
68	Federal Income Tax Expense	2 8 0 0 00		(i) 1 5 8 60		68
69		708 6 5 2 50	708 6 5 2 50	29 5 1 8 50	29 5 1 8 50	69
70	*Net Income after Fed. Inc. Tax*					70
71						71
72						72
73						73
74						74
75						75
76						76
77						77
78						78

18-5   MASTERY PROBLEM (continued)

[3]

Furniture DeCor, Inc.

Departmental Margin Statement—Furniture

For Year Ended December 31, 20--

				% OF NET SALES
Operating Revenue:				
Sales		357 5 7 3 50		100.5
Less: Sales Discount	8 9 3 20			0.3
Sales Returns & Allow.	8 4 1 30	1 7 3 4 50		0.2
Net Sales			355 8 3 9 00	100.0
Cost of Merchandise Sold:				
Mdse. Inv., Jan. 1, 20--		103 8 3 6 30		29.2
Purchases	233 5 2 1 60			65.6
Less: Purchases Discount	1 5 5 8 40			0.4
Purchases Returns & Allow.	1 0 3 8 90	2 5 9 7 30		0.3
Net Purchases		230 9 2 4 30		64.9
Total Cost of Mdse. Avail. for Sale		334 7 6 0 60		94.1
Less Mdse. Inv., Dec. 31, 20--		112 4 6 0 00		31.6
Cost of Merchandise Sold			222 3 0 0 60	62.5
Gross Profit on Operations			133 5 3 8 40	37.5
Direct Expenses:				
Advertising Expense		2 8 3 8 40		0.8
Depr. Exp.—Store Equipment		2 1 3 1 30		0.6
Insurance Expense		1 3 9 5 00		0.4
Payroll Taxes Expense		5 5 6 8 00		1.6
Salary Expense		56 2 4 0 00		15.8
Supplies Expense		1 4 0 9 00		0.4
Uncollectible Accounts Expense		1 0 1 60		0.0
Total Direct Expenses			69 6 8 3 30	19.6
Departmental Margin			63 8 5 5 10	17.9

18-5 MASTERY PROBLEM (continued)

[3]

Furniture DeCor, Inc.

Departmental Margin Statement—Accessories

For Year Ended December 31, 20--

			% OF NET SALES
Operating Revenue:			
Sales		112 1 9 7 30	100.5
Less: Sales Discount	3 7 2 60		0.3
Sales Returns & Allow.	1 5 9 80	5 3 2 40	0.1
Net Sales		111 6 6 4 90	100.0
Cost of Merchandise Sold			
Mdse. Inv., Jan. 1, 20--		35 3 9 4 70	31.7
Purchases	81 6 7 9 30		73.1
Less: Purchases Discount	2 7 7 40		0.2
Purchases Returns & Allow.	1 1 8 90	3 9 6 30	0.1
Net Purchases		81 2 8 3 00	72.8
Total Cost of Mdse. Avail. for Sale		116 6 7 7 70	104.5
Less Mdse. Inv., Dec. 31, 20--		46 5 4 3 80	41.7
Cost of Merchandise Sold		70 1 3 3 90	62.8
Gross Profit on Operations		41 5 3 1 00	37.2
Direct Expenses:			
Advertising Expense	7 1 5 60		0.6
Depr. Exp.—Store Equipment	9 8 1 70		0.9
Insurance Expense	1 3 9 5 00		1.2
Payroll Taxes Expense	2 3 6 5 00		2.1
Salary Expense	23 8 9 0 00		21.4
Supplies Expense	8 9 6 30		0.8
Total Direct Expenses		30 2 4 3 60	27.1
Departmental Margin		11 2 8 7 40	10.1

18-5 MASTERY PROBLEM (continued)

[4]

Furniture DeCor, Inc.

Income Statement

For Year Ended December 31, 20--

| | DEPARTMENTAL | | COMPANY | |
	FURNITURE	ACCESSORIES	AMOUNTS	% OF NET SALES
Net Sales	355 8 3 9 00	111 6 6 4 90	467 5 0 3 90	100.0
Cost of Merchandise Sold	222 3 0 0 60	70 1 3 3 90	292 4 3 4 50	62.6
Gross Profit on Operations	133 5 3 8 40	41 5 3 1 00	175 0 6 9 40	37.4
Direct Expenses	69 6 8 3 30	30 2 4 3 60	99 9 2 6 90	21.4
Departmental Margin	63 8 5 5 10	11 2 8 7 40	75 1 4 2 50	16.1
Indirect Expenses:				
Credit Card Fee Expense			6 2 5 5 30	1.3
Depr. Exp.—Office Equip.			5 2 9 50	0.1
Insurance Expense—Admin.			3 2 5 00	0.1
Miscellaneous Expense			8 0 7 6 80	1.7
Payroll Taxes Expense—Admin.			1 8 7 3 00	0.4
Rent Expense			15 0 0 0 00	3.2
Salary Expense—Admin.			18 9 2 0 00	4.0
Supplies Expense—Admin.			4 2 2 70	0.1
Utilities Expense			4 0 1 6 20	0.9
Total Indirect Expenses			55 4 1 8 50	11.9
Net Income before Fed. Inc. Tax			19 7 2 4 00	4.2
Less Federal Income Tax Expense			2 9 5 8 60	0.6
Net Income after Fed. Inc. Tax			16 7 6 5 40	3.6

18-5 MASTERY PROBLEM

Extra form

	DEPARTMENTAL		COMPANY	
	FURNITURE	ACCESSORIES	AMOUNTS	% OF NET SALES

Name _____ Date _____ Class _____

18-6 CHALLENGE PROBLEM, p. 520

Analyzing a departmental margin statement   [1]

Ultra Video, Inc.

Departmental Margin Statement—Camcorder

For Years Ended December 31, 20X7 and 20X6

	20X7 AMOUNTS	20X7 % OF NET SALES	20X6 AMOUNTS	20X6 % OF NET SALES
Operating Revenue:				
Sales	432 6 1 1 90	100.4	384 8 0 5 90	100.4
Less Sales Returns and Allowances	1 7 1 8 80	0.4	1 5 3 3 10	0.4
Net Sales	430 8 9 3 10	100.0	383 2 7 2 80	100.0
Cost of Merchandise Sold:				
Merchandise Inventory, January 1, 20--	46 1 6 6 80	10.7	41 0 1 0 20	10.7
Purchases	237 2 0 4 90	55.0	203 9 0 1 10	53.2
Total Cost of Mdse. Available for Sale	283 3 7 1 70	65.8	244 9 1 1 30	63.9
Less Mdse. Inventory, Dec. 31, 20--	42 0 4 8 50	9.8	45 6 0 9 50	11.9
Cost of Merchandise Sold	241 3 2 3 20	56.0	199 3 0 1 80	52.0
Gross Profit on Operations	189 5 6 9 90	44.0	183 9 7 1 00	48.0
Direct Expenses:				
Advertising Expense	4 3 2 0 90	1.0	3 4 4 9 50	0.9
Delivery Expense	10 2 3 7 20	2.4	8 4 3 2 00	2.2
Depr. Expense—Delivery Equipment	5 9 6 0 10	1.4	4 5 9 9 30	1.2
Depr. Expense—Store Equipment	3 9 0 1 60	0.9	3 4 3 2 60	0.9
Insurance Expense	3 3 9 8 20	0.8	3 0 2 3 70	0.8
Payroll Taxes Expense	5 2 6 5 30	1.2	4 3 6 0 40	1.1
Salary Expense	50 2 4 3 70	11.7	42 9 6 0 00	11.2
Supplies Expense	3 9 2 2 80	0.9	2 9 8 1 90	0.8
Uncollectible Accounts Expense	4 8 9 9 60	1.1	3 8 2 7 90	1.0
Total Direct Expenses	92 1 4 9 40	21.4	77 0 6 7 30	20.1
Departmental Margin	97 4 2 0 50	22.6	106 9 0 3 70	27.9

18-6 CHALLENGE PROBLEM (concluded)

[2]

Change in % of Net Sales	
a. Cost of Merchandise Sold	**+4.0%**
b. Gross Profit	**−4.0%**
c. Total Direct Departmental Expenses	**+1.3%**
d. Departmental Margin	**−5.3%**

[3]

a. Is the departmental margin for the camcorder department at a satisfactory percentage of sales? Explain why it is or is not satisfactory.

**Not satisfactory. The departmental margin for the camcorder department is not at a** _**satisfactory percentage of sales. Specifically, the 22.6% departmental margin for 20X7 does not**_ _**meet the minimum guidelines percentage of 25.0%. This is due primarily to an increase as a**_ _**percentage of sales of 4.0% in cost of merchandise sold and a 1.3% increase in total direct**_ _**departmental expenses.**_

b. Is the trend of the cost of merchandise sold percentage favorable or unfavorable? Explain why it is or is not favorable. Can you suggest some possible reasons for the change in cost of merchandise sold from 20X6 to 20X7?

**Unfavorable. Cost of merchandise sold percentage increased from 52.0% in 20X6 to** _**56.0% in 20X7. This increase is directly reflected in the gross profit percentage reduction as well**_ _**as the departmental margin percentage reduction. Possible reasons for the change in cost of**_ _**merchandise sold percentage are a higher cost per unit of merchandise purchased and/or a**_ _**decrease in the selling price per unit of merchandise sold.**_

c. Is the trend of the total direct departmental expenses percentage favorable or unfavorable? Explain why the trend is or is not favorable.

**Unfavorable. Total departmental expenses percentage has increased from 20.1% in** _**20X6 to 21.4% in 20X7, a 1.3% increase. This increase is largely due to a 0.5% increase in**_ _**salary expense and a 0.2% increase in delivery expense and depreciation expense—delivery**_ _**equipment.**_

19-1 WORK TOGETHER, p. 530

Classifying manufacturing costs; specifying the ledger used for initial recording [4, 5]

	Direct Materials	Direct Labor	Factory Overhead	Materials Ledger	Cost Ledger (Sheet)	Finished Goods Ledger
a. Wages earned by production employees		✓			✓	
b. Aluminum used to produce gutters	✓			✓		
c. Factory rent			✓		✓	
d. Cleaning solvent used to clean production machinery			✓		✓	
e. Production employees' fringe benefits			✓		✓	

19-1 ON YOUR OWN, p. 530

Classifying manufacturing costs; specifying the ledger used for initial recording [6, 7]

	Direct Materials	Direct Labor	Factory Overhead	Materials Ledger	Cost Ledger (Sheet)	Finished Goods Ledger
a. Rivets used in production of gutters			✓		✓	
b. Wages earned by maintenance employees			✓		✓	
c. Factory property taxes			✓		✓	
d. Fringe benefits of factory supervisor			✓		✓	
e. Wages earned by gutter inspector		✓*	✓*		✓	
* *Depends on employer classification*						

19-1 WORK TOGETHER ON YOUR OWN

Extra form

COST SHEET

Job No. _____   Date _____

Item _____   Date wanted _____

No. of items _____   Date completed _____

Ordered for _____

DIRECT MATERIALS		DIRECT LABOR				SUMMARY	
REQ. NO.	AMOUNT	DATE	AMOUNT	DATE	AMOUNT	ITEM	AMOUNT

19-2 WORK TOGETHER, p. 538

Determining total cost and unit cost for a job and determining total cost for a finished item [6]

COST SHEET

Job No. _____657_____   Date _July 18, 20--_

Item _K-39 Sofa_   Date wanted _July 25, 20--_

No. of items _70_   Date completed _July 25, 20--_

Ordered for _Stock_

DIRECT MATERIALS		DIRECT LABOR				SUMMARY	
REQ. NO.	AMOUNT	DATE	AMOUNT	DATE	AMOUNT	ITEM	AMOUNT
147	$1,105.58	July 18	$1,378.65			*Direct Materials*	*$6,444.65*
149	1,264.79	20	1,195.03			*Direct Labor*	*5,967.94*
152	963.02	21	979.84			*Factory Overhead*	
154	586.98	22	1,036.01			*($15 × 530 direct*	
155	1,435.76	24	1,378.41			*labor hours)*	*7,950.00*
159	1,088.52		*$5,967.94*			*Total Cost*	*$20,362.59*
	$6,444.65						
						No. of units finished	*70*
						Cost per unit	*$290.89*

Space for calculations:

Estimated Factory Overhead	÷	*Estimated Direct Labor Hours*	=	*Overhead Application Rate*
$3,000,000.00	÷	*200,000*		*$15 per DLH*

[7]

FINISHED GOODS LEDGER CARD

Description _Sofa_   Stock No. _K-39_

Minimum _80_   Location _S-9_

MANUFACTURED/RECEIVED					SHIPPED/ISSUED					BALANCE			
DATE	JOB NO.	QUAN-TITY	UNIT COST	TOTAL COST	DATE	SALES INVOICE NO.	QUAN-TITY	UNIT COST	TOTAL COST	DATE	QUAN-TITY	UNIT COST	TOTAL COST
										July 23	150	$285.00	$42,750.00
July 25	*657*	*70*	*$290.89*	*$20,362.59*						25	150	285.00	
											70	290.89	63,112.59

19-2 WORK TOGETHER

Extra form

COST SHEET

Job No. _____   Date _____

Item _____   Date wanted _____

No. of items _____   Date completed _____

Ordered for _____

DIRECT MATERIALS		DIRECT LABOR				SUMMARY	
REQ. NO.	AMOUNT	DATE	AMOUNT	DATE	AMOUNT	ITEM	AMOUNT

Name _____ Date _____ Class _____

19-2 ON YOUR OWN, p. 538

Determining total cost and unit cost for a job and determining total cost for a finished item [8]

COST SHEET

Job No. ___711___   Date _August 3, 20--_

Item _S-68 Chair_   Date wanted _August 10, 20--_

No. of items _80_   Date completed _August 10, 20--_

Ordered for _Stock_

DIRECT MATERIALS		DIRECT LABOR				SUMMARY	
REQ. NO.	AMOUNT	DATE	AMOUNT	DATE	AMOUNT	ITEM	AMOUNT
211	$ 2,106.44	Aug. 3	$1,286.90			*Direct Materials*	*$11,466.73*
212	1,865.22	5	843.62			*Direct Labor*	*5,605.21*
215	1,954.57	6	1,140.74			*Factory Overhead*	
217	2,284.05	8	971.20			*($15 × 743 direct*	
218	1,372.91	9	1,362.75			*labor hours)*	*11,145.00*
221	1,883.54		*$5,605.21*			*Total Cost*	*$28,216.94*
	$11,466.73						
						No. of units finished	*80*
						Cost per unit	*$352.71*

Space for calculations:

Estimated Factory Overhead	÷	Estimated Direct Labor Hours	=	Overhead Application Rate
$3,000.000.00	÷	200,000		$15 per DLH

[9]

FINISHED GOODS LEDGER CARD

Description _Chair_   Stock No. _S-68_

Minimum _100_   Location _L-7_

MANUFACTURED/RECEIVED					SHIPPED/ISSUED					BALANCE			
DATE	JOB NO.	QUAN-TITY	UNIT COST	TOTAL COST	DATE	SALES INVOICE NO.	QUAN-TITY	UNIT COST	TOTAL COST	DATE	QUAN-TITY	UNIT COST	TOTAL COST
										Aug. 9	185	$374.00	$69,190.00
Aug. 10	*711*	*80*	*$352.71*	*$28,216.94*						10	185	374.00	
											80	352.71	97,406.94

19-2 ON YOUR OWN

Extra form

COST SHEET

Job No. _____   Date _____

Item _____   Date wanted _____

No. of items _____   Date completed _____

Ordered for _____

REQ. NO.	DIRECT MATERIALS AMOUNT	DATE	DIRECT LABOR AMOUNT	DATE	AMOUNT	SUMMARY ITEM	AMOUNT

19-1 APPLICATION PROBLEM, p. 540

Classifying manufacturing costs and determining which ledger to use   [1, 2]
for initial recording

	Direct Materials	Direct Labor	Factory Overhead	None	Materials Ledger	Cost Ledger (Sheet)	Finished Goods Ledger
a. Wages of factory supervisor			✓			✓	
b. Fringe benefits of factory supervisor			✓			✓	
c. Rent of company headquarters				✓			
d. Rubber to produce tires	✓				✓		
e. Factory property taxes			✓			✓	
f. Wages of production employees		✓				✓	
g. Glue used in tire production			✓			✓	
h. Cleaning solvent used to clean factory equipment			✓			✓	
i. Inspector's wages		✓*	✓*			✓	
j. Wages of marketing manager				✓			

* *Depends on employer classification*

19-1 APPLICATION PROBLEM

Extra form

COST SHEET

Job No. _____

Item _____

No. of items _____

Ordered for _____

Date _____

Date wanted _____

Date completed _____

DIRECT MATERIALS		DIRECT LABOR				SUMMARY	
REQ. NO.	AMOUNT	DATE	AMOUNT	DATE	AMOUNT	ITEM	AMOUNT

19-2 APPLICATION PROBLEM, p. 540

Classifying manufacturing costs and determining which ledger to use [1–3]
for initial recording

MATERIALS LEDGER CARD

Article _T-S Thermostats_ _____ Acct. No. _76_ _____

Reorder _500_ _____ Minimum _175_ _____ Location _A-18_ _____

ORDERED			RECEIVED					ISSUED					BALANCE			
DATE	PUR-CHASE ORDER NO.	QUAN-TITY	DATE	PUR-CHASE ORDER NO.	QUAN-TITY	UNIT PRICE	VALUE	DATE	REQUI-SITION NO.	QUAN-TITY	UNIT PRICE	VALUE	DATE	QUAN-TITY	UNIT PRICE	VALUE
													Oct. 1	175	39.50	6,912.50
Oct. 1	83	500														
								Oct. 3	196	110	39.50	4,345.00	3	65	39.50	2,567.50
								4	200	45	39.50	1,777.50	4	20	39.50	790.00
			Oct. 7	83	500	39.50	19,750.00						7	520	39.50	20,540.00
								12	207	220	39.50	8,690.00	12	300	39.50	11,850.00
								17	218	85	39.50	3,357.50	17	215	39.50	8,492.50
								29	231	55	39.50	2,172.50	29	160	39.50	6,320.00
29	88	500														

19-3 APPLICATION PROBLEM, p. 541

Calculating factory overhead applied rate

Estimated Factory Overhead	÷	_Estimated Direct Labor Cost_	=	_Factory Overhead Applied Rate_
_$336,000.00_	÷	_$420,000.00_	=	_80% of Direct Labor Cost_

19-2 APPLICATION PROBLEM

Extra form

MATERIALS LEDGER CARD

Article _____ Acct. No. _____

Reorder _____ Minimum _____ Location _____

ORDERED			RECEIVED					ISSUED					BALANCE			
DATE	PURCHASE ORDER NO.	QUANTITY	DATE	PURCHASE ORDER NO.	QUANTITY	UNIT PRICE	VALUE	DATE	REQUISITION NO.	QUANTITY	UNIT PRICE	VALUE	DATE	QUANTITY	UNIT PRICE	VALUE

19-4 APPLICATION PROBLEM, p. 541

Preparing a cost sheet [1, 2]

COST SHEET

Job No. _309_

Item _ET42 Game Tables_

No. of items _45_

Ordered for _Stock_

Date _July 1, 20--_

Date wanted _July 10, 20--_

Date completed _July 8, 20--_

REQ. NO.	DIRECT MATERIALS AMOUNT	DATE	DIRECT LABOR AMOUNT	DATE	AMOUNT	SUMMARY ITEM	AMOUNT
432	$ 641.25	July 1	$465.00			Direct Materials	$1,247.25
438	345.00	2	364.50			Direct Labor	1,617.00
447	261.00	3	301.50			Factory Overhead	
	$1,247.25	5	285.00			(75% of direct	
		8	201.00			labor costs)	1,212.75
			$1,617.00			Total Costs	$4,077.00
						No. of units finished	45
						Cost per unit	$90.60

19-4 APPLICATION PROBLEM

Extra form

COST SHEET

Job No. _____   Date _____

Item _____   Date wanted _____

No. of items _____   Date completed _____

Ordered for _____

DIRECT MATERIALS		DIRECT LABOR				SUMMARY	
REQ. NO.	AMOUNT	DATE	AMOUNT	DATE	AMOUNT	ITEM	AMOUNT

Name _____ Date _____ Class _____

19-5 APPLICATION PROBLEM, p. 541

Recording entries in a finished goods ledger   [1–3]

FINISHED GOODS LEDGER CARD

Description Baseball Bat   Stock No. C45

Minimum 250   Location R-12

MANUFACTURED/RECEIVED					SHIPPED/ISSUED					BALANCE			
DATE	JOB NO.	QUAN-TITY	UNIT COST	TOTAL COST	DATE	SALES INVOICE NO.	QUAN-TITY	UNIT COST	TOTAL COST	DATE	QUAN-TITY	UNIT COST	TOTAL COST
										Apr. 1	280	$8.70	$2,436.00
Apr. 2	315	210	$8.80	$1,848.00						2	280	$8.70	
											210	$8.80	4,284.00
					8	511	90	$8.70	$ 783.00	8	190	$8.70	
											210	$8.80	3,501.00
9	334	140	$9.00	1,260.00						9	190	$8.70	
											210	$8.80	
											140	$9.00	4,761.00
					14	521	75	$8.70	652.50	14	115	$8.70	
											210	$8.80	
											140	$9.00	4,108.50
16	339	100	$8.60	860.00						16	115	$8.70	
											210	$8.80	
											140	$9.00	
											100	$8.60	4,968.50
					23	536	115	$8.70		23	25	$8.80	
							185	$8.80	2,628.50		140	$9.00	
											100	$8.60	2,340.00
					27	543	25	$8.80		27	90	$9.00	
							50	$9.00	670.00		100	$8.60	1,670.00
28	363	120	$8.85	1,062.00						28	90	$9.00	
											100	$8.60	
											120	$8.85	2,732.00

Name _____ Date _____ Class _____

APPLICATION PROBLEM

Extra form

FINISHED GOODS LEDGER CARD													

Description _____ Stock No. _____

Minimum _____ Location _____

MANUFACTURED/RECEIVED					SHIPPED/ISSUED					BALANCE			
DATE	JOB NO.	QUAN-TITY	UNIT COST	TOTAL COST	DATE	SALES INVOICE NO.	QUAN-TITY	UNIT COST	TOTAL COST	DATE	QUAN-TITY	UNIT COST	TOTAL COST

19-6 MASTERY PROBLEM, p. 542

Preparing cost records   [1]

Estimated Factory Overhead	÷	Estimated Direct Labor Costs	=	Factory Overhead Applied Rate
$398,800.00	÷	$498,500.00	=	80% of Direct Labor Cost

[2, 3]

COST SHEET

Job No. __283__   Date _May 3, 20--_

Item _52L Athletic Shoes_   Date wanted _May 13, 20--_

No. of items _150_   Date completed _May 12, 20--_

Ordered for _Stock_

DIRECT MATERIALS		DIRECT LABOR				SUMMARY	
REQ. NO.	AMOUNT	DATE	AMOUNT	DATE	AMOUNT	ITEM	AMOUNT
392	$ 862.50	May 3	$ 129.00			Direct Materials	$1,695.00
399	472.50	4	248.00			Direct Labor	1,480.00
428	360.00	5	175.00			Factory Overhead	
	$1,695.00	6	192.00			(80% of direct	
		7	295.00			labor costs)	1,184.00
		10	165.00			Total Cost	$4,359.00
		11	152.00				
		12	124.00			No. units finished	150
			$1,480.00			Cost per unit	$29.06

19-6 MASTERY PROBLEM (concluded)

[4-6]

FINISHED GOODS LEDGER CARD

Description _Athletic Shoes_ Stock No. _52L_

Minimum _100_ Location _C-50_

MANUFACTURED/RECEIVED					SHIPPED/ISSUED					BALANCE			
DATE	JOB NO.	QUAN-TITY	UNIT COST	TOTAL COST	DATE	SALES INVOICE NO.	QUAN-TITY	UNIT COST	TOTAL COST	DATE	QUAN-TITY	UNIT COST	TOTAL COST
										20-- May 1	140	30.45	4,263.00
					20-- May 5	633	60	30.45	1,827.00	5	80	30.45	2,436.00
20-- May 12	283	150	29.06	4,359.00						12	80	30.45	
											150	29.06	6,795.00
					18	652	30	30.45	913.50	18	50	30.45	
											150	29.06	5,881.50

Extra form

FINISHED GOODS LEDGER CARD

Description _____ Stock No. _____

Minimum _____ Location _____

MANUFACTURED/RECEIVED					SHIPPED/ISSUED					BALANCE			
DATE	JOB NO.	QUAN-TITY	UNIT COST	TOTAL COST	DATE	SALES INVOICE NO.	QUAN-TITY	UNIT COST	TOTAL COST	DATE	QUAN-TITY	UNIT COST	TOTAL COST

19-7 CHALLENGE PROBLEM, p. 543

Preparing cost records [1]

a. Direct materials cost

10,000 Suits × $80.00 per Suit Cost = $800,000.00 Estimated Direct Materials Cost

Estimated Factory Overhead		Estimated Direct Materials Cost		Factory Overhead Applied Rate
$600,000.00	÷	$800,000.00	=	75% of Direct Materials Cost

b. Direct labor cost

10,000 Suits × 4 Labor Hours per Suit × $12.50 per Hour = $500,000.00 Estimated Direct Labor Cost

Estimated Factory Overhead		Estimated Direct Labor Cost		Factory Overhead Applied Rate
$600,000.00	÷	$500,000.00	=	120% of Direct Labor Cost

c. Direct labor hours

10,000 Suits × 4 Labor Hours per Suit = 40,000 Estimated Direct Labor Hours

Estimated Factory Overhead		Estimated Direct Labor Hours		Factory Overhead Applied Rate
$600,000.00	÷	40,000.00	=	$15.00 of Direct Labor Hour

[2, 3]

COST SHEET

Job No. 365   Date May 9, 20--

Item SE80 Diving Suit   Date wanted May 19, 20--

No. of items 55   Date completed May 18, 20--

Ordered for Stock

DIRECT MATERIALS		DIRECT LABOR					SUMMARY	
REQ. NO.	AMOUNT	DATE	AMOUNT	DATE	AMOUNT		ITEM	AMOUNT
421	$1,160.50	May 9	$ 274.75				Direct Materials	$ 4,499.00
430	2,321.00	10	441.00				Direct Labor	2,873.75
438	1,017.50	11	392.00				Factory Overhead	
	$4,499.00	12	423.00				(75% of direct	
		13	440.00				materials cost)	3,374.25
		16	370.00				Total Costs	$10,747.00
		17	352.00					
		18	181.00				No. units finished	55
			$2,873.75				Cost per unit	$195.40

19-7 CHALLENGE PROBLEM (concluded)

[4–6]

FINISHED GOODS LEDGER CARD

Description _Diving Suit_ _____ Stock No. _SE80_ _____

Minimum _30_ _____ Location _J16_ _____

MANUFACTURED/RECEIVED					SHIPPED/ISSUED					BALANCE			
DATE	JOB NO.	QUAN-TITY	UNIT COST	TOTAL COST	DATE	SALES INVOICE NO.	QUAN-TITY	UNIT COST	TOTAL COST	DATE	QUAN-TITY	UNIT COST	TOTAL COST
										20-- May 1	40	191.50	7,660.00
					20-- May 11	450	10	191.50	1,915.00	11	30	191.50	5,745.00
20-- May 18	365	55	195.40	10,747.00						18	30	191.50	⌐
											55	195.40	16,492.00
					23	494	30	195.40	5,862.00	23	30	191.50	⌐
											25	195.40	10,630.00
					25	523	25	195.40	4,885.00	25	30	191.50	5,745.00

20-1 WORK TOGETHER, p. 555

Preparing manufacturing journal entries   [4]

MATERIALS PURCHASES JOURNAL   PAGE 12

	DATE		ACCOUNT CREDITED	PURCH. NO.	POST. REF.	MATERIALS DR. ACCTS. PAY. CR.	
1	20-- May	3	Bushnell Corrugated			15 4 0 0 00	1
2							2

GENERAL JOURNAL   PAGE 18

	DATE		ACCOUNT TITLE	DOC. NO.	POST. REF.	DEBIT	CREDIT	
1	20-- May	5	Work in Process			2 6 5 0 00		1
2			Factory Overhead			3 5 0 00		2
3			Materials				3 0 0 0 00	3
4		21	Work in Process			4 7 0 0 00		4
5			Factory Overhead			2 1 0 0 00		5
6			Materials				6 8 0 0 00	6
7		31	Factory Overhead			4 7 0 0 00		7
8			Depr. Expense—Building				7 5 0 00	8
9			Depr. Expense—Factory Equipment				1 2 0 0 00	9
10			Insurance Expense—Factory				3 2 5 00	10
11			Property Tax Expense—Factory				5 4 5 00	11
12			Utilities Expense				1 8 8 0 00	12
13		31	Work in Process			10 6 7 5 00		13
14			Factory Overhead				10 6 7 5 00	14
15		31	Factory Overhead			5 5 5 00		15
16			Income Summary				5 5 5 00	16
17		31	Finished Goods			29 9 2 0 00		17
18			Work in Process				29 9 2 0 00	18
19		31	Cost of Goods Sold			24 7 6 0 00		19
20			Finished Goods				24 7 6 0 00	20
21								21
22								22
23								23
24								24
25								25
26								26

20-1 WORK TOGETHER (concluded)

[4]

CASH PAYMENTS JOURNAL

PAGE 8

	DATE	ACCOUNT TITLE	CK. NO.	POST. REF.	GENERAL DEBIT	GENERAL CREDIT	ACCOUNTS PAYABLE DEBIT	CASH CREDIT	
1	20-- May 15	Work in Process			1120000			1034080	1
2		Factory Overhead			160000				2
3		Employee Income Tax Payable				148000			3
4		Social Security Tax Payable				79360			4
5		Medicare Tax Payable				18560			5
6	31	Work in Process			1015000			941872	6
7		Factory Overhead			137000				7
8		Employee Income Tax Payable				122000			8
9		Social Security Tax Payable				71424			9
10		Medicare Tax Payable				16704			10
11									11
12									12
13									13
14									14
15									15
16									16
17									17
18									18
19									19
20									20
21									21
22									22
23									23
24									24
25									25

20-1 ON YOUR OWN, p. 556

Preparing manufacturing journal entries [5]

MATERIALS PURCHASES JOURNAL

PAGE 18

	DATE		ACCOUNT CREDITED	PURCH. NO.	POST. REF.	MATERIALS DR. ACCTS. PAY. CR.	
1	20-- June	4	Fresno, Inc.			8 1 0 0 00	1
2							2

GENERAL JOURNAL

PAGE 23

	DATE		ACCOUNT TITLE	DOC. NO.	POST. REF.	DEBIT	CREDIT	
1	20-- June	7	Work in Process			3 7 7 0 00		1
2			Factory Overhead			7 3 0 00		2
3			Materials				4 5 0 0 00	3
4		15	Work in Process			2 3 0 0 00		4
5			Factory Overhead			1 5 3 0 00		5
6			Materials				3 8 3 0 00	6
7		30	Factory Overhead			4 8 0 5 00		7
8			Depr. Expense—Building				7 5 0 00	8
9			Depr. Expense—Factory Equipment				1 2 0 0 00	9
10			Insurance Expense—Factory				3 2 5 00	10
11			Property Tax Expense—Factory				5 7 0 00	11
12			Utilities Expense				1 9 6 0 00	12
13		30	Work in Process			11 7 2 5 00		13
14			Factory Overhead				11 7 2 5 00	14
15		30	Factory Overhead			9 3 5 00		15
16			Income Summary				9 3 5 00	16
17		30	Finished Goods			35 5 0 0 00		17
18			Work in Process				35 5 0 0 00	18
19		30	Cost of Goods Sold			32 1 6 0 00		19
20			Finished Goods				32 1 6 0 00	20
21								21
22								22
23								23
24								24
25								25
26								26

20-1 ON YOUR OWN (concluded)

[5]

CASH PAYMENTS JOURNAL   PAGE 22

	DATE	ACCOUNT TITLE	CK. NO.	POST. REF.	GENERAL DEBIT (1)	GENERAL CREDIT (2)	ACCOUNTS PAYABLE DEBIT (3)	CASH CREDIT (4)	
1	20-- June 15	Work in Process			1259000			1163845	1
2		Factory Overhead			194000				2
3		Employee Income Tax Payable				178000			3
4		Social Security Tax Payable				90086			4
5		Medicare Tax Payable				21069			5
6	31	Work in Process			1086000			1006266	6
7		Factory Overhead			178500				7
8		Employee Income Tax Payable				161500			8
9		Social Security Tax Payable				78399			9
10		Medicare Tax Payable				18335			10
11									11
12									12
13									13
14									14
15									15
16									16
17									17
18									18
19									19
20									20
21									21
22									22
23									23
24									24
25									25

20-2 WORK TOGETHER, p. 563

Preparing statement of cost of goods manufactured, income statement, and balance sheet [4]

Work sheet begins on page 290.

Bedthings, Inc.

Statement of Cost of Goods Manufactured

For Month Ended April 30, 20--

Direct Materials	110	9	5	0	00
Direct Labor	82	1	6	5	00
Factory Overhead Applied	62	3	1	0	00
Total Cost of Work Placed in Process	255	4	2	5	00
Work in Process Inventory, March 1, 20--	78	1	0	0	00
Total Cost of Work in Process During March	333	5	2	5	00
Less Work in Process Inventory, March 31, 20--	78	3	6	0	00
Cost of Goods Manufactured	255	1	6	5	00

Extra form

Bedthings, Inc.

Work Sheet

For Month Ended March 31, 20--

ACCOUNT TITLE	TRIAL BALANCE DEBIT	TRIAL BALANCE CREDIT	ADJUSTMENTS DEBIT	ADJUSTMENTS CREDIT	INCOME STATEMENT DEBIT	INCOME STATEMENT CREDIT	BALANCE SHEET DEBIT	BALANCE SHEET CREDIT
1 Cash	25700000						25700000	
2 Accounts Receivable	16187500						16187500	
3 Allowance for Uncollectible Accounts		304000		(a) 120000				424000
4 Materials	9222000						9222000	
5 Work in Process	7836000						7836000	
6 Finished Goods	11852000						11852000	
7 Supplies—Factory	262000						262000	
8 Supplies—Sales	2400000			(b) 820000			1580000	
9 Factory Equipment	17550000						17550000	
10 Accum. Depr.—Factory Equipment		3218000						3218000
11 Office Equipment	1990000						1990000	
12 Accum. Depr.—Office Equipment		826000		(c) 60000				886000
13 Building	28800000						28800000	
14 Accum. Depr.—Building		13071000						13071000
15 Land	12564000						12564000	
16 Accounts Payable		14785000						14785000
17 Employee Income Tax Payable		843000						843000
18 Federal Income Tax Payable				(d) 1207000				1207000
19 Social Security Tax Payable		834400						834400
20 Medicare Tax Payable		192600						192600
21 Mortgage Payable		8500000						8500000
22 Capital Stock		43000000						43000000
23 Retained Earnings		19603000						19603000
24 Income Summary		1160000				1160000		
25 Sales		32870000				32870000		
26 Cost of Goods Sold	23949000				23949000			
27 Factory Overhead								
28 Depr. Expense—Factory Equipment								
29 Depr. Expense—Building								
30 Utilities Expense—Factory								

20-2 WORK TOGETHER (continued)

	ACCOUNT TITLE	TRIAL BALANCE DEBIT	TRIAL BALANCE CREDIT	ADJUSTMENTS DEBIT	ADJUSTMENTS CREDIT	INCOME STATEMENT DEBIT	INCOME STATEMENT CREDIT	BALANCE SHEET DEBIT	BALANCE SHEET CREDIT
31	Insurance Expense—Factory								
32	Payroll Taxes Expense—Factory								
33	Property Tax Expense—Factory								
34	Supplies Expense—Factory								
35	Advertising Expense	5 3 3 0 00				5 3 3 0 00			
36	Salary Expense—Sales	22 6 5 0 00				22 6 5 0 00			
37	Supplies Expense—Sales			(b) 8 2 0 00		8 2 0 00			
38	Depr. Expense—Office Equipment			(c) 6 0 0 00		6 0 0 00			
39	Payroll Taxes Expense—Admin.	5 3 8 0 00				5 3 8 0 00			
40	Property Tax Expense—Admin.	2 5 5 00				2 5 5 00			
41	Salary Expense—Admin.	17 0 0 0 00				17 0 0 0 00			
42	Uncollectible Accounts Expense			(a) 1 2 0 0 00		1 2 0 0 00			
43	Utilities Expense—Admin.	7 9 0 00				7 9 0 00			
44	Federal Income Tax Expense	12 0 7 0 00		(d)12 0 7 0 00		12 0 7 0 00			
45		1381 6 3 0 00	1381 6 3 0 00	14 6 9 0 00	14 6 9 0 00	305 5 8 5 00	329 8 6 0 00	1089 9 1 5 00	1065 6 4 0 00
46	Net Income after Federal Income Tax					24 2 7 5 00			24 2 7 5 00
47						329 8 6 0 00	329 8 6 0 00	1089 9 1 5 00	1089 9 1 5 00
48									
49									
50									
51									
52									
53									
54									
55									
56									
57									
58									
59									
60									
61									

20-2 WORK TOGETHER (continued)

[5]

Bedthings, Inc.

Income Statement

For Month Ended March 31, 20--

Operating Revenue:					
Sales				328 7 0 0 00	
Cost of Goods Sold:					
Finished Goods Inventory, March 1, 20--		102 8 4 5 00			
Cost of Goods Manufactured		255 1 6 5 00			
Total Cost of Finished Goods Available for Sale		358 0 1 0 00			
Less Finished Goods Inventory, March 31, 20--		118 5 2 0 00			
Cost of Goods Sold		239 4 9 0 00			
Overapplied Overhead		1 1 6 0 00			
Net Cost of Goods Sold				238 3 3 0 00	
Gross Profit on Operations				90 3 7 0 00	
Operating Expenses:					
Selling Expenses:					
Advertising Expense	5 3 3 0 00				
Salary Expense	22 6 5 0 00				
Supplies Expense	8 2 0 00				
Total Selling Expenses		28 8 0 0 00			
Administrative Expenses:					
Depr. Expense—Office Equip.	6 0 0 00				
Payroll Taxes Expense—Admin.	5 3 8 0 00				
Property Tax Expense—Admin.	2 5 5 00				
Salary Expense—Admin.	17 0 0 0 00				
Uncollectible Accts. Expense	1 2 0 0 00				
Utilities Expense—Admin.	7 9 0 00				
Total Administrative Expense		25 2 2 5 00			
Total Operating Expenses				54 0 2 5 00	
Net Income before Fed. Inc. Tax				36 3 4 5 00	
Less Fed. Inc. Tax Expense				12 0 7 0 00	
Net Income				24 2 7 5 00	

20-2 WORK TOGETHER (continued)

[6]

Bedthings, Inc.

Balance Sheet

March 31, 20--

ASSETS					
Current Assets:					
Cash			25 7 0 0 00		
Accounts Receivable	161 8 7 5 00				
Less Allowance for Uncollectible Accounts	4 2 4 0 00		157 6 3 5 00		
Materials			92 2 2 0 00		
Work in Process			78 3 6 0 00		
Finished Goods			118 5 2 0 00		
Supplies—Factory			2 6 2 0 00		
Supplies—Sales			1 5 8 0 00		
Total Current Assets				476 6 3 5 00	
Plant Assets:					
Factory Equipment	175 5 0 0 00				
Less Accum. Depr.—Factory Equipment	32 1 8 0 00		143 3 2 0 00		
Office Equipment	19 9 0 0 00				
Less Accum. Depr.—Office Equipment	8 8 6 0 00		11 0 4 0 00		
Building	288 0 0 0 00				
Less Accum. Depr.—Building	130 7 1 0 00		157 2 9 0 00		
Land			125 6 4 0 00		
Total Plant Assets				437 2 9 0 00	
Total Assets				913 9 2 5 00	
LIABILITIES					
Current Liabilities:					
Accounts Payable			147 8 5 0 00		
Employee Income Tax Payable			8 4 3 0 00		
Federal Income Tax Payable			12 0 7 0 00		
Social Security Tax Payable			8 3 4 4 00		
Medicare Tax Payable			1 9 2 6 00		
Total Current Liabilities				178 6 2 0 00	
Long-Term Liability:					
Mortgage Payable				85 0 0 0 00	
Total Liabilities				263 6 2 0 00	
STOCKHOLDERS' EQUITY					
Capital Stock			430 0 0 0 00		
Retained Earnings			220 3 0 5 00		
Total Stockholders' Equity				650 3 0 5 00	
Total Liabilities and Stockholders' Equity				913 9 2 5 00	

20-2 WORK TOGETHER

Extra form

20-2 ON YOUR OWN, p. 563

Preparing statement of cost of goods manufactured, income statement, and balance sheet [7]

Work sheet begins on page 296.

Bedthings, Inc.

Statement of Cost of Goods Manufactured

For Month Ended April 30, 20--

Direct Materials	123 4 9 0 00
Direct Labor	88 2 0 5 00
Factory Overhead Applied	63 7 3 0 00
Total Cost of Work Placed in Process	275 4 2 5 00
Work in Process Inventory, April 1, 20--	78 3 6 0 00
Total Cost of Work in Process During April	353 7 8 5 00
Less Work in Process Inventory, April 30, 20--	85 4 6 0 00
Cost of Goods Manufactured	268 3 2 5 00

Extra form

20-2 ON YOUR OWN (continued)

Bedthings, Inc.
Work Sheet
For Month Ended April 30, 20--

#	ACCOUNT TITLE	TRIAL BALANCE DEBIT	TRIAL BALANCE CREDIT	ADJUSTMENTS DEBIT	ADJUSTMENTS CREDIT	INCOME STATEMENT DEBIT	INCOME STATEMENT CREDIT	BALANCE SHEET DEBIT	BALANCE SHEET CREDIT
1	Cash	31 2 8 0 00						31 2 8 0 00	
2	Accounts Receivable	155 1 9 0 00						155 1 9 0 00	
3	Allowance for Uncollectible Accounts		4 2 4 0 00		(a) 4 0 0 00				4 6 4 0 00
4	Materials	108 5 6 0 00						108 5 6 0 00	
5	Work in Process	85 4 6 0 00						85 4 6 0 00	
6	Finished Goods	120 5 2 0 00						120 5 2 0 00	
7	Supplies—Factory	2 6 2 0 00						2 6 2 0 00	
8	Supplies—Sales	2 1 7 0 00			(b) 7 8 0 00			1 3 9 0 00	
9	Factory Equipment	175 5 0 0 00						175 5 0 0 00	
10	Accum. Depr.—Factory Equipment		32 1 8 0 00						32 1 8 0 00
11	Office Equipment	19 9 0 0 00						19 9 0 0 00	
12	Accum. Depr.—Office Equipment		8 8 6 0 00		(c) 6 0 0 00				9 4 6 0 00
13	Building	288 0 0 0 00						288 0 0 0 00	
14	Accum. Depr.—Building		130 7 1 0 00						130 7 1 0 00
15	Land	135 4 0 5 00						135 4 0 5 00	
16	Accounts Payable		151 4 4 0 00						151 4 4 0 00
17	Employee Income Tax Payable		11 3 8 0 00						11 3 8 0 00
18	Federal Income Tax Payable				(d) 10 3 7 0 00				10 3 7 0 00
19	Social Security Tax Payable		12 0 5 0 00						12 0 5 0 00
20	Medicare Tax Payable		2 7 8 0 00						2 7 8 0 00
21	Mortgage Payable		85 0 0 0 00						85 0 0 0 00
22	Capital Stock		430 0 0 0 00						430 0 0 0 00
23	Retained Earnings		220 3 0 5 00						220 3 0 5 00
24	Income Summary	5 9 0 00				5 9 0 00			
25	Sales		362 3 7 5 00				362 3 7 5 00		
26	Cost of Goods Sold	266 3 2 5 00				266 3 2 5 00			
27	Factory Overhead								
28	Depr. Expense—Factory Equipment								
29	Depr. Expense—Building								
30	Utilities Expense—Factory								

20-2 ON YOUR OWN (continued)

	Account Title	Trial Balance Debit	Trial Balance Credit	Adjustments Debit	Adjustments Credit	Income Statement Debit	Income Statement Credit	Balance Sheet Debit	Balance Sheet Credit
31	Insurance Expense—Factory								
32	Payroll Taxes Expense—Factory								
33	Property Tax Expense—Factory								
34	Supplies Expense—Factory								
35	Advertising Expense	6 050 00				6 050 00			
36	Salary Expense—Sales	27 940 00				27 940 00			
37	Supplies Expense—Sales			(b) 780 00		780 00			
38	Depr. Expense—Office Equipment			(c) 600 00		600 00			
39	Payroll Taxes Expense—Admin.	5 890 00				5 890 00			
40	Property Tax Expense—Admin.	255 00				255 00			
41	Salary Expense—Admin.	18 800 00				18 800 00			
42	Uncollectible Accounts Expense			(a) 400 00		400 00			
43	Utilities Expense—Admin.	865 00				865 00			
44	Federal Income Tax Expense			(d)10 370 00		10 370 00			
45		1451 320 00	1451 320 00	12 150 00	12 150 00	338 865 00	362 375 00	1123 825 00	1100 315 00
46	Net Income after Federal Income Tax					23 510 00			23 510 00
47						362 375 00	362 375 00	1123 825 00	1123 825 00
48									
49									
50									
51									
52									
53									
54									
55									
56									
57									
58									
59									
60									
61									

20-2 ON YOUR OWN (continued)

[8]

Bedthings, Inc.

Income Statement

For Month Ended March 31, 20--

Operating Revenue:				
Sales				362 3 7 5 00
Cost of Goods Sold:				
Finished Goods Inventory, March 1, 20--		118 5 2 0 00		
Cost of Goods Manufactured		268 3 2 5 00		
Total Cost of Finished Goods Available for Sale		386 8 4 5 00		
Less Finished Goods Inventory, March 31, 20--		120 5 2 0 00		
Cost of Goods Sold		266 3 2 5 00		
Underapplied Overhead		5 9 0 00		
Net Cost of Goods Sold				266 9 1 5 00
Gross Profit on Operations				95 4 6 0 00
Operating Expenses:				
Selling Expenses:				
Advertising Expense	6 0 5 0 00			
Salary Expense	27 9 4 0 00			
Supplies Expense	7 8 0 00			
Total Selling Expenses		34 7 7 0 00		
Administrative Expenses:				
Depr. Expense—Office Equip.	6 0 0 00			
Payroll Taxes Expense—Admin.	5 8 9 0 00			
Property Tax Expense—Admin.	2 5 5 00			
Salary Expense—Admin.	18 8 0 0 00			
Uncollectible Accts. Expense	4 0 0 00			
Utilities Expense—Admin.	8 6 5 00			
Total Administrative Expense		26 8 1 0 00		
Total Operating Expenses				61 5 8 0 00
Net Income before Fed. Inc. Tax				33 8 8 0 00
Less Fed. Inc. Tax Expense				10 3 7 0 00
Net Income				23 5 1 0 00

20-2 ON YOUR OWN (continued)

Bedthings, Inc.

Balance Sheet

March 31, 20--

ASSETS															
Current Assets:															
Cash						31	2	8	0	00					
Accounts Receivable	155	1	9	0	00										
Less Allowance for Uncollectible Accounts	4	6	4	0	00	150	5	5	0	00					
Materials						108	5	6	0	00					
Work in Process						85	4	6	0	00					
Finished Goods						120	5	2	0	00					
Supplies—Factory						2	6	2	0	00					
Supplies—Sales						1	3	9	0	00					
Total Current Assets											500	3	8	0	00
Plant Assets:															
Factory Equipment	175	5	0	0	00										
Less Accum. Depr.—Factory Equipment	32	1	8	0	00	143	3	2	0	00					
Office Equipment	19	9	0	0	00										
Less Accum. Depr.—Office Equipment	9	4	6	0	00	10	4	4	0	00					
Building	288	0	0	0	00										
Less Accum. Depr.—Building	130	7	1	0	00	157	2	9	0	00					
Land						135	4	0	5	00					
Total Plant Assets											446	4	5	5	00
Total Assets											946	8	3	5	00
LIABILITIES															
Current Liabilities:															
Accounts Payable						151	4	4	0	00					
Employee Income Tax Payable						11	3	8	0	00					
Federal Income Tax Payable						10	3	7	0	00					
Social Security Tax Payable						12	0	5	0	00					
Medicare Tax Payable						2	7	8	0	00					
Total Current Liabilities											188	0	2	0	00
Long-Term Liability:															
Mortgage Payable											85	0	0	0	00
Total Liabilities											273	0	2	0	00
STOCKHOLDERS' EQUITY															
Capital Stock						430	0	0	0	00					
Retained Earnings						243	8	1	5	00					
Total Stockholders' Equity											673	8	1	5	00
Total Liabilities and Stockholders' Equity											946	8	3	5	00

20-2 ON YOUR OWN

Extra form

20-1 APPLICATION PROBLEM, p. 565

Journalizing cost accounting transactions for a manufacturing company [1, 2]

MATERIALS PURCHASES JOURNAL

PAGE 4

	DATE		ACCOUNT CREDITED	PURCH. NO.	POST. REF.	MATERIALS DR. ACCTS. PAY. CR.	
1	20-- Aug.	4	Sharon Company	047		6 1 5 2 80	1
2		24	Hubbard Company	048		3 5 1 0 72	2
3		31	Total			9 6 6 3 52	3
4							4
5							5
6							6
7							7
8							8
9							9
10							10
11							11
12							12
13							13
14							14
15							15
16							16
17							17
18							18
19							19
20							20
21							21
22							22
23							23
24							24
25							25
26							26
27							27
28							28
29							29
30							30
31							31

CASH PAYMENTS JOURNAL

PAGE 8

	DATE	ACCOUNT TITLE	CK. NO.	POST. REF.	GENERAL DEBIT (1)	GENERAL CREDIT (2)	ACCOUNTS PAYABLE DEBIT (3)	PURCHASES DISCOUNT CREDIT (4)	CASH CREDIT (5)	
1	20-- Aug. 7	Factory Equipment	651		345800				345800	1
2	15	Supplies—Factory	658		58383				58383	2
3	21	Miscellaneous Expense—Factory	667		112300				112300	3
4	24	Work in Process	679		720000				759932	4
5		Factory Overhead			192000					5
6		Employee Income Tax Payable				82300				6
7		Social Security Tax Payable				56687				7
8		Medicare Tax Payable				13081				8
9	31	Totals			1428483	152068			1276415	9
10										10
11										11
12										12
13										13
14										14
15										15
16										16
17										17
18										18
19										19
20										20
21										21
22										22
23										23
24										24
25										25

20-2 APPLICATION PROBLEM, p. 565

Journalizing and posting entries that summarize cost records at the end of a fiscal period [1–5]

The ledger and journals prepared in this problem are needed to complete Application Problem 20-3.

CASH PAYMENTS JOURNAL

PAGE 6

	DATE	ACCOUNT TITLE	CK. NO.	POST. REF.	GENERAL DEBIT	GENERAL CREDIT	ACCOUNTS PAYABLE DEBIT	PURCHASES DISCOUNT CREDIT	CASH CREDIT	
1	20-- Mar. 31	Work in Process	371	1130	102570 00				99249 10	1
2		Factory Overhead		5505	19960 00					2
3		Employee Income Tax Payable		2110		1347850				3
4		Social Security Tax Payable		2120		796445				4
5		Medicare Tax Payable		2130		183795				5
6										6
7										7
8										8
9										9
10										10
11										11
12										12
13										13
14										14
15										15
16										16
17										17
18										18
19										19
20										20
21										21
22										22
23										23
24										24
25										25

20-2 APPLICATION PROBLEM (continued)

[2, 3]

GENERAL JOURNAL   PAGE 3

	DATE		ACCOUNT TITLE	DOC. NO.	POST. REF.	DEBIT	CREDIT	
1	20– Mar.	31	Work in Process	M34	1130	139 4 1 9 80		1
2			Factory Overhead		5505	4 5 0 5 00		2
3			Materials		1125		143 9 2 4 80	3
4		31	Factory Overhead	M35	5505	46 0 5 0 40		4
5			Depreciation Expense—Factory Equipment		5510		7 6 2 8 40	5
6			Depreciation Expense—Building		5515		2 0 8 1 30	6
7			Heat, Light, and Power Expense		5520		5 7 7 8 50	7
8			Insurance Expense—Factory		5525		9 7 3 70	8
9			Miscellaneous Expense—Factory		5530		6 0 9 50	9
10			Payroll Taxes Expense—Factory		5535		17 1 5 4 20	10
11			Property Tax Expense—Factory		5540		3 7 8 1 70	11
12			Supplies Expense—Factory		5545		8 0 4 3 10	12
13		31	Work in Process	M36	1130	69 7 4 7 60		13
14			Factory Overhead		5505		69 7 4 7 60	14
15		31	Income Summary	M37	3120	7 6 7 80		15
16			Factory Overhead		5505		7 6 7 80	16
17		31	Finished Goods	M38	1135	294 3 1 3 50		17
18			Work in Process		1130		294 3 1 3 50	18
19		31	Cost of Goods Sold	M39	5105	395 8 0 0 00		19
20			Finished Goods		1135		395 8 0 0 00	20
21								21
22								22
23								23
24								24
25								25
26								26
27								27
28								28
29								29
30								30
31								31

20-2 **APPLICATION PROBLEM (continued)**

[1–5]

GENERAL LEDGER

ACCOUNT Materials   ACCOUNT NO. 1125

DATE		ITEM	POST. REF.	DEBIT	CREDIT	BALANCE DEBIT	BALANCE CREDIT
20-- Mar.	1	Balance	✓			138 4 1 9 00	
	31		MP3	51 5 2 4 00		189 9 4 3 00	
	31		G3		143 9 2 4 80	46 0 1 8 20	

ACCOUNT Work in Process   ACCOUNT NO. 1130

DATE		ITEM	POST. REF.	DEBIT	CREDIT	BALANCE DEBIT	BALANCE CREDIT
20-- Mar.	1	Balance	✓			17 7 8 1 00	
	31		CP6	102 5 7 0 00		120 3 5 1 00	
	31		G3	139 4 1 9 80		259 7 7 0 80	
	31		G3	69 7 4 7 60		329 5 1 8 40	
	31		G3		294 3 1 3 50	35 2 0 4 90	

ACCOUNT Finished Goods   ACCOUNT NO. 1135

DATE		ITEM	POST. REF.	DEBIT	CREDIT	BALANCE DEBIT	BALANCE CREDIT
20-- Mar.	1	Balance	✓			156 1 9 6 00	
	31		G3	294 3 1 3 50		450 5 0 9 50	
	31		G3		395 8 0 0 00	54 7 0 9 50	

ACCOUNT Employee Income Tax Payable   ACCOUNT NO. 2110

DATE		ITEM	POST. REF.	DEBIT	CREDIT	BALANCE DEBIT	BALANCE CREDIT
20-- Mar.	31		CP6		13 4 7 8 50		13 4 7 8 50

20-2 APPLICATION PROBLEM (continued)

[1–5]

GENERAL LEDGER

ACCOUNT Social Security Tax Payable   ACCOUNT NO. 2120

DATE	ITEM	POST. REF.	DEBIT	CREDIT	BALANCE DEBIT	BALANCE CREDIT
20-- Mar. 31		CP6		7 9 6 4 45		7 9 6 4 45

ACCOUNT Medicare Tax Payable   ACCOUNT NO. 2130

DATE	ITEM	POST. REF.	DEBIT	CREDIT	BALANCE DEBIT	BALANCE CREDIT
20-- Mar. 31		CP6		1 8 3 7 95		1 8 3 7 95

ACCOUNT Income Summary   ACCOUNT NO. 3120

DATE	ITEM	POST. REF.	DEBIT	CREDIT	BALANCE DEBIT	BALANCE CREDIT
20-- Mar. 31		G3	7 6 7 80		7 6 7 80	

ACCOUNT Cost of Goods Sold   ACCOUNT NO. 5105

DATE	ITEM	POST. REF.	DEBIT	CREDIT	BALANCE DEBIT	BALANCE CREDIT
20-- Mar. 31		G3	395 8 0 0 00		395 8 0 0 00	

20-2 APPLICATION PROBLEM (continued)

[1–5]

GENERAL LEDGER

ACCOUNT Factory Overhead   ACCOUNT NO. 5505

DATE		ITEM	POST. REF.	DEBIT	CREDIT	BALANCE DEBIT	BALANCE CREDIT
20-- Mar.	31		CP6	19 9 6 0 00		19 9 6 0 00	
	31		G3	4 5 0 5 00		24 4 6 5 00	
	31		G3	46 0 5 0 40		70 5 1 5 40	
	31		G3		69 7 4 7 60	7 6 7 80	
	31		G3		7 6 7 80	—	—

ACCOUNT Depreciation Expense—Factory Equipment   ACCOUNT NO. 5510

DATE		ITEM	POST. REF.	DEBIT	CREDIT	BALANCE DEBIT	BALANCE CREDIT
20-- Mar.	31	Balance	✓			7 6 2 8 40	
	31		G3		7 6 2 8 40	—	—

ACCOUNT Depreciation Expense—Building   ACCOUNT NO. 5515

DATE		ITEM	POST. REF.	DEBIT	CREDIT	BALANCE DEBIT	BALANCE CREDIT
20-- Mar.	31	Balance	✓			2 0 8 1 30	
	31		G3		2 0 8 1 30	—	—

ACCOUNT Heat, Light, and Power Expense   ACCOUNT NO. 5520

DATE		ITEM	POST. REF.	DEBIT	CREDIT	BALANCE DEBIT	BALANCE CREDIT
20-- Mar.	31	Balance	✓			5 7 7 8 50	
	31		G3		5 7 7 8 50	—	—

20-2 APPLICATION PROBLEM (concluded)

[1–5]

GENERAL LEDGER

ACCOUNT Insurance Expense—Factory   ACCOUNT NO. 5525

DATE		ITEM	POST. REF.	DEBIT	CREDIT	BALANCE DEBIT	BALANCE CREDIT
20-- Mar.	31	Balance	✓			9 7 3 70	
	31		G3		9 7 3 70	—	—

ACCOUNT Miscellaneous Expense—Factory   ACCOUNT NO. 5530

DATE		ITEM	POST. REF.	DEBIT	CREDIT	BALANCE DEBIT	BALANCE CREDIT
20-- Mar.	31	Balance	✓			6 0 9 50	
	31		G3		6 0 9 50	—	—

ACCOUNT Payroll Taxes Expense—Factory   ACCOUNT NO. 5535

DATE		ITEM	POST. REF.	DEBIT	CREDIT	BALANCE DEBIT	BALANCE CREDIT
20-- Mar.	31	Balance	✓			17 1 5 4 20	
	31		G3		17 1 5 4 20	—	—

ACCOUNT Property Tax Expense—Factory   ACCOUNT NO. 5540

DATE		ITEM	POST. REF.	DEBIT	CREDIT	BALANCE DEBIT	BALANCE CREDIT
20-- Mar.	31	Balance	✓			3 7 8 1 70	
	31		G3		3 7 8 1 70	—	—

ACCOUNT Supplies Expense—Factory   ACCOUNT NO. 5545

DATE		ITEM	POST. REF.	DEBIT	CREDIT	BALANCE DEBIT	BALANCE CREDIT
20-- Mar.	31	Balance	✓			8 0 4 3 10	
	31		G3		8 0 4 3 10		

20-3 APPLICATION PROBLEM, p. 566

Preparing a statement of cost of goods manufactured

The ledger and journals prepared in Application Problem 20-2 are needed to complete this problem.

Cramer Corporation

Statement of Cost of Goods Manufactured

For Month Ended March 31, 20--

Direct Materials	139	4 1 9	80
Direct Labor	102	5 7 0	00
Factory Overhead Applied	69	7 4 7	60
Total Cost of Work Placed in Process	311	7 3 7	40
Work in Process Inventory, March 1, 20--	17	7 8 1	00
Total Cost of Work in Process During March	329	5 1 8	40
Less Work in Process Inventory, March 31, 20--	35	2 0 4	90
Cost of Goods Manufactured	294	3 1 3	50

20-3 APPLICATION PROBLEM

Extra form

20-4 MASTERY PROBLEM, p. 566

Journalizing entries that summarize cost records at the end of a fiscal period [1]

CASH PAYMENTS JOURNAL

PAGE 10

	DATE	ACCOUNT TITLE	CK. NO.	POST. REF.	GENERAL DEBIT	GENERAL CREDIT	ACCOUNTS PAYABLE DEBIT	PURCHASES DISCOUNT CREDIT	CASH CREDIT	
1	20-- May 31	Work in Process	711	1130	5816000				6260810	1
2		Factory Overhead		5505	1927000					2
3		Employee Income Tax Payable		2110		862750				3
4		Social Security Tax Payable		2120		503295				4
5		Medicare Tax Payable		2125		116145				5
6										6
7										7
8										8
9										9
10										10
11										11
12										12
13										13
14										14
15										15
16										16
17										17
18										18
19										19
20										20
21										21
22										22
23										23
24										24
25										25

20-4 MASTERY PROBLEM (continued)

[2–5]

GENERAL JOURNAL   PAGE 5

	DATE		ACCOUNT TITLE	DOC. NO.	POST. REF.	DEBIT	CREDIT	
1	20-- May	31	Work in Process	M211	1130	64 3 4 4 00		1
2			Factory Overhead		5505	5 8 3 5 00		2
3			Materials		1125		70 1 7 9 00	3
4		31	Factory Overhead	M212	5505	21 8 6 7 80		4
5			Depreciation Expense—Factory Equipment		5510		1 4 7 3 60	5
6			Depreciation Expense—Building		5515		7 2 0 00	6
7			Heat, Light, and Power Expense		5520		2 3 1 0 00	7
8			Insurance Expense—Factory		5525		3 8 4 00	8
9			Miscellaneous Expense—Factory		5530		3 2 0 00	9
10			Payroll Taxes Expense		5535		10 8 4 0 20	10
11			Property Tax Expense—Factory		5540		1 8 1 2 00	11
12			Supplies Expense—Factory		5545		4 0 0 8 00	12
13		31	Work in Process	M213	1130	46 5 2 8 00		13
14			Factory Overhead		5505		46 5 2 8 00	14
15		31	Income Summary	M214	3120	4 4 4 80		15
16			Factory Overhead		5505		4 4 4 80	16
17		31	Finished Goods	M215	1135	166 4 2 5 00		17
18			Work in Process		1130		166 4 2 5 00	18
19		31	Cost of Goods Sold	M216	5105	258 7 0 5 00		19
20			Finished Goods		1135		258 7 0 5 00	20
21								21
22								22
23								23
24								24
25								25
26								26
27								27
28								28
29								29
30								30
31								31

20-4 MASTERY PROBLEM (continued)

[1–5]

GENERAL LEDGER

ACCOUNT Materials   **ACCOUNT NO.** 1125

DATE		ITEM	POST. REF.	DEBIT	CREDIT	BALANCE DEBIT	BALANCE CREDIT
20-- May	1	Balance	✓			77 3 1 6 00	
	31		MP5	67 5 8 9 00		144 9 0 5 00	
	31		G5		70 1 7 9 00	74 7 2 6 00	

ACCOUNT Work in Process   **ACCOUNT NO.** 1130

DATE		ITEM	POST. REF.	DEBIT	CREDIT	BALANCE DEBIT	BALANCE CREDIT
20-- May	1	Balance	✓			48 9 6 0 00	
	31		CP10	58 1 6 0 00		107 1 2 0 00	
	31		G5	64 3 4 4 00		171 4 6 4 00	
	31		G5	46 5 2 8 00		217 9 9 2 00	
	31		G5		166 4 2 5 00	51 5 6 7 00	

ACCOUNT Finished Goods   **ACCOUNT NO.** 1135

DATE		ITEM	POST. REF.	DEBIT	CREDIT	BALANCE DEBIT	BALANCE CREDIT
20-- May	1	Balance	✓			120 7 5 0 00	
	31		G5	166 4 2 5 00		287 1 7 5 00	
	31		G5		258 7 0 5 00	28 4 7 0 00	

ACCOUNT Employee Income Tax Payable   **ACCOUNT NO.** 2110

DATE		ITEM	POST. REF.	DEBIT	CREDIT	BALANCE DEBIT	BALANCE CREDIT
20-- May	31		CP10		8 6 2 7 50		8 6 2 7 50

ACCOUNT Social Security Tax Payable   **ACCOUNT NO.** 2120

DATE		ITEM	POST. REF.	DEBIT	CREDIT	BALANCE DEBIT	BALANCE CREDIT
20-- May	31		CP10		5 0 3 2 95		5 0 3 2 95

ACCOUNT Medicare Tax Payable   **ACCOUNT NO.** 2125

DATE		ITEM	POST. REF.	DEBIT	CREDIT	BALANCE DEBIT	BALANCE CREDIT
20-- May	31		CP10		1 1 6 1 45		1 1 6 1 45

20-4 MASTERY PROBLEM (continued)

[1-5]

GENERAL LEDGER

ACCOUNT Income Summary   ACCOUNT NO. 3120

DATE		ITEM	POST. REF.	DEBIT	CREDIT	BALANCE DEBIT	BALANCE CREDIT
20-- May	31		G5	4 4 4 80		4 4 4 80	

ACCOUNT Cost of Goods Sold   ACCOUNT NO. 5105

DATE		ITEM	POST. REF.	DEBIT	CREDIT	BALANCE DEBIT	BALANCE CREDIT
20-- May	31		G5	258 7 0 5 00		258 7 0 5 00	

ACCOUNT Factory Overhead   ACCOUNT NO. 5505

DATE		ITEM	POST. REF.	DEBIT	CREDIT	BALANCE DEBIT	BALANCE CREDIT
20-- May	31		CP10	19 2 7 0 00		19 2 7 0 00	
	31		G5	5 8 3 5 00		25 1 0 5 00	
	31		G5	21 8 6 7 80		46 9 7 2 80	
	31		G5		46 5 2 8 00	4 4 4 80	
	31		G5		4 4 4 80	—	—

ACCOUNT Depreciation Expense—Factory Equipment   ACCOUNT NO. 5510

DATE		ITEM	POST. REF.	DEBIT	CREDIT	BALANCE DEBIT	BALANCE CREDIT
20-- May	31	Balance	✓			1 4 7 3 60	
	31		G5		1 4 7 3 60	—	—

ACCOUNT Depreciation Expense—Building   ACCOUNT NO. 5515

DATE		ITEM	POST. REF.	DEBIT	CREDIT	BALANCE DEBIT	BALANCE CREDIT
20-- May	31	Balance	✓			7 2 0 00	
	31		G5		7 2 0 00	—	—

ACCOUNT Heat, Light, and Power Expense   ACCOUNT NO. 5520

DATE		ITEM	POST. REF.	DEBIT	CREDIT	BALANCE DEBIT	BALANCE CREDIT
20-- May	31	Balance	✓			2 3 1 0 00	
	31		G5		2 3 1 0 00	—	—

20-4 MASTERY PROBLEM (continued)

[1–5]

GENERAL LEDGER

ACCOUNT Insurance Expense—Factory   ACCOUNT NO. 5525

DATE		ITEM	POST. REF.	DEBIT	CREDIT	BALANCE DEBIT	BALANCE CREDIT
20-- May	31	Balance	✓			3 8 4 00	
	31		G5		3 8 4 00	—	—

ACCOUNT Miscellaneous Expense—Factory   ACCOUNT NO. 5530

DATE		ITEM	POST. REF.	DEBIT	CREDIT	BALANCE DEBIT	BALANCE CREDIT
20-- May	31	Balance	✓			3 2 0 00	
	31		G5		3 2 0 00	—	—

ACCOUNT Payroll Taxes Expense—Factory   ACCOUNT NO. 5535

DATE		ITEM	POST. REF.	DEBIT	CREDIT	BALANCE DEBIT	BALANCE CREDIT
20-- May	31	Balance	✓			10 8 4 0 20	
	31		G5		10 8 4 0 20	—	—

ACCOUNT Property Tax Expense—Factory   ACCOUNT NO. 5540

DATE		ITEM	POST. REF.	DEBIT	CREDIT	BALANCE DEBIT	BALANCE CREDIT
20-- May	31	Balance	✓			1 8 1 2 00	
	31		G5		1 8 1 2 00	—	—

ACCOUNT Supplies Expense—Factory   ACCOUNT NO. 5545

DATE		ITEM	POST. REF.	DEBIT	CREDIT	BALANCE DEBIT	BALANCE CREDIT
20-- May	31	Balance	✓			4 0 0 8 00	
	31		G5		4 0 0 8 00	—	—

20-4 MASTERY PROBLEM (concluded)

[6]

Simmons Corporation

Statement of Cost of Goods Manufactured

For Month Ended May 31, 20--

Direct Materials	64	3	4	4	00
Direct Labor	58	1	6	0	00
Factory Overhead Applied	46	5	2	8	00
Total Cost of Work Placed in Process	169	0	3	2	00
Work in Process Inventory, May 1, 20--	48	9	6	0	00
Total Cost of Work in Process During May	217	9	9	2	00
Less Work in Process Inventory, May 31, 20--	51	5	6	7	00
Cost of Goods Manufactured	166	4	2	5	00

20-5 CHALLENGE PROBLEM, p. 567

Journalizing entries that summarize cost records at the end of a fiscal period; preparing financial statements [1]

CASH PAYMENTS JOURNAL

PAGE 14

	DATE	ACCOUNT TITLE	CK. NO.	POST. REF.	GENERAL DEBIT	GENERAL CREDIT	ACCOUNTS PAYABLE DEBIT	PURCHASES DISCOUNT CREDIT	CASH CREDIT	
1	20-- July 31	Work in Process	341	1130	4660000				5103000	1
2		Factory Overhead		5505	1640000					2
3		Employee Income Tax Payable		2110		693000				3
4		Social Security Tax Payable		2120		409500				4
5		Medicare Tax Payable		2125		94500				5
6										6
7										7
8										8
9										9
10										10
11										11
12										12
13										13
14										14
15										15
16										16
17										17
18										18
19										19
20										20
21										21
22										22
23										23
24										24
25										25

20-5 CHALLENGE PROBLEM (continued)

[2-5]

GENERAL JOURNAL   PAGE 7

	DATE		ACCOUNT TITLE	DOC. NO.	POST. REF.	DEBIT	CREDIT	
1	20-- July	31	Work in Process	M698	1130	67 76 0 00		1
2			Factory Overhead		5505	6 99 0 00		2
3			Materials		1125		74 75 0 00	3
4		31	Factory Overhead	M699	5505	20 688 17		4
5			Depreciation Expense—Factory Equipment		5510		2 179 34	5
6			Depreciation Expense—Building		5515		1 618 75	6
7			Heat, Light, and Power Expense		5520		3 822 24	7
8			Insurance Expense—Factory		5525		1 352 60	8
9			Miscellaneous Expense—Factory		5530		1 566 65	9
10			Payroll Taxes Expense—Factory		5535		6 993 00	10
11			Property Tax Expense—Factory		5540		1 355 55	11
12			Supplies Expense—Factory		5545		1 800 04	12
13		31	Work in Process	M700	1130	44 270 00		13
14			Factory Overhead		5505		44 270 00	14
15		31	Factory Overhead	M701	5505	1 91 83		15
16			Income Summary		3120		1 91 83	16
17		31	Finished Goods	M702	1135	140 984 00		17
18			Work in Process		1130		140 984 00	18
19		31	Cost of Goods Sold	M703	5105	112 176 83		19
20			Finished Goods		1135		112 176 83	20
21								21
22								22
23								23
24								24
25								25
26								26
27								27
28								28
29								29
30								30
31								31

20-5 CHALLENGE PROBLEM (continued)

[1-5]

GENERAL LEDGER

ACCOUNT Materials   ACCOUNT NO. 1125

DATE		ITEM	POST. REF.	DEBIT	CREDIT	BALANCE DEBIT	BALANCE CREDIT
20-- July	1	Balance	✓			35 6 1 2 28	
	31		MP7	83 2 5 0 00		118 8 6 2 28	
	31		G7		74 7 5 0 00	44 1 1 2 28	

ACCOUNT Work in Process   ACCOUNT NO. 1130

DATE		ITEM	POST. REF.	DEBIT	CREDIT	BALANCE DEBIT	BALANCE CREDIT
20-- July	1	Balance	✓			20 2 1 4 00	
	31		CP14	46 6 0 0 00		66 8 1 4 00	
	31		G7	67 7 6 0 00		134 5 7 4 00	
	31		G7	44 2 7 0 00		178 8 4 4 00	
	31		G7		140 9 8 4 00	37 8 6 0 00	

ACCOUNT Finished Goods   ACCOUNT NO. 1135

DATE		ITEM	POST. REF.	DEBIT	CREDIT	BALANCE DEBIT	BALANCE CREDIT
20-- July	1	Balance	✓			38 4 0 9 28	
	31		G7	140 9 8 4 00		179 3 9 3 28	
	31		G7		112 1 7 6 83	67 2 1 6 45	

ACCOUNT Employee Income Tax Payable   ACCOUNT NO. 2110

DATE		ITEM	POST. REF.	DEBIT	CREDIT	BALANCE DEBIT	BALANCE CREDIT
20-- July	31		CP14		6 9 3 0 00		6 9 3 0 00

ACCOUNT Social Security Tax Payable   ACCOUNT NO. 2120

DATE		ITEM	POST. REF.	DEBIT	CREDIT	BALANCE DEBIT	BALANCE CREDIT
20-- July	31		CP14		4 0 9 5 00		4 0 9 5 00

ACCOUNT Medicare Tax Payable   ACCOUNT NO. 2125

DATE		ITEM	POST. REF.	DEBIT	CREDIT	BALANCE DEBIT	BALANCE CREDIT
20-- July	31		CP14		9 4 5 00		9 4 5 00

20-5 CHALLENGE PROBLEM (continued)

[1–5]

GENERAL LEDGER

ACCOUNT Income Summary ACCOUNT NO. 3120

DATE		ITEM	POST. REF.	DEBIT	CREDIT	BALANCE	
						DEBIT	CREDIT
20-- July	31		G7		1 9 1 83		1 9 1 83

ACCOUNT Cost of Goods Sold ACCOUNT NO. 5105

DATE		ITEM	POST. REF.	DEBIT	CREDIT	BALANCE	
						DEBIT	CREDIT
20-- July	31		G7	112 1 7 6 83		112 1 7 6 83	

ACCOUNT Factory Overhead ACCOUNT NO. 5505

DATE		ITEM	POST. REF.	DEBIT	CREDIT	BALANCE	
						DEBIT	CREDIT
20-- July	31		CP14	16 4 0 0 00		16 4 0 0 00	
	31		G7	6 9 9 0 00		23 3 9 0 00	
	31		G7	20 6 8 8 17		44 0 7 8 17	
	31		G7		44 2 7 0 00		1 9 1 83
	31		G7	1 9 1 83		—	—

ACCOUNT Depreciation Expense—Factory Equipment ACCOUNT NO. 5510

DATE		ITEM	POST. REF.	DEBIT	CREDIT	BALANCE	
						DEBIT	CREDIT
20-- July	31	Balance	✓			2 1 7 9 34	
	31		G7		2 1 7 9 34	—	—

ACCOUNT Depreciation Expense—Building ACCOUNT NO. 5515

DATE		ITEM	POST. REF.	DEBIT	CREDIT	BALANCE	
						DEBIT	CREDIT
20-- July	31	Balance	✓			1 6 1 8 75	
	31		G7		1 6 1 8 75	—	—

ACCOUNT Heat, Light, and Power Expense ACCOUNT NO. 5520

DATE		ITEM	POST. REF.	DEBIT	CREDIT	BALANCE	
						DEBIT	CREDIT
20-- July	31	Balance	✓			3 8 2 2 24	
	31		G7		3 8 2 2 24	—	—

20-5 CHALLENGE PROBLEM (continued)

[1–6]

GENERAL LEDGER

ACCOUNT Insurance Expense—Factory   ACCOUNT NO. 5525

DATE		ITEM	POST. REF.	DEBIT	CREDIT	BALANCE DEBIT	BALANCE CREDIT
20-- July	31	Balance	✓			1 3 5 2 60	
	31		G7		1 3 5 2 60		

ACCOUNT Miscellaneous Expense—Factory   ACCOUNT NO. 5530

DATE		ITEM	POST. REF.	DEBIT	CREDIT	BALANCE DEBIT	BALANCE CREDIT
20-- July	31	Balance	✓			1 5 6 6 65	
	31		G7		1 5 6 6 65		

ACCOUNT Payroll Taxes Expense—Factory   ACCOUNT NO. 5535

DATE		ITEM	POST. REF.	DEBIT	CREDIT	BALANCE DEBIT	BALANCE CREDIT
20-- July	31	Balance	✓			6 9 9 3 00	
	31		G7		6 9 9 3 00		

ACCOUNT Property Tax Expense—Factory   ACCOUNT NO. 5540

DATE		ITEM	POST. REF.	DEBIT	CREDIT	BALANCE DEBIT	BALANCE CREDIT
20-- July	31	Balance	✓			1 3 5 5 55	
	31		G7		1 3 5 5 55		

ACCOUNT Supplies Expense—Factory   ACCOUNT NO. 5545

DATE		ITEM	POST. REF.	DEBIT	CREDIT	BALANCE DEBIT	BALANCE CREDIT
20-- July	31	Balance	✓			1 8 0 0 04	
	31		G7		1 8 0 0 04		

Cozart Company	
Statement of Cost of Goods Manufactured	
For Month Ended July 31, 20--	

Direct Materials	67 7 6 0 00
Direct Labor	46 6 0 0 00
Factory Overhead Applied	44 2 7 0 00
Total Cost of Work Placed in Process	158 6 3 0 00
Work in Process Inventory, July 1, 20--	20 2 1 4 00
Total Cost of Work in Process During July	178 8 4 4 00
Less Work in Process Inventory, July 31, 20--	37 8 6 0 00
Cost of Goods Manufactured	140 9 8 4 00

20-5 CHALLENGE PROBLEM (continued)

[7]

Cozart Company
Work Sheet
For Month Ended July 31, 20--

#	ACCOUNT TITLE	TRIAL BALANCE DEBIT	TRIAL BALANCE CREDIT	ADJUSTMENTS DEBIT	ADJUSTMENTS CREDIT	INCOME STATEMENT DEBIT	INCOME STATEMENT CREDIT	BALANCE SHEET DEBIT	BALANCE SHEET CREDIT
1	Cash	6306156						6306156	
2	Petty Cash	37500						37500	
3	Accounts Receivable	11530030						11530030	
4	Allowance for Uncollectible Accounts		281965		(a) 76275				358240
5	Materials	4411228						4411228	
6	Work in Process	3786000						3786000	
7	Finished Goods	6721645						6721645	
8	Supplies—Factory	247455						247455	
9	Supplies—Sales	310703			(b) 134453			176250	
10	Supplies—Administrative	79420			(c) 27346			52074	
11	Prepaid Insurance	142223			(d) 3893			138330	
12	Factory Equipment	10300500						10300500	
13	Accum. Depr.—Factory Equipment		2811600						2811600
14	Office Equipment	861300						861300	
15	Accum. Depr.—Office Equipment		276930		(e) 6851				283781
16	Store Equipment	777150						777150	
17	Accum. Depr.—Store Equipment		288456		(f) 6188				294644
18	Building	23760000						23760000	
19	Accum. Depr.—Building		2376000						2376000
20	Land	9944589						9944589	
21	Accounts Payable		1653586						1653586
22	Employee Income Tax Payable		989072						989072
23	Federal Income Tax Payable				(g) 780700				780700
24	Social Security Tax Payable		1168885						1168885
25	Medicare Tax Payable		269743						269743
26	Unemployment Tax Payable—Federal		107880						107880
27	Unemployment Tax Payable—State		728190						728190
28	Mortgage Payable		5625000						5625000
29	Capital Stock		45000000						45000000
30	Retained Earnings		14596058						14596058
31	Income Summary		19183				19183		
32	Sales		18358000				18358000		
33	Cost of Goods Sold	11217683				11217683			

20-5 CHALLENGE PROBLEM (continued)

	ACCOUNT TITLE	TRIAL BALANCE DEBIT	TRIAL BALANCE CREDIT	ADJUSTMENTS DEBIT	ADJUSTMENTS CREDIT	INCOME STATEMENT DEBIT	INCOME STATEMENT CREDIT	BALANCE SHEET DEBIT	BALANCE SHEET CREDIT
34	Factory Overhead								
35	Depr. Expense—Factory Equipment								
36	Depr. Expense—Building								
37	Heat, Light, and Power Expense								
38	Insurance Expense—Factory								
39	Miscellaneous Expense—Factory								
40	Payroll Taxes Expense—Factory								
41	Property Tax Expense—Factory								
42	Supplies Expense—Factory								
43	Advertising Expense	241605				241605			
44	Delivery Expense	584224				584224			
45	Depr. Expense—Store Equipment			(f) 6188		6188			
46	Miscellaneous Expense—Sales	150033				150033			
47	Salary Expense—Sales	1160438				1160438			
48	Supplies Expense—Sales			(b) 134453		134453			
49	Depr. Expense—Office Equipment			(e) 6851		6851			
50	Insurance Expense—Admin.			(d) 3893		3893			
51	Miscellaneous Expense—Admin.	156141				156141			
52	Payroll Taxes Expense—Admin.	252995				252995			
53	Property Tax Expense—Admin.	9259				9259			
54	Salary Expense—Admin.	1530990				1530990			
55	Supplies Expense—Admin.			(c) 27346		27346			
56	Uncollectible Accounts Expense			(a) 76275		76275			
57	Gain on Plant Assets		15593				15593		
58	Miscellaneous Revenue								
59	Interest Expense	46874				46874			
60	Loss on Plant Assets								
61	Federal Income Tax Expense			(g) 780700		780700			
62		94566141	94566141	1035706	1035706	16385948	18392776	79050207	77043379
63	Net Inc. after Fed. Inc. Tax					2006828			2006828
64						18392776	18392776	79050207	79050207
65									
66									

20-5 CHALLENGE PROBLEM

Extra form

[7]

ACCOUNT TITLE	TRIAL BALANCE		ADJUSTMENTS		INCOME STATEMENT		BALANCE SHEET	
	DEBIT	CREDIT	DEBIT	CREDIT	DEBIT	CREDIT	DEBIT	CREDIT
	1	2	3	4	5	6	7	8

20-5 CHALLENGE PROBLEM (continued)

[8]

Cozart Company

Income Statement

For Month Ended July 31, 20--

															% OF NET SALES
Operating Revenue:															
Sales										183	5	8	0	00	100.0
Cost of Goods Sold:															
Finished Goods Inventory, July 1, 20--						38	4	0	9	28					
Cost of Goods Manufactured						140	9	8	4	00					
Total Cost of Finished Goods Available for Sale						179	3	9	3	28					
Less Finished Goods Inventory, July 31, 20--						67	2	1	6	45					
Cost of Goods Sold						112	1	7	6	83					
Overapplied Overhead							1	9	1	83					
Net Cost of Goods Sold											111	9	8	5	00	61.0
Gross Profit on Operations											71	5	9	5	00	39.0
Operating Expenses:															
Selling Expenses:															
Advertising Expense	2	4	1	6	05										
Delivery Expense	5	8	4	2	24										
Depreciation Expense—Store Equipment			6	1	88										
Miscellaneous Expense—Sales	1	5	0	0	33										
Salary Expense—Sales	11	6	0	4	38										
Supplies Expense—Sales	1	3	4	4	53										
Total Selling Expenses						22	7	6	9	41					
Administrative Expenses:															
Depreciation Expense—Office Equipment			6	8	51										
Insurance Expense—Administrative			3	8	93										
Miscellaneous Expense—Administrative	1	5	6	1	41										
Payroll Taxes Expense—Administrative	2	5	2	9	95										
Property Tax Expense—Administrative			9	2	59										
Salary Expense—Administrative	15	3	0	9	90										
Supplies Expense—Administrative		2	7	3	46										
Uncollectible Accounts Expense		7	6	2	75										
Total Administrative Expenses						20	6	3	7	50					

20-5 CHALLENGE PROBLEM (continued)

[8]

Cozart Company

Income Statement (continued)

For Month Ended July 31, 20--

																	% OF NET SALES
Total Operating Expenses													43 4 0 6 91				23.6
Net Income from Operations													28 1 8 8 09				15.4
Other Revenue:																	
Gain on Plant Assets							1 5 5 93										
Other Expense:																	
Interest Expense							4 6 8 74										
Net Deduction													3 1 2 81				0.2
Net Income before Federal Income Tax													27 8 7 5 28				15.2
Less Federal Income Tax Expense													7 8 0 7 00				4.3
Net Income after Federal Income Tax													20 0 6 8 28				10.9

20-5 CHALLENGE PROBLEM (continued)

[9]

Cozart Company

Balance Sheet

July 31, 20--

ASSETS								
Current Assets:								
Cash					63 0 6 1 56			
Petty Cash					3 7 5 00			
Accounts Receivable	115 3 0 0 30							
Less Allowance for Uncollectible Accounts	3 5 8 2 40				111 7 1 7 90			
Materials					44 1 1 2 28			
Work in Process					37 8 6 0 00			
Finished Goods					67 2 1 6 45			
Supplies—Factory					2 4 7 4 55			
Supplies—Sales					1 7 6 2 50			
Supplies—Administrative					5 2 0 74			
Prepaid Insurance					1 3 8 3 30			
Total Current Assets						330 4 8 4 28		
Plant Assets:								
Factory Equipment	103 0 0 5 00							
Less Accumulated Depr.—Factory Equipment	28 1 1 6 00				74 8 8 9 00			
Office Equipment	8 6 1 3 00							
Less Accumulated Depr.—Office Equipment	2 8 3 7 81				5 7 7 5 19			
Store Equipment	7 7 7 1 50							
Less Accumulated Depr.—Store Equipment	2 9 4 6 44				4 8 2 5 06			
Building	237 6 0 0 00							
Less Accumulated Depr.—Building	23 7 6 0 00				213 8 4 0 00			
Land					99 4 4 5 89			
Total Plant Assets						398 7 7 5 14		
Total Assets						729 2 5 9 42		
LIABILITIES								
Current Liabilities:								
Accounts Payable					16 5 3 5 86			
Employee Income Tax Payable					9 8 9 0 72			
Federal Income Tax Payable					7 8 0 7 00			

20-5 CHALLENGE PROBLEM (concluded)

[9]

Cozart Company

Balance Sheet (continued)

July 31, 20--

Social Security Tax Payable		11 6 8 8 85		
Medicare Tax Payable		2 6 9 7 43		
Unemployment Tax Payable—Federal		1 0 7 8 80		
Unemployment Tax Payable—State		7 2 8 1 90		
Total Current Liabilities			56 9 8 0 56	
Long-Term Liability:				
Mortgage Payable			56 2 5 0 00	
Total Liabilities			113 2 3 0 56	
STOCKHOLDERS' EQUITY				
Capital Stock	450 0 0 0 00			
Retained Earnings	166 0 2 8 86			
Total Stockholders' Equity			616 0 2 8 86	
Total Liabilities and Stockholders' Equity			729 2 5 9 42	

3 REINFORCEMENT ACTIVITY, p. 570

Processing and reporting cost accounting data for a manufacturing business

[1]

Estimated Factory Overhead	÷	Estimated Direct Labor Cost	=	Factory Overhead Applied Rate (as % of Direct Labor Cost)
$306,000.00	÷	$255,000.00 (17,000 DL hours × $15.00/hr)	=	120%

[2, 4]

MATERIALS PURCHASES JOURNAL   PAGE 1

	DATE		ACCOUNT CREDITED	PURCH. NO.	POST. REF.	MATERIALS DR. ACCTS. PAY. CR.	
1	20-- Jan.	10	Plastics Unlimited	521		12 0 0 0 00	1
2		12	Wood Craft, Inc.	520		6 0 0 0 00	2
3		12	Wheels Galore	522		2 0 0 0 00	3
4		12	Simpson Company	525		3 0 0 00	4
5		21	Cal Adhesives	524		1 6 0 0 00	5
6		21	Simpson Company	526		7 5 0 00	6
7		24	Simpson Company	523		1 0 0 0 00	7
8		31	Simpson Company	527		3 0 0 00	8
9		31	Grant Hardware Supplies	519		1 2 0 0 00	9
10		31	Total			25 1 5 0 00	10
11						(1125) (2105)	11
12							12
13							13
14							14
15							15
16							16
17							17
18							18
19							19
20							20
21							21
22							22
23							23

3 REINFORCEMENT ACTIVITY (continued)

[2, 6–9]

GENERAL JOURNAL   PAGE 1

	DATE		ACCOUNT TITLE	DOC. NO.	POST. REF.	DEBIT	CREDIT	
1	20-- Jan.	17	Payroll Taxes Expense–Factory	M308	5535	1 9 4 2 56		1
2			Social Security Tax Payable		2120		8 8 9 20	2
3			Medicare Tax Payable		2125		2 0 5 20	3
4			Unemployment Tax Pay.—Fed.		2130		1 0 9 44	4
5			Unemployment Tax Pay.—State		2135		7 3 8 72	5
6		31	Payroll Taxes Expense—Factory	M345	5535	2 2 7 6 97		6
7			Social Security Tax Payable		2120		1 0 4 2 28	7
8			Medicare Tax Payable		2125		2 4 0 52	8
9			Unemployment Tax Pay.—Fed.		2130		1 2 8 28	9
10			Unemployment Tax Pay.—State		2135		8 6 5 89	10
11		31	Work in Process	M346	1130	33 6 1 9 00		11
12			Factory Overhead		5505	1 1 8 1 00		12
13			Materials		1125		34 8 0 0 00	13
14		31	Factory Overhead	M347	5505	15 6 2 0 25		14
15			Depreciation Exp.—Factory Equip.		5510		2 1 9 6 00	15
16			Depreciation Exp.—Building		5515		1 1 5 3 00	16
17			Heat, Light & Power Exp.		5520		5 2 4 4 20	17
18			Insurance Exp.—Factory		5525		1 9 2 00	18
19			Miscellaneous Exp.—Factory		5530		4 7 0 47	19
20			Payroll Taxes Exp.—Factory		5535		4 2 1 9 53	20
21			Property Tax Exp.—Factory		5540		6 5 9 80	21
22			Supplies Exp.—Factory		5545		1 4 8 5 25	22
23		31	Work in Process	M348	1130	25 3 1 7 00		23
24			Factory Overhead		5505		25 3 1 7 00	24
25		31	Income Summary	M349	3120	1 0 1 75		25
26			Factory Overhead		5505		1 0 1 75	26
27		31	Finished Goods	M350	1135	73 1 8 1 50		27
28			Work in Process		1130		73 1 8 1 50	28
29		31	Cost of Goods Sold	M351	5105	61 1 3 7 50		29
30			Finished Goods		1135		61 1 3 7 50	30
31								31

3 REINFORCEMENT ACTIVITY (continued)

[2, 5]

CASH PAYMENTS JOURNAL   PAGE 1

	DATE	ACCOUNT TITLE	CK. NO.	POST. REF.	GENERAL DEBIT	GENERAL CREDIT	ACCOUNTS PAYABLE DEBIT	PURCHASES DISCOUNT CREDIT	CASH CREDIT	
1	20-- Jan. 17	Work in Process	782	1130	9712 50				11080 80	1
2		Factory Overhead		5505	3967 50					2
3		Employee Income Tax Payable		2110		1504 80				3
4		Social Security Tax Payable		2120		889 20				4
5		Medicare Tax Payable		2125		205 20				5
6	31	Work in Process	856	1130	11385 00				12988 20	6
7		Factory Overhead		5505	4650 00					7
8		Employee Income Tax Payable		2110		1764 00				8
9		Social Security Tax Payable		2120		1042 28				9
10		Medicare Tax Payable		2125		240 52				10
11	31	Totals			29715 00	5646 00			24069 00	11
12					(✓)	(✓)				12
13										13
14										14
15										15
16										16
17										17
18										18
19										19
20										20
21										21
22										22
23										23
24										24
25										25

3 REINFORCEMENT ACTIVITY (continued)

[4, 6–9]

GENERAL LEDGER

ACCOUNT Materials   **ACCOUNT NO.** 1125

DATE		ITEM	POST. REF.	DEBIT	CREDIT	BALANCE DEBIT	BALANCE CREDIT
20-- Jan.	1	Balance	✓			20 0 4 8 00	
	31		MP1	25 1 5 0 00		45 1 9 8 00	
	31		G1		34 8 0 0 00	10 3 9 8 00	

ACCOUNT Work in Process   **ACCOUNT NO.** 1130

DATE		ITEM	POST. REF.	DEBIT	CREDIT	BALANCE DEBIT	BALANCE CREDIT
20-- Jan.	17	Balance	CP1	9 7 1 2 50		9 7 1 2 50	
	31		CP1	11 3 8 5 00		21 0 9 7 50	
	31		G1	33 6 1 9 00		54 7 1 6 50	
	31		G1	25 3 1 7 00		80 0 3 3 50	
	31		G1		73 1 8 1 50	6 8 5 2 00	

ACCOUNT Finished Goods   **ACCOUNT NO.** 1135

DATE		ITEM	POST. REF.	DEBIT	CREDIT	BALANCE DEBIT	BALANCE CREDIT
20-- Jan.	1	Balance	✓			43 1 9 0 00	
	31		G1	73 1 8 1 50		116 3 7 1 50	
	31		G1		61 1 3 7 50	55 2 3 4 00	

ACCOUNT Accounts Payable   **ACCOUNT NO.** 2105

DATE		ITEM	POST. REF.	DEBIT	CREDIT	BALANCE DEBIT	BALANCE CREDIT
20-- Jan.	31	Balance	✓			11 7 7 2 40	
	31		MP1		25 1 5 0 00		13 3 7 7 60

ACCOUNT Employee Income Tax Payable   **ACCOUNT NO.** 2110

DATE		ITEM	POST. REF.	DEBIT	CREDIT	BALANCE DEBIT	BALANCE CREDIT
20-- Jan.	31	Balance	✓				1 6 2 4 10
	17		CP1		1 5 0 4 80		3 1 2 8 90
	31		CP1		1 7 6 4 00		4 8 9 2 90

ACCOUNT Social Security Tax Payable   **ACCOUNT NO.** 2120

DATE		ITEM	POST. REF.	DEBIT	CREDIT	BALANCE DEBIT	BALANCE CREDIT
20-- Jan.	31	Balance	✓				1 8 5 4 21
	17		CP1		8 8 9 20		2 7 4 3 41
	17		G1		8 8 9 20		3 6 3 2 61
	31		CP1		1 0 4 2 28		4 6 7 4 89
	31		G1		1 0 4 2 28		5 7 1 7 17

3 **REINFORCEMENT ACTIVITY (continued)**

[4, 6–9]

GENERAL LEDGER

ACCOUNT Medicare Tax Payable   ACCOUNT NO. 2125

DATE		ITEM	POST. REF.	DEBIT	CREDIT	BALANCE DEBIT	BALANCE CREDIT
20-- Jan.	31	Balance	✓				4 2 7 89
	17		CP1		2 0 5 20		6 3 3 09
	17		G1		2 0 5 20		8 3 8 29
	31		CP1		2 4 0 52		1 0 7 8 81
	31		G1		2 4 0 52		1 3 1 9 33

ACCOUNT Unemployment Tax Payable—Federal   ACCOUNT NO. 2130

DATE		ITEM	POST. REF.	DEBIT	CREDIT	BALANCE DEBIT	BALANCE CREDIT
20-- Jan.	31	Balance	✓				1 1 4 05
	17		G1		1 0 9 44		2 2 3 49
	31		G1		1 2 8 28		3 5 1 77

ACCOUNT Unemployment Tax Payable—State   ACCOUNT NO. 2135

DATE		ITEM	POST. REF.	DEBIT	CREDIT	BALANCE DEBIT	BALANCE CREDIT
20-- Jan.	31	Balance	✓				7 7 0 21
	17		G1		7 3 8 72		1 5 0 8 93
	31		G1		8 6 5 89		2 3 7 4 82

ACCOUNT Income Summary   ACCOUNT NO. 3120

DATE		ITEM	POST. REF.	DEBIT	CREDIT	BALANCE DEBIT	BALANCE CREDIT
20-- Jan.	31		G1	1 0 1 75		1 0 1 75	

ACCOUNT Cost of Goods Sold   ACCOUNT NO. 5105

DATE		ITEM	POST. REF.	DEBIT	CREDIT	BALANCE DEBIT	BALANCE CREDIT
20-- Jan.	31		G1	61 1 3 7 50		61 1 3 7 50	

ACCOUNT Factory Overhead   ACCOUNT NO. 5505

DATE		ITEM	POST. REF.	DEBIT	CREDIT	BALANCE DEBIT	BALANCE CREDIT
20-- Jan.	17		CP1	3 9 6 7 50		3 9 6 7 50	
	31		CP1	4 6 5 0 00		8 6 1 7 50	
	31		G1	1 1 8 1 00		9 7 9 8 50	
	31		G1	15 6 2 0 25		25 4 1 8 75	
	31		G1		25 3 1 7 00	1 0 1 75	
	31		G1		1 0 1 75	—	

3 REINFORCEMENT ACTIVITY (continued)

[4, 6–9]

GENERAL LEDGER

ACCOUNT Depreciation Expense—Factory Equipment   ACCOUNT NO. 5510

DATE		ITEM	POST. REF.	DEBIT	CREDIT	BALANCE DEBIT	BALANCE CREDIT
20-- Jan.	31	Balance	✓			2 1 9 6 00	
	31		G1		2 1 9 6 00		

ACCOUNT Depreciation Expense—Building   ACCOUNT NO. 5515

DATE		ITEM	POST. REF.	DEBIT	CREDIT	BALANCE DEBIT	BALANCE CREDIT
20-- Jan.	31	Balance	✓			1 1 5 3 00	
	31		G1		1 1 5 3 00		

ACCOUNT Heat, Light, and Power Expense   ACCOUNT NO. 5520

DATE		ITEM	POST. REF.	DEBIT	CREDIT	BALANCE DEBIT	BALANCE CREDIT
20-- Jan.	31	Balance	✓			5 2 4 4 20	
	31		G1		5 2 4 4 20		

ACCOUNT Insurance Expense—Factory   ACCOUNT NO. 5525

DATE		ITEM	POST. REF.	DEBIT	CREDIT	BALANCE DEBIT	BALANCE CREDIT
20-- Jan.	31	Balance	✓			1 9 2 00	
	31		G1		1 9 2 00		

ACCOUNT Miscellaneous Expense—Factory   ACCOUNT NO. 5530

DATE		ITEM	POST. REF.	DEBIT	CREDIT	BALANCE DEBIT	BALANCE CREDIT
20-- Jan.	31	Balance	✓			4 7 0 47	
	31		G1		4 7 0 47		

ACCOUNT Payroll Taxes Expense—Factory   ACCOUNT NO. 5535

DATE		ITEM	POST. REF.	DEBIT	CREDIT	BALANCE DEBIT	BALANCE CREDIT
20-- Jan.	17		G1	1 9 4 2 56		1 9 4 2 56	
	31		G1	2 2 7 6 97		4 2 1 9 53	
	31		G1		4 2 1 9 53		

ACCOUNT Property Tax Expense—Factory   ACCOUNT NO. 5540

DATE		ITEM	POST. REF.	DEBIT	CREDIT	BALANCE DEBIT	BALANCE CREDIT
20-- Jan.	31	Balance	✓			6 5 9 80	
	31		G1		6 5 9 80		

ACCOUNT Supplies Expense—Factory   ACCOUNT NO. 5545

DATE		ITEM	POST. REF.	DEBIT	CREDIT	BALANCE DEBIT	BALANCE CREDIT
20-- Jan.	31	Balance	✓			1 4 8 5 25	
	31		G1		1 4 8 5 25		

3 REINFORCEMENT ACTIVITY (continued)

[2, 10]

MATERIALS LEDGER CARD

Article Base Wood   Acct. No. 110

Reorder 30,000   Minimum 10,000   Location B10

ORDERED			RECEIVED					ISSUED					BALANCE			
DATE	PUR-CHASE ORDER NO.	QUAN-TITY	DATE	PUR-CHASE ORDER NO.	QUAN-TITY	UNIT PRICE	VALUE	DATE	REQUI-SITION NO.	QUAN-TITY	UNIT PRICE	VALUE	DATE	QUAN-TITY	UNIT PRICE	VALUE
													20-- Jan. 1	18,000	0.20	3,600.00
								20-- Jan. 3	750	6,000	0.20	1,200.00	3	12,000	0.20	2,400.00
								5	751	4,000	0.20	800.00	5	8,000	0.20	1,600.00
20-- Jan. 5	520	30,000						12	754	6,000	0.20	1,200.00	12	2,000	0.20	400.00
			20-- Jan. 12	520	30,000	0.20	6,000.00						12	32,000	0.20	6,400.00
								14	755	2,400	0.20	480.00	14	29,600	0.20	5,920.00
								18	757	8,000	0.20	1,600.00	18	21,600	0.20	4,320.00
								25	760	2,240	0.20	448.00	25	19,360	0.20	3,872.00
								28	762	4,800	0.20	960.00	28	14,560	0.20	2,912.00

MATERIALS LEDGER CARD

Article Laminate   Acct. No. 120

Reorder 20,000   Minimum 10,000   Location B20

ORDERED			RECEIVED					ISSUED					BALANCE			
DATE	PUR-CHASE ORDER NO.	QUAN-TITY	DATE	PUR-CHASE ORDER NO.	QUAN-TITY	UNIT PRICE	VALUE	DATE	REQUI-SITION NO.	QUAN-TITY	UNIT PRICE	VALUE	DATE	QUAN-TITY	UNIT PRICE	VALUE
													20-- Jan. 1	17,000	0.60	10,200.00
								20-- Jan. 3	750	6,000	0.60	3,600.00	3	11,000	0.60	6,600.00
								5	751	4,000	0.60	2,400.00	5	7,000	0.60	4,200.00
20-- Jan. 5	521	20,000	20-- Jan. 10	521	20,000	0.60	12,000.00						10	27,000	0.60	16,200.00
								12	754	6,000	0.60	3,600.00	12	21,000	0.60	12,600.00
								14	755	2,400	0.60	1,440.00	14	18,600	0.60	11,160.00
								18	757	8,000	0.60	4,800.00	18	10,600	0.60	6,360.00
	24	528	20,000					25	760	2,240	0.60	1,344.00	25	8,360	0.60	5,016.00
								28	762	4,800	0.60	2,880.00	28	3,560	0.60	2,136.00

3 ■ REINFORCEMENT ACTIVITY (continued)

[2, 10]

MATERIALS LEDGER CARD

Article Adhesive   Acct. No. 210

Reorder 1,000   Minimum 520   Location C10

ORDERED			RECEIVED					ISSUED					BALANCE		
DATE	PUR-CHASE ORDER NO.	QUAN-TITY	DATE	PUR-CHASE ORDER NO.	QUAN-TITY	UNIT PRICE	VALUE	DATE	REQUI-SITION NO.	QUAN-TITY	UNIT PRICE	VALUE	DATE	QUAN-TITY	UNIT PRICE	VALUE
													20-- Jan. 1	830.0	1.60	1,328.00
								20-- Jan. 3	750	187.5	1.60	300.00	3	642.50	1.60	1,028.00
								5	751	125.0	1.60	200.00	5	517.5	1.60	828.00
20-- Jan. 7	524	1,000						12	754	187.5	1.60	300.00	12	330.0	1.60	528.00
								14	755	75.0	1.60	120.00	14	255.0	1.60	408.00
								18	757	250.0	1.60	400.00	18	5.0	1.60	8.00
			20-- Jan. 21	524	1,000	1.60	1,600.00						21	1,005.0	1.60	1,608.00
								25	760	70.0	1.60	112.00	25	935.0	1.60	1,496.00
								28	762	150.0	1.60	240.00	28	785.0	1.60	1,256.00

MATERIALS LEDGER CARD

Article Casters   Acct. No. 310

Reorder 1,600   Minimum 800   Location D10

ORDERED			RECEIVED					ISSUED					BALANCE		
DATE	PUR-CHASE ORDER NO.	QUAN-TITY	DATE	PUR-CHASE ORDER NO.	QUAN-TITY	UNIT PRICE	VALUE	DATE	REQUI-SITION NO.	QUAN-TITY	UNIT PRICE	VALUE	DATE	QUAN-TITY	UNIT PRICE	VALUE
													20-- Jan. 1	1,800	1.25	2,250.00
20-- Jan. 7	522	1,600						20-- Jan. 7	752	1,000	1.25	1,250.00	7	800	1.25	1,000.00
								10	753	800	1.25	1,000.00	10	-0-		-0-
			20-- Jan. 12	522	1,600	1.25	2,000.00						12	1,600	1.25	2,000.00
								28	761	640	1.25	800.00	28	960	1.25	1,200.00

MATERIALS LEDGER CARD

Article Metal Glides (set of 2)   Acct. No. 320

Reorder 300   Minimum 100   Location D20

ORDERED			RECEIVED					ISSUED					BALANCE		
DATE	PUR-CHASE ORDER NO.	QUAN-TITY	DATE	PUR-CHASE ORDER NO.	QUAN-TITY	UNIT PRICE	VALUE	DATE	REQUI-SITION NO.	QUAN-TITY	UNIT PRICE	VALUE	DATE	QUAN-TITY	UNIT PRICE	VALUE
													20-- Jan. 1	300	1.00	300.00
								20-- Jan. 10	753	200	1.00	200.00	10	100	1.00	100.00
20-- Jan. 10	525	300	20-- Jan. 12	525	300	1.00	300.00						12	400	1.00	400.00
								21	758	300	1.00	300.00	21	100	1.00	100.00
21	527	300	31	527	300	1.00	300.00						31	400	1.00	400.00

3 REINFORCEMENT ACTIVITY (continued)

[2, 10]

MATERIALS LEDGER CARD

Article Hinges (set of 2) Acct. No. 330

Reorder 1,000 Minimum 300 Location D30

ORDERED			RECEIVED					ISSUED					BALANCE			
DATE	PUR-CHASE ORDER NO.	QUAN-TITY	DATE	PUR-CHASE ORDER NO.	QUAN-TITY	UNIT PRICE	VALUE	DATE	REQUI-SITION NO.	QUAN-TITY	UNIT PRICE	VALUE	DATE	QUAN-TITY	UNIT PRICE	VALUE
													20-- Jan. 1	600	1.00	600.00
20-- Jan. 7	523	1,000						20-- Jan. 18	756	240	1.00	240.00	18	360	1.00	360.00
								21	758	300	1.00	300.00	21	60	1.00	60.00
			20-- Jan. 24	523	1,000	1.00	1,000.00						24	1,060	1.00	1,060.00
								25	759	400	1.00	400.00	25	660	1.00	660.00

MATERIALS LEDGER CARD

Article Fasteners Acct. No. 340

Reorder 1,000 Minimum 600 Location D40

ORDERED			RECEIVED					ISSUED					BALANCE			
DATE	PUR-CHASE ORDER NO.	QUAN-TITY	DATE	PUR-CHASE ORDER NO.	QUAN-TITY	UNIT PRICE	VALUE	DATE	REQUI-SITION NO.	QUAN-TITY	UNIT PRICE	VALUE	DATE	QUAN-TITY	UNIT PRICE	VALUE
													20-- Jan. 1	560	0.75	420.00
20-- Jan. 10	526	1,000						20-- Jan. 18	756	240	0.75	180.00	18	320	0.75	240.00
								21	758	300	0.75	225.00	21	20	0.75	15.00
			20-- Jan. 21	526	1,000	0.75	750.00						21	1,020	0.75	765.00
								25	759	400	0.75	300.00	25	620	0.75	465.00

3 REINFORCEMENT ACTIVITY (continued)

[2, 3, 10]

COST SHEET

Job No. 232

Item C200 Computer Desk

No. of items 250

Ordered for Stock

Date January 3, 20--

Date wanted January 12, 20--

Date completed January 11, 20--

DIRECT MATERIALS		DIRECT LABOR				SUMMARY	
REQ. NO.	AMOUNT	DATE	AMOUNT	DATE	AMOUNT	ITEM	AMOUNT
750	$5,100.00	20-- Jan. 7	$3,300.00			Direct Materials	$ 6,350.00
752	1,250.00	11	1,387.50			Direct Labor	4,687.50
	$6,350.00		$4,687.50			Factory Overhead	
						(120% of direct	
						labor costs)	5,625.00
						Total Cost	$16,662.50
						No. of units finished	250
						Cost per unit	$66.65

COST SHEET

Job No. 233

Item P150 Printer Table

No. of items 200

Ordered for Stock

Date January 5, 20--

Date wanted January 17, 20--

Date completed January 14, 20--

DIRECT MATERIALS		DIRECT LABOR				SUMMARY	
REQ. NO.	AMOUNT	DATE	AMOUNT	DATE	AMOUNT	ITEM	AMOUNT
751	$3,400.00	20-- Jan. 7	$1,125.00			Direct Materials	$ 4,600.00
753	1,200.00	14	1,875.00			Direct Labor	3,000.00
	$4,600.00		$3,000.00			Factory Overhead	
						(120% of direct	
						labor costs)	3,600.00
						Total Cost	$11,200.00
						No. of units finished	200
						Cost per unit	$56.00

3 REINFORCEMENT ACTIVITY (continued)

[2, 3, 10]

COST SHEET

Job No. 234

Item E400 Entertainment Center

No. of items 120

Ordered for Stock

Date January 12, 20--

Date wanted January 18, 20--

Date completed January 19, 20--

DIRECT MATERIALS		DIRECT LABOR				SUMMARY	
REQ. NO.	AMOUNT	DATE	AMOUNT	DATE	AMOUNT	ITEM	AMOUNT
754	$5,100.00	20-- Jan. 14	$1,800.00			Direct Materials	$ 5,520.00
756	420.00	19	1,800.00			Direct Labor	3,600.00
	$5,520.00		$3,600.00			Factory Overhead	
						(120% of direct	
						labor cost)	4,320.00
						Total Cost	$13,440.00
						No. of units finished	120
						Cost per unit	$112.00

COST SHEET

Job No. 235

Item V110 Video Tape Cabinet

No. of items 150

Ordered for Stock

Date January 14, 20--

Date wanted January 27, 20--

Date completed January 27, 20--

DIRECT MATERIALS		DIRECT LABOR				SUMMARY	
REQ. NO.	AMOUNT	DATE	AMOUNT	DATE	AMOUNT	ITEM	AMOUNT
755	$2,040.00	20-- Jan. 14	$ 225.00			Direct Materials	$2,865.00
758	825.00	21	1,125.00			Direct Labor	2,250.00
		27	900.00			Factory Overhead	
	$2,865.00		$2,250.00			(120% of direct	
						labor cost)	2,700.00
						Total Cost	$7,815.00
						No. of units finished	150
						Cost per unit	$52.10

3 REINFORCEMENT ACTIVITY (continued)

[2, 3, 10]

COST SHEET

Job No. 236

Item B160 Book Case

No. of items 200

Ordered for Stock

Date January 18, 20--

Date wanted January 28, 20--

Date completed January 28, 20--

DIRECT MATERIALS		DIRECT LABOR				SUMMARY	
REQ. NO.	AMOUNT	DATE	AMOUNT	DATE	AMOUNT	ITEM	AMOUNT
757	$6,800.00	20-- Jan. 21	$2,250.00			Direct Materials	$ 7,500.00
759	700.00	28	2,250.00			Direct Labor	4,500.00
	$7,500.00		$4,500.00			Factory Overhead	
						(120% of direct	
						labor cost)	5,400.00
						Total Cost	$17,400.00
						No. of units finished	200
						Cost per unit	$87.00

COST SHEET

Job No. 237

Item T120 TV Cart

No. of items 160

Ordered for Stock

Date January 25, 20--

Date wanted January 31, 20--

Date completed January 31, 20--

DIRECT MATERIALS		DIRECT LABOR				SUMMARY	
REQ. NO.	AMOUNT	DATE	AMOUNT	DATE	AMOUNT	ITEM	AMOUNT
760	$1,904.00	20-- Jan. 28	$1,440.00			Direct Materials	$2,704.00
761	800.00	31	360.00			Direct Labor	1,800.00
	$2,704.00		$1,800.00			Factory Overhead	
						(120% of direct	
						labor cost)	2,160.00
						Total Cost	$6,664.00
						No. of units finished	160
						Cost per unit	$41.65

3 REINFORCEMENT ACTIVITY (continued)

[2, 3, 10]

COST SHEET

Job No. 238

Item C200 Computer Desk

No. of items 200

Ordered for Stock

Date January 28, 20--

Date wanted February 8, 20--

Date completed _____

DIRECT MATERIALS		DIRECT LABOR				SUMMARY	
REQ. NO.	AMOUNT	DATE	AMOUNT	DATE	AMOUNT	ITEM	AMOUNT
762	$4,080.00	20-- Jan. 28	$630.00			*Factory Overhead*	
		31	630.00			*for January*	
						(120% of direct	
						labor cost)	$1,512.00

FINISHED GOODS LEDGER CARD

Description Computer Desk

Minimum 100

Stock No. C200

Location J10

MANUFACTURED/RECEIVED					SHIPPED/ISSUED					BALANCE			
DATE	JOB NO.	QUAN-TITY	UNIT COST	TOTAL COST	DATE	SALES INVOICE NO.	QUAN-TITY	UNIT COST	TOTAL COST	DATE	QUAN-TITY	UNIT COST	TOTAL COST
										20-- Jan. 1	150	65.00	9,750.00
					20-- Jan. 10	323	100	65.00	6,500.00	10	50	65.00	3,250.00
20-- Jan. 11	232	250	66.65	16,662.50						11	50	65.00	⌐ 19,912.50
											250	66.65	
					31	329	50	65.00	⌐ 13,247.50	31	100	66.65	6,665.00
							150	66.65					

FINISHED GOODS LEDGER CARD

Description Printer Table

Minimum 50

Stock No. P150

Location J20

MANUFACTURED/RECEIVED					SHIPPED/ISSUED					BALANCE			
DATE	JOB NO.	QUAN-TITY	UNIT COST	TOTAL COST	DATE	SALES INVOICE NO.	QUAN-TITY	UNIT COST	TOTAL COST	DATE	QUAN-TITY	UNIT COST	TOTAL COST
										20-- Jan. 1	50	55.00	2,750.00
20-- Jan. 14	233	200	56.00	11,200.00						14	50	55.00	⌐ 13,950.00
											200	56.00	
					20-- Jan. 17	324	50	55.00	⌐ 8,350.00	17	100	56.00	5,600.00
							100	56.00					

3 REINFORCEMENT ACTIVITY (continued)

[2, 10]

FINISHED GOODS LEDGER CARD

Description Entertainment Center   Stock No. E400

Minimum 50   Location K10

MANUFACTURED/RECEIVED					SHIPPED/ISSUED					BALANCE			
DATE	JOB NO.	QUAN-TITY	UNIT COST	TOTAL COST	DATE	SALES INVOICE NO.	QUAN-TITY	UNIT COST	TOTAL COST	DATE	QUAN-TITY	UNIT COST	TOTAL COST
										20--Jan. 1	40	110.00	4,400.00
20--Jan. 19	234	120	112.00	13,440.00						19	40	110.00	⌐
											120	112.00	17,840.00
					20--Jan. 26	326	40	110.00	⌐				
							50	112.00	10,000.00	26	70	112.00	7,840.00

FINISHED GOODS LEDGER CARD

Description Video Tape Cabinet   Stock No. V110

Minimum 200   Location K20

MANUFACTURED/RECEIVED					SHIPPED/ISSUED					BALANCE			
DATE	JOB NO.	QUAN-TITY	UNIT COST	TOTAL COST	DATE	SALES INVOICE NO.	QUAN-TITY	UNIT COST	TOTAL COST	DATE	QUAN-TITY	UNIT COST	TOTAL COST
										20--Jan. 1	350	51.00	17,850.00
20--Jan. 27	235	150	52.10	7,815.00						27	350	51.00	⌐
											150	52.10	25,665.00
					20--Jan. 27	327	200	51.00	10,200	27	150	51.00	⌐
											150	52.10	15,465.00

FINISHED GOODS LEDGER CARD

Description Book Case   Stock No. B160

Minimum 50   Location L10

MANUFACTURED/RECEIVED					SHIPPED/ISSUED					BALANCE			
DATE	JOB NO.	QUAN-TITY	UNIT COST	TOTAL COST	DATE	SALES INVOICE NO.	QUAN-TITY	UNIT COST	TOTAL COST	DATE	QUAN-TITY	UNIT COST	TOTAL COST
										20--Jan. 1	60	86.00	5,160.00
20--Jan. 28	236	200	87.00	17,400.00						28	60	86.00	⌐
											200	87.00	22,560.00
					20--Jan. 28	328	60	86.00	⌐				
							60	87.00	10,380	28	140	87.00	12,180.00

3   REINFORCEMENT ACTIVITY (continued)

[2, 10]

FINISHED GOODS LEDGER CARD

Description TV Cart   Stock No. T120

Minimum 25   Location L20

MANUFACTURED/RECEIVED					SHIPPED/ISSUED					BALANCE			
DATE	JOB NO.	QUAN-TITY	UNIT COST	TOTAL COST	DATE	SALES INVOICE NO.	QUAN-TITY	UNIT COST	TOTAL COST	DATE	QUAN-TITY	UNIT COST	TOTAL COST
										20-- Jan. 1	80	41.00	3,280.00
					20-- Jan. 20	325	60	41.00	2,460.00	20	20	41.00	820.00
20-- Jan. 31	237	160	41.65	6,664.00						31	20	41.00	⌐
											160	41.65	⌐ 7,484.00

[10]

Direct and Indirect Materials Ledger Proof	Cost Ledger Proof	Finished Goods Ledger Proof
$ 2,912.00	$4,080.00	$ 6,665.00
2,136.00	630.00	5,600.00
1,256.00	630.00	7,840.00
1,200.00	1,512.00	15,465.00
400.00	$6,852.00	12,180.00
660.00		7,484.00
465.00		$55,234.00
1,369.00		
$10,398.00		

[11]

Furniture Decor, Inc.

Statement of Cost of Goods Manufactured

For Month Ended January 31, 20--

Direct Materials	33	6	1	9	00
Direct Labor	21	0	9	7	50
Factory Overhead Applied	25	3	1	7	00
Total Cost of Work Placed in Process	80	0	3	3	50
Work in Process Inventory, January 1, 20--				-0-	
Total Cost of Work in Process During January	80	0	3	3	50
Less Work in Process Inventory, January 31, 20--		6	8	5	2	00
Cost of Goods Manufactured	73	1	8	1	50

3 REINFORCEMENT ACTIVITY (continued)

[12, 13]

Cozart Company
Work Sheet
For Month Ended July 31, 20--

	ACCOUNT TITLE	TRIAL BALANCE DEBIT	TRIAL BALANCE CREDIT	ADJUSTMENTS DEBIT	ADJUSTMENTS CREDIT	INCOME STATEMENT DEBIT	INCOME STATEMENT CREDIT	BALANCE SHEET DEBIT	BALANCE SHEET CREDIT
1	Cash	30 200 50						30 200 50	
2	Petty Cash	25 000						25 000	
3	Accounts Receivable	46 687 50						46 687 50	
4	Allowance for Uncollectible Accounts		80 600		(a) 27 000				107 600
5	Materials	10 398 00						10 398 00	
6	Work in Process	6 852 00						6 852 00	
7	Finished Goods	55 234 00						55 234 00	
8	Supplies—Factory	1 237 25						1 237 25	
9	Supplies—Sales	1 553 50			(b) 44 215			1 111 35	
10	Supplies—Administrative	397 10			(c) 9 463			302 47	
11	Prepaid Insurance	280 80			(d) 23 40			257 40	
12	Factory Equipment	113 100 00						113 100 00	
13	Accum. Depr.—Factory Equipment		33 930 00						33 930 00
14	Office Equipment	4 320 00						4 320 00	
15	Accum. Depr.—Office Equipment		1 296 00		(e) 34 25				1 330 25
16	Store Equipment	3 895 00						3 895 00	
17	Accum. Depr.—Store Equipment		1 363 00		(f) 31 00				1 394 00
18	Building	150 000 00						150 000 00	
19	Accum. Depr.—Building		22 500 00						22 500 00
20	Land	50 600 00						50 600 00	
21	Accounts Payable		13 377 60						13 377 60
22	Employee Income Tax Payable		4 892 90						4 892 90
23	Federal Income Tax Payable				(g) 3 682 38				3 682 38
24	Social Security Tax Payable		5 717 17						5 717 17
25	Medicare Tax Payable		1 319 33						1 319 33
26	Salaries Payable								
27	Unemployment Tax Payable—Federal		351 77						351 77
28	Unemployment Tax Payable—State		2 374 82						2 374 82
29	Dividends Payable								
30	Mortgage Payable		300 000 00						300 000 00

3 REINFORCEMENT ACTIVITY (continued)

[12, 13]

	ACCOUNT TITLE	TRIAL BALANCE DEBIT	TRIAL BALANCE CREDIT	ADJUSTMENTS DEBIT	ADJUSTMENTS CREDIT	INCOME STATEMENT DEBIT	INCOME STATEMENT CREDIT	BALANCE SHEET DEBIT	BALANCE SHEET CREDIT	
31	Capital Stock		2000000 00						2000000 00	31
32	Retained Earnings		143160 56						143160 56	32
33	Dividends									33
34	Income Summary	10175				10175				34
35	Sales		9575000				9575000			35
36	Cost of Goods Sold	6113750				6113750				36
37	Factory Overhead									37
38	Depr. Expense—Factory Equipment									38
39	Depr. Expense—Building									39
40	Heat, Light, and Power Expense									40
41	Insurance Expense—Factory									41
42	Miscellaneous Expense—Factory									42
43	Payroll Taxes Expense—Factory									43
44	Property Tax Expense—Factory									44
45	Supplies Expense—Factory									45
46	Advertising Expense	83595				83595				46
47	Delivery Expense	205345				205345				47
48	Depr. Expense—Store Equipment			(f) 3100		3100				48
49	Miscellaneous Expense—Sales	519910				519910				49
50	Salary Expense—Sales	613325				613325				50
51	Supplies Expense—Sales			(b) 44215		44215				51
52	Depr. Expense—Office Equipment			(e) 3425		3425				52
53	Insurance Expense—Admin.			(d) 2340		2340				53
54	Miscellaneous Expense—Admin.	44185				44185				54
55	Payroll Taxes Expense—Admin.	202535				202535				55
56	Property Tax Expense—Admin.	5690				5690				56
57	Salary Expense—Admin.	813000				813000				57
58	Supplies Expense—Admin.			(c) 9463		9463				58
59	Uncollectible Accounts Expense			(a) 27000		27000				59
60	Utilities Expense—Admin.	9840				9840				60

3 REINFORCEMENT ACTIVITY (continued)

[12, 13]

	ACCOUNT TITLE	TRIAL BALANCE DEBIT	TRIAL BALANCE CREDIT	ADJUSTMENTS DEBIT	ADJUSTMENTS CREDIT	INCOME STATEMENT DEBIT	INCOME STATEMENT CREDIT	BALANCE SHEET DEBIT	BALANCE SHEET CREDIT
61	Gain on Plant Assets								
62	Miscellaneous Revenue								
63	Interest Expense	3 0 0 00				3 0 0 00			
64	Loss on Plant Assets								
65	Federal Income Tax Expense			(8) 3 6 8 2 38		3 6 8 2 38			
66		556 8 3 9 15	556 8 3 9 15	4 5 7 7 81	4 5 7 7 81	86 4 1 1 31	95 7 5 0 00	474 4 4 5 47	465 1 0 6 78
67	Net Inc. after Fed. Inc. Tax					9 3 3 8 69			9 3 3 8 69
68						95 7 5 0 00	95 7 5 0 00	474 4 4 5 47	474 4 4 5 47
69									
70									
71									
72									
73									
74									
75									
76									
77									
78									
79									
80									
81									
82									
83									
84									
85									
86									
87									
88									
89									
90									
91									

3 **REINFORCEMENT ACTIVITY (continued)**

[14]

Furniture Decor, Inc.

Income Statement

For Month Ended January 31, 20--

				% OF NET SALES
Operating Revenue:				
Sales			95 7 5 0 00	100.0
Cost of Goods Sold:				
Finished Goods Inventory, Jan. 1, 20--		43 1 9 0 00		
Cost of Goods Manufactured		73 1 8 1 50		
Total Cost of Finished Goods Available for Sale		116 3 7 1 50		
Less Finished Goods Inventory, Jan. 31, 20--		55 2 3 4 00		
Cost of Goods Sold		61 1 3 7 50		
Underapplied Overhead		1 0 1 75		
Net Cost of Goods Sold			61 2 3 9 25	64.0
Gross Profit on Operations			34 5 1 0 75	36.0
Operating Expenses:				
Selling Expenses:				
Advertising Expense	8 3 5 95			
Delivery Expense	2 0 5 3 45			
Depreciation Expense—Store Equipment	3 1 00			
Miscellaneous Expense—Sales	5 1 9 10			
Salary Expense—Sales	6 1 3 3 25			
Supplies Expense—Sales	4 4 2 15			
Total Selling Expenses		10 0 1 4 90		
Administrative Expenses:				
Depreciation Expense—Office Equipment	3 4 25			
Insurance Expense—Administrative	2 3 40			
Miscellaneous Expense—Administrative	4 4 1 85			
Payroll Taxes Expense—Administrative	2 0 2 5 35			
Property Tax Expense—Administrative	5 6 90			
Salary Expense—Administrative	8 1 3 0 00			
Supplies Expense—Administrative	9 4 63			
Uncollectible Accounts Expense	2 7 0 00			
Utilities Expense—Administrative	9 8 40			
Total Administrative Expenses		11 1 7 4 78		

3 REINFORCEMENT ACTIVITY (continued)

[14]

Furniture Decor, Inc.

Income Statement (continued)

For Month Ended January 31, 20--

									% OF NET SALES
Total Operating Expenses							21 1 8 9 68		22.1
Net Income from Operations							13 3 2 1 07		13.9
Other Expense:									
Interest Expense							3 0 0 00		0.3
Net Income before Federal Income Tax							13 0 2 1 07		13.6
Less Federal Income Tax Expense							3 6 8 2 38		3.8
Net Income after Federal Income Tax							9 3 3 8 69		9.8

3 REINFORCEMENT ACTIVITY (continued)

[15]

Furniture Decor, Inc.

Balance Sheet

January 31, 20--

ASSETS																
Current Assets:																
Cash							30	2	0	0	50					
Petty Cash								2	5	0	00					
Accounts Receivable	46	6	8	7	50											
Less Allowance for Uncollectible Accounts	1	0	7	6	00		45	6	1	1	50					
Materials							10	3	9	8	00					
Work in Process							6	8	5	2	00					
Finished Goods							55	2	3	4	00					
Supplies—Factory							1	2	3	7	25					
Supplies—Sales							1	1	1	1	35					
Supplies—Administrative								3	0	2	47					
Prepaid Insurance								2	5	7	40					
Total Current Assets												151	4	5	4	47
Plant Assets:																
Factory Equipment	113	1	0	0	00											
Less Accumulated Depr.—Factory Equipment	33	9	3	0	00		79	1	7	0	00					
Office Equipment	4	3	2	0	00											
Less Accumulated Depr.—Office Equipment	1	3	3	0	25		2	9	8	9	75					
Store Equipment	3	8	9	5	00											
Less Accumulated Depr.—Store Equipment	1	3	9	4	00		2	5	0	1	00					
Building	150	0	0	0	00											
Less Accumulated Depr.—Building	22	5	0	0	00		127	5	0	0	00					
Land							50	6	0	0	00					
Total Plant Assets												262	7	6	0	75
Total Assets												414	2	1	5	22
LIABILITIES																
Current Liabilities:																
Accounts Payable							13	3	7	7	60					
Employee Income Tax Payable							4	8	9	2	90					
Federal Income Tax Payable							3	6	8	2	38					
Social Security Tax Payable							5	7	1	7	17					
Medicare Tax Payable							1	3	1	9	33					

3 REINFORCEMENT ACTIVITY (concluded)

[15]

Furniture Decor, Inc.

Balance Sheet (continued)

January 31, 20--

Unemployment Tax Payable—Federal			3 5 1 77		
Unemployment Tax Payable—State		2 3 7 4 82		
Total Current Liabilities				31 7 1 5 97	
Long-Term Liability:					
Mortgage Payable				30 0 0 0 00	
Total Liabilities				61 7 1 5 97	
STOCKHOLDERS' EQUITY					
Capital Stock		200 0 0 0 00			
Retained Earnings		152 4 9 9 25			
Total Stockholders' Equity				352 4 9 9 25	
Total Liabilities and Stockholders' Equity				414 2 1 5 22	

21-1 WORK TOGETHER, p. 586

Forming a partnership

Jensen's Boutique
Balance Sheet
March 31, 20--

ASSETS

Current Assets:

Cash		$ 11,371.85	
Accounts Receivable	$ 2,434.95		
Less Allowance for Uncollectible Accounts	73.45	2,361.50	
Merchandise Inventory		24,350.00	
Supplies		620.90	
Total Current Assets			$ 38,704.25
Plant Assets:			
Equipment			8,778.75
Total Assets			$ 47,483.00

LIABILITIES

Accounts Payable			$ 5,483.00

OWNERS' EQUITY

Betty Jensen, Capital			42,000.00
Total Liabilities and Owner's Equity			$ 47,483.00

21-1 WORK TOGETHER (concluded)

[4]

CASH RECEIPTS JOURNAL

PAGE 1

DATE		ACCOUNT TITLE	DOC. NO.	POST. REF.	GENERAL DEBIT	GENERAL CREDIT	ACCOUNTS RECEIVABLE CREDIT	SALES CREDIT	SALES TAX PAYABLE CREDIT	CASH DEBIT	
20-- April	1	Glen Chau, Capital	R1			4200000				4200000	1
	1	Accounts Receivable	R2		2434495					1137185	2
		Merchandise Inventory			2435000						3
		Supplies			62090						4
		Equipment			877875						5
		Allowance for Uncoll. Accounts				7345					6
		Accounts Payable				548300					7
		Betty Jensen, Capital				4200000					8
											9
											10
											11
											12
											13
											14
											15
											16
											17
											18
											19
											20
											21
											22
											23
											24
											25

21-1 ON YOUR OWN, p. 586

Forming a partnership

Rice Patch
Balance Sheet
June 30, 20--

ASSETS			
Current Assets:			
Cash		$ 12,379.10	
Accounts Receivable	$ 3,191.40		
Less Allowance for Uncollectible Accounts	63.80	3,127.60	
Merchandise Inventory		18,402.30	
Supplies		571.25	
Total Current Assets			$ 34,480.25
Plant Assets:			
Equipment			8,076.50
Total Assets			$ 42,556.75
LIABILITIES			
Accounts Payable			$ 10,556.75
OWNERS' EQUITY			
David Rice, Capital			32,000.00
Total Liabilities and Owner's Equity			$ 42,556.75

21-1 ON YOUR OWN (concluded)

[5]

CASH RECEIPTS JOURNAL

PAGE 1

DATE		ACCOUNT TITLE	DOC. NO.	POST. REF.	GENERAL DEBIT (1)	GENERAL CREDIT (2)	ACCOUNTS RECEIVABLE CREDIT (3)	SALES CREDIT (4)	SALES TAX PAYABLE CREDIT (5)	CASH DEBIT (6)
20-- July	1	Tanya Taylor, Capital	R1			3200000				3200000	1
	1	Accounts Receivable	R2		319140					1237910	2
		Merchandise Inventory			1840230						3
		Supplies			57125						4
		Equipment			807650						5
		Allowance for Uncoll. Accounts				6380					6
		Accounts Payable				1055675					7
		David Rice, Capital				3200000					8

21-2 WORK TOGETHER, p. 592

Admitting partners to an existing partnership

[4–7]

GENERAL JOURNAL

PAGE 6

	DATE		ACCOUNT TITLE	DOC. NO.	POST. REF.	DEBIT	CREDIT	
1	20-- Apr.	1	Maria Heath, Capital	M32		8 000 00		1
2			Lisa Curtis, Capital			8 000 00		2
3			Wade Torres, Capital				16 000 00	3
4								4
5								5
6								6
7	20-- Apr.	1	Maria Heath, Capital	M31		5 000 00		7
8			Lisa Curtis, Capital			5 000 00		8
9			Wade Torres, Capital				10 000 00	9
10								10
11								11
12								12
13	20-- Apr.	1	Goodwill	M22		12 000 00		13
14			Maria Heath, Capital				6 000 00	14
15			Lisa Curtis, Capital				6 000 00	15
16								16
17								17
18								18
19								19
20								20
21								21
22								22
23								23
24								24
25								25
26								26
27								27
28								28
29								29
30								30
31								31

21-2 WORK TOGETHER (concluded)

[4–7]

CASH RECEIPTS JOURNAL

PAGE 12

	DATE		ACCOUNT TITLE	DOC. NO.	POST. REF.	GENERAL DEBIT	GENERAL CREDIT	ACCOUNTS RECEIVABLE CREDIT	SALES CREDIT	SALES TAX PAYABLE CREDIT	CASH DEBIT	
1	20-- Apr.	1	Wade Torres, Capital	R101			8000000				8000000	1
2												2
3												3
4												4
5												5
6												6
7	Apr.	1	Wade Torres, Capital	R125			3500000				3500000	7
8												8
9												9
10												10
11												11
12												12
13	Apr.	1	Wade Torres, Capital	R89			4000000				4000000	13
14												14
15												15
16												16
17												17
18												18
19												19
20												20
21												21
22												22
23												23
24												24
25												25

21-2 ON YOUR OWN, p. 593

Admitting partners to an existing partnership [8–11]

GENERAL JOURNAL

PAGE 9

	DATE		ACCOUNT TITLE	DOC. NO.	POST. REF.	DEBIT	CREDIT	
8 1	20-- June	1	Kyle Bowen, Capital	M36		12 00 00 0		1
2			Susan Wong, Capital			12 00 00 0		2
3			Angie Mills, Capital				24 00 00 0	3
4								4
5								5
6								6
10 7	20-- June	1	Kyle Bowen, Capital	M40		2 00 00 0		7
8			Susan Wong, Capital			2 00 00 0		8
9			Angie Mills, Capital				4 00 00 0	9
10								10
11								11
12								12
11 13	20-- June	1	Goodwill	M46		16 00 00 0		13
14			Kyle Bowen, Capital				8 00 00 0	14
15			Susan Wong, Capital				8 00 00 0	15
16								16
17								17
18								18
19								19
20								20
21								21
22								22
23								23
24								24
25								25
26								26
27								27
28								28
29								29
30								30
31								31

21-2 ON YOUR OWN (concluded)

[8–11]

CASH RECEIPTS JOURNAL

PAGE 18

	DATE	ACCOUNT TITLE	DOC. NO.	POST. REF.	GENERAL DEBIT	GENERAL CREDIT	ACCOUNTS RECEIVABLE CREDIT	SALES CREDIT	SALES TAX PAYABLE CREDIT	CASH DEBIT	
1	20-- June 1	Angie Mills, Capital	R142			75000000				75000000	1
2											2
3											3
4											4
5											5
6											6
7	20-- June 1	Angie Mills, Capital	R130			30000000				30000000	7
8											8
9											9
10											10
11											11
12											12
13	20-- June 1	Angie Mills, Capital	R160			60000000				60000000	13
14											14
15											15
16											16
17											17
18											18
19											19
20											20
21											21
22											22
23											23
24											24
25											25

6

10

11

21-1/21-2 APPLICATION PROBLEMS, p. 595

Forming a partnership; admitting a partner with no change in total equity

Application Problem 21-1

CASH RECEIPTS JOURNAL PAGE 1

	DATE		ACCOUNT TITLE	DOC. NO.	POST. REF.	GENERAL DEBIT	GENERAL CREDIT	ACCOUNTS RECEIVABLE CREDIT	SALES CREDIT	SALES TAX PAYABLE CREDIT	CASH DEBIT	
1	June	1	Paula Jeter, Capital	R1			46000000				46000000	1
2		1	Accounts Receivable	R2		374647					1453200	2
3			Merchandise Inventory			2629834						3
4			Supplies			67059						4
5			Equipment			948112						5
6			Allowance for Uncoll. Accounts				7492					6
7			Accounts Payable				865360					7
8			Carmen Estrada, Capital				46000000					8
9												9
10												10

Application Problem 21-2

GENERAL JOURNAL PAGE 12

	DATE		ACCOUNT TITLE	DOC. NO.	POST. REF.	DEBIT	CREDIT	
1	Oct.	1	Steven Myer, Capital	M24		10000000		1
2			William Riggs, Capital			10000000		2
3			Sandra DeVito, Capital				20000000	3
4								4
5								5
6								6
7								7

Name _____ Date _____ Class _____

Extra form

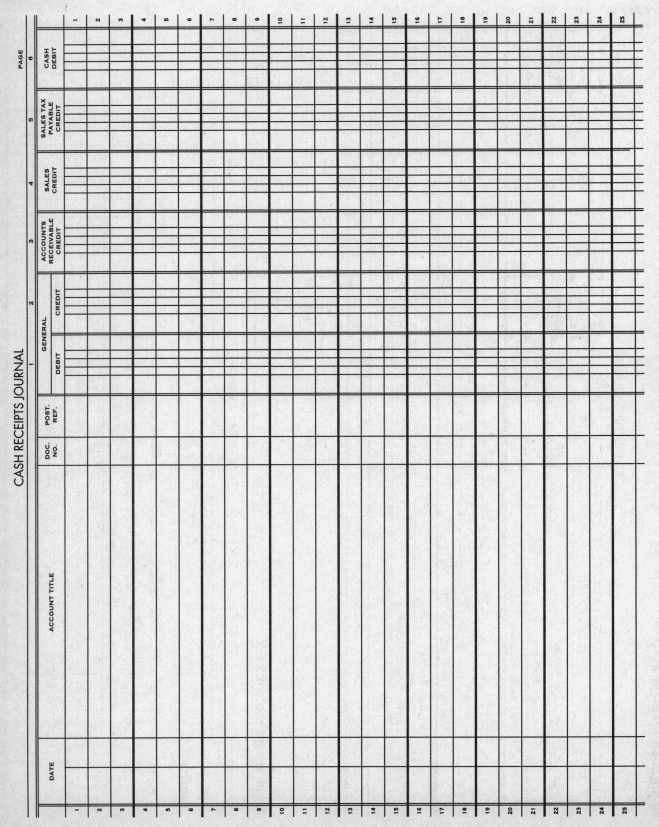

CASH RECEIPTS JOURNAL

		DOC. NO.	POST. REF.	GENERAL DEBIT	GENERAL CREDIT	ACCOUNTS RECEIVABLE CREDIT	SALES CREDIT	SALES TAX PAYABLE CREDIT	CASH DEBIT
DATE	ACCOUNT TITLE			1	2	3	4	5	6

PAGE ____

21-3 - 21-5 APPLICATION PROBLEMS, p. 596

Admitting a partner with equity equal to new partner's investment; admitting a partner with equity greater than new partner's investment; admitting a partner when goodwill is recognized

Application Problem 21-3

CASH RECEIPTS JOURNAL   PAGE 13

DATE		ACCOUNT TITLE	DOC. NO.	POST. REF.	GENERAL DEBIT	GENERAL CREDIT	ACCOUNTS RECEIVABLE CREDIT	SALES CREDIT	SALES TAX PAYABLE CREDIT	CASH DEBIT	
20-- Apr.	1	Daryl Wetzel, Capital	R95			6000000				6000000	1
											2
											3

Application Problem 21-4

The general journal for this problem appears on page 362.

CASH RECEIPTS JOURNAL   PAGE 14

DATE		ACCOUNT TITLE	DOC. NO.	POST. REF.	GENERAL DEBIT	GENERAL CREDIT	ACCOUNTS RECEIVABLE CREDIT	SALES CREDIT	SALES TAX PAYABLE CREDIT	CASH DEBIT	
20-- Aug.	1	Greg Talbot, Capital	R116			2200000				2200000	1
											2
											3

Application Problem 21-5

The general journal for this problem appears on page 362.

CASH RECEIPTS JOURNAL   PAGE 5

DATE		ACCOUNT TITLE	DOC. NO.	POST. REF.	GENERAL DEBIT	GENERAL CREDIT	ACCOUNTS RECEIVABLE CREDIT	SALES CREDIT	SALES TAX PAYABLE CREDIT	CASH DEBIT	
20-- Mar.	1	Dean McGee, Capital	R67			3600000				3600000	1
											2
											3

21-3 – 21-5 APPLICATION PROBLEMS (concluded)

Application Problem 21-4

GENERAL JOURNAL

PAGE 7

DATE		ACCOUNT TITLE	DOC. NO.	POST. REF.	DEBIT	CREDIT	
20–							
Aug.	1	Stanley Neal, Capital	M25		6000000		1
	2	Helen Jobe, Capital			6000000		2
	3	Greg Talbot, Capital				1200000	3
	4						4
	5						5
	6						6
	7						7
	8						8
	9						9

Application Problem 21-5

GENERAL JOURNAL

PAGE 3

DATE		ACCOUNT TITLE	DOC. NO.	POST. REF.	DEBIT	CREDIT	
20–							
Mar.	1	Goodwill	M10		18000000		1
	2	Arthur Jansky, Capital				9000000	2
	3	Edward Thayer, Capital				9000000	3
	4						4
	5						5
	6						6
	7						7
	8						8
	9						9

21-6 MASTERY PROBLEM, p. 597

Forming and expanding a partnership

CASH RECEIPTS JOURNAL

PAGE 1

	DATE		ACCOUNT TITLE	DOC. NO.	POST. REF.	GENERAL DEBIT	GENERAL CREDIT	ACCOUNTS RECEIVABLE CREDIT	SALES CREDIT	SALES TAX PAYABLE CREDIT	CASH DEBIT	
1	20-- July	1	Michelle Allen, Capital	R1			1200000				1200000	1
2		1	Accounts Receivable	R2		330360					429123	2
3			Supplies			29019						3
4			Equipment			437814						4
5			Allowance for Uncollectible Accounts				3579					5
6			Accounts Payable				22737					6
7			Roy Hatfield, Capital				1200000					7
8	Oct.	1	Danita McGrew, Capital	R80			800000				800000	8
9		20	Donna Wells, Capital	R92			700000				700000	9
10	Dec.	5	Pearl Morgan, Capital	R118			820000				820000	10
11												11
12												12
13												13
14												14
15												15
16												16
17												17
18												18
19												19
20												20
21												21
22												22
23												23
24												24
25												25

21-6 MASTERY PROBLEM (concluded)

GENERAL JOURNAL

PAGE 1

	DATE		ACCOUNT TITLE	DOC. NO.	POST. REF.	DEBIT	CREDIT	
1	20-- Aug.	1	Michelle Allen, Capital	M8		4 0 0 0 00		1
2			Roy Hatfield, Capital			4 0 0 0 00		2
3			Frank Boyd, Capital				8 0 0 0 00	3
4	Oct.	20	Michelle Allen, Capital	M18		2 0 0 00		4
5			Roy Hatfield, Capital			2 0 0 00		5
6			Frank Boyd, Capital			2 0 0 00		6
7			Danita McGrew, Capital			2 0 0 00		7
8			Donna Wells, Capital				8 0 0 00	8
9	Dec.	5	Goodwill	M24		2 0 0 0 00		9
10			Roy Hatfield, Capital				4 0 0 00	10
11			Michelle Allen, Capital				4 0 0 00	11
12			Frank Boyd, Capital				4 0 0 00	12
13			Danita McGrew, Capital				4 0 0 00	13
14			Donna Wells, Capital				4 0 0 00	14
15								15
16								16
17								17
18								18
19								19
20								20
21								21
22								22
23								23
24								24
25								25
26								26
27								27
28								28
29								29
30								30
31								31

21-7 CHALLENGE PROBLEM, p. 598

Forming and expanding a partnership

CASH RECEIPTS JOURNAL

PAGE 8

	DATE		ACCOUNT TITLE	DOC. NO.	POST. REF.	GENERAL DEBIT	GENERAL CREDIT	ACCOUNTS RECEIVABLE CREDIT	SALES CREDIT	SALES TAX PAYABLE CREDIT	CASH DEBIT	
1	May	1	Accounts Receivable	R1							425832	1
2			Merchandise Inventory			623729						2
3			Office Equipment			294349						3
4			Allowance for Uncollectible Accounts				3543					4
5			Accounts Payable				368423					5
6			Marsha Huerta, Capital				1200000					6
7		1	Supplies	R2		207521					432349	7
8			Merchandise Inventory			634204						8
9			Office Equipment			295988						9
10			Accounts Payable				370062					10
11			John Ward, Capital				1200000					11
12	July	20	Pam Wise, Capital	R24			1500000				1500000	12
13	Nov.	5	Merchandise Inventory	R92		800000					500000	13
14			Rodney Stein, Capital				1300000					14
15												15
16												16
17												17
18												18
19												19
20												20
21												21
22												22
23												23
24												24
25												25

21-7 CHALLENGE PROBLEM (concluded)

GENERAL JOURNAL

PAGE 4

	DATE		ACCOUNT TITLE	DOC. NO.	POST. REF.	DEBIT	CREDIT	
1	20-- July	1	Merchandise Inventory	M80		12 0 0 0 00		1
2			Dan Ogden, Capital				12 0 0 0 00	2
3		20	Pam Wise, Capital	M85		2 2 5 0 00		3
4			Marsha Huerta, Capital				7 5 0 00	4
5			John Ward, Capital				7 5 0 00	5
6			Dan Ogden, Capital				7 5 0 00	6
7	Nov.	5	Goodwill	M105		1 0 0 0 00		7
8			Marsha Huerta, Capital				2 5 0 00	8
9			John Ward, Capital				2 5 0 00	9
10			Dan Ogden, Capital				2 5 0 00	10
11			Pam Wise, Capital				2 5 0 00	11
12								12
13								13
14								14
15								15
16								16
17								17
18								18
19								19
20								20
21								21
22								22
23								23
24								24
25								25
26								26
27								27
28								28
29								29
30								30
31								31

22-1 WORK TOGETHER, p. 608

Calculating partnership earnings and journalizing partnership withdrawals

[5a]

Fixed percentage:

	Total Net Income	×	Fixed %	=	Partner's Share of Net Income
Badger	$60,000.00	×	50%	=	$30,000.00
Giesen	60,000.00	×	50%	=	30,000.00
Total net income					$60,000.00

[5b]

Percentage of total equity:

	Partner's Equity	÷	Total Equity	=	%	×	Net Income	=	Partner's Share
Badger	$60,000.00	÷	$150,000.00	=	40%	×	$60,000.00	=	$24,000.00
Giesen	90,000.00	÷	150,000.00	=	60%	×	60,000.00	=	36,000.00
Total net income									$60,000.00

[5c]

Interest on equity plus fixed percentage:

	Partner's Equity	×	Interest Rate	=	Partner's Interest
Badger	$60,000.00	×	10%	=	$ 6,000.00
Giesen	90,000.00	×	10%	=	9,000.00
Total interest					$15,000.00

Net Income	–	Total Interest	=	Remaining Net Income
$60,000.00	–	$15,000.00	=	$45,000.00

	Remaining Net Income	×	Fixed %	=	Partner's Share
Badger	$45,000.00	×	50%	=	$22,500.00
Giesen	45,000.00	×	50%	=	22,500.00
Total remaining net income					$45,000.00

	Interest	+	Remaining Net Income	=	Partner's Share
Badger	$6,000.00	+	$22,500.00	=	$28,500.00
Giesen	9,000.00	+	22,500.00	=	31,500.00
Total net income					$60,000.00

22-1 WORK TOGETHER (continued)

[5d]

Interest on equity, salary, and fixed percentage:

	Partner's Equity	×	Interest Rate	=	Interest on Equity	+	Salary	=	Total Allowance
Badger	$60,000.00	×	8%	=	$4,800.00	+	$18,000.00	=	$22,800.00
Giesen	90,000.00	×	8%	=	7,200.00	+	22,500.00	=	29,700.00
Total allowance									$52,500.00

Net Income	–	Total Allowance	=	Remaining Net Income
$60,000.00	–	$52,500.00	=	$7,500.00

	Remaining Net Income	×	Fixed %	=	Partner's Share	+	Total Allowance	=	Partner's Total Share
Badger	$7,500.00	×	50%	=	$3,750.00	+	$22,800.00	=	$26,550.00
Giesen	7,500.00	×	50%	=	3,750.00	+	29,700.00	=	33,450.00
Total net income									$60,000.00

[6]

GENERAL JOURNAL
PAGE 7

	DATE		ACCOUNT TITLE	DOC. NO.	POST. REF.	DEBIT	CREDIT	
1	20-- July	1	Maxine Giesen, Drawing	M23		4 5 00		1
2			Supplies—Office				4 5 00	2
3								3
4								4
5								5
6								6
7								7
8								8
9								9
10								10
11								11
12								12
13								13
14								14

Name _____ Date _____ Class _____

22-1 **WORK TOGETHER (concluded)**

[6]

CASH PAYMENTS JOURNAL

PAGE 12

	DATE		ACCOUNT TITLE	CK. NO.	POST. REF.	GENERAL DEBIT 1	GENERAL CREDIT 2	ACCOUNTS PAYABLE DEBIT 3	CASH CREDIT 4	
1	20-- June	20	Scott Badger, Drawing	133		75000			75000	1
2										2
3										3
4										4
5										5
6										6
7										7
8										8
9										9
10										10
11										11
12										12
13										13
14										14
15										15
16										16
17										17
18										18
19										19
20										20
21										21
22										22
23										23
24										24
25										25

22-1 WORK TOGETHER

Extra form

GENERAL JOURNAL   PAGE _____

	DATE	ACCOUNT TITLE	DOC. NO.	POST. REF.	DEBIT	CREDIT	
1							1
2							2
3							3
4							4
5							5
6							6
7							7
8							8
9							9
10							10
11							11
12							12
13							13
14							14
15							15
16							16
17							17
18							18
19							19
20							20
21							21
22							22
23							23
24							24
25							25
26							26
27							27
28							28
29							29
30							30
31							31

22-1 ON YOUR OWN, p. 609

Calculating partnership earnings and journalizing partnership withdrawals

[7a]

Fixed percentage:

	Total Net Income	×	Fixed %	=	Partner's Share of Net Income
Nabors	$50,000.00	×	50%	=	$25,000.00
Ives	50,000.00	×	50%	=	25,000.00
Total net income					$50,000.00

[7b]

Percentage of total equity:

	Partner's Equity	÷	Total Equity	=	%	×	Net Income	=	Partner's Share
Nabors	$50,000.00	÷	$125,000.00	=	40%	×	$50,000.00	=	$20,000.00
Ives	75,000.00	÷	125,000.00	=	60%	×	50,000.00	=	30,000.00
Total net income									$50,000.00

[7c]

Interest on equity plus fixed percentage:

	Partner's Equity	×	Interest Rate	=	Partner's Interest
Nabors	$50,000.00	×	8%	=	$ 4,000.00
Ives	75,000.00	×	8%	=	6,000.00
Total interest					$10,000.00

Net Income	−	Total Interest	=	Remaining Net Income
$50,000.00	−	$10,000.00	=	$40,000.00

	Remaining Net Income	×	Fixed %	=	Partner's Share
Nabors	$40,000.00	×	50%	=	$20,000.00
Ives	40,000.00	×	50%	=	20,000.00
Total remaining net income					$40,000.00

	Interest	+	Remaining Net Income	=	Partner's Share
Nabors	$4,000.00	+	$20,000.00	=	$24,000.00
Ives	6,000.00	+	20,000.00	=	26,000.00
Total net income					$50,000.00

22-1 ON YOUR OWN (continued)

[7d]

Interest on equity, salary, and fixed percentage:

	Partner's Equity	×	Interest Rate	=	Interest on Equity	+	Salary	=	Total Allowance
Nabors	$50,000.00	×	10%	=	$5,000.00	+	$16,000.00	=	$21,000.00
Ives	75,000.00	×	10%	=	7,500.00	+	14,000.00	=	21,500.00
Total allowance									$42,500.00

Net Income	−	Total Allowance	=	Remaining Net Income
$50,000.00	−	$42,500.00	=	$7,500.00

	Remaining Net Income	×	Fixed %	=	Partner's Share	+	Total Allowance	=	Partner's Total Share
Nabors	$7,500.00	×	50%	=	$3,750.00	+	$21,000.00	=	$24,750.00
Ives	7,500.00	×	50%	=	3,750.00	+	21,500.00	=	25,250.00
Total net income									$50,000.00

[8]

GENERAL JOURNAL PAGE 4

	DATE		ACCOUNT TITLE	DOC. NO.	POST. REF.	DEBIT	CREDIT	
1	20-- Oct.	3	Sam Ives, Drawing	M18		1 2 0 00		1
2			Supplies—Store				1 2 0 00	2
3								3

22-1 ON YOUR OWN (concluded)

[8]

CASH PAYMENTS JOURNAL

PAGE 8

	DATE		ACCOUNT TITLE	CK. NO.	POST. REF.	GENERAL DEBIT 1	GENERAL CREDIT 2	ACCOUNTS PAYABLE DEBIT 3	CASH CREDIT 4	
1	Apr. 20--	15	Rose Nabors, Drawing	126		80000			80000	1
2										2
3										3
4										4
5										5
6										6
7										7
8										8
9										9
10										10
11										11
12										12
13										13
14										14
15										15
16										16
17										17
18										18
19										19
20										20
21										21
22										22
23										23
24										24
25										25

22-1 ON YOUR OWN

Extra form

GENERAL JOURNAL   PAGE _____

	DATE	ACCOUNT TITLE	DOC. NO.	POST. REF.	DEBIT	CREDIT	
1							1
2							2
3							3
4							4
5							5
6							6
7							7
8							8
9							9
10							10
11							11
12							12
13							13
14							14
15							15
16							16
17							17
18							18
19							19
20							20
21							21
22							22
23							23
24							24
25							25
26							26
27							27
28							28
29							29
30							30
31							31

22-2 WORK TOGETHER, p. 618

End-of-fiscal-period-work for a partnership

Maria and Kelso Shop

Work Sheet

For Year Ended December 31, 20--

	ACCOUNT TITLE	INCOME STATEMENT		BALANCE SHEET		
		DEBIT	CREDIT	DEBIT	CREDIT	
13	Maria Delgado, Capital				93 6 0 0 00	13
14	Maria Delgado, Drawing			17 6 0 0 00		14
15	Oren Kelso, Capital				50 4 0 0 00	15
16	Oren Kelso, Drawing			10 4 0 0 00		16
17	Income Summary					17
18	Sales		133 5 1 0 00			18
19	Advertising Expense	2 4 0 0 00				19
20	Depr. Expense—Equipment	3 0 6 3 00				20
21	Depr. Expense—Truck	2 2 5 0 00				21
22	Insurance Expense	1 2 2 5 00				22
23	Miscellaneous Expense	4 3 4 7 00				23
24	Rent Expense	18 0 0 0 00				24
25	Supplies Expense—Service	18 8 0 7 00				25
26	Supplies Expense—Office	3 4 7 5 00				26
27	Truck Expense	13 2 5 0 00				27
28	Uncollectible Accounts Expense	2 9 3 00				28
29	Utilities Expense	4 9 0 0 00				29
30		72 0 1 0 00	133 5 1 0 00	291 8 6 0 00	230 3 6 0 00	30
31	Net Income	61 5 0 0 00			61 5 0 0 00	31
32		133 5 1 0 00	133 5 1 0 00	291 8 6 0 00	291 8 6 0 00	32
33						33
34						34
35						35
36						36
37						37
38						38
39						39
40						40
41						41
42						42
43						43
44						44
45						45
46						46
47						47

22-2 WORK TOGETHER (continued)

[4]

Maria and Kelso Shop
Income Statement
For Year Ended December 31, 20--

			% OF NET SALES
Operating Revenue:			
Sales		133 5 1 0 00	100.0
Operating Expenses:			
Advertising Expense	2 4 0 0 00		
Depreciation Expense—Equipment	3 0 6 3 00		
Depreciation Expense—Truck	2 2 5 0 00		
Insurance Expense	1 2 2 5 00		
Miscellaneous Expense	4 3 4 7 00		
Rent Expense	18 0 0 0 00		
Supplies Expense—Service	18 8 0 7 00		
Supplies Expense—Office	3 4 7 5 00		
Truck Expense	13 2 5 0 00		
Uncollectible Accounts Expense	2 9 3 00		
Utilities Expense	4 9 0 0 00		
Total Operating Expenses		72 0 1 0 00	53.9
Net Income		61 5 0 0 00	46.1

[5]

Maria and Kelso Shop
Distribution of Net Income Statement
For Year Ended December 31, 20--

Maria Delgado:		
8% Interest on Equity	7 4 8 8 00	
Salary	15 0 0 0 00	
Share of Remaining Net Income	10 4 9 0 00	
Total Share of Net Income		32 9 7 8 00
Oren Kelso:		
8% Interest on Equity	4 0 3 2 00	
Salary	14 0 0 0 00	
Share of Remaining Net Income	10 4 9 0 00	
Total Share of Net Income		28 5 2 2 00
Total Net Income		61 5 0 0 00

22-2 WORK TOGETHER (continued)

[6]

Maria and Kelso Shop

Owners' Equity Statement

For Year Ended December 31, 20--

Maria Delgado:					
Capital, January 1, 20--			93 6 0 0 00		
Share of Net Income	32 9 7 8 00				
Less Withdrawals	17 6 0 0 00				
Net Increase in Capital		15 3 7 8 00			
Capital, December 31, 20--				108 9 7 8 00	
Oren Kelso:					
Capital, January 1, 20--			50 4 0 0 00		
Share of Net Income	28 5 2 2 00				
Less Withdrawals	10 4 0 0 00				
Net Increase in Capital		18 1 2 2 00			
Capital, December 31, 20--				68 5 2 2 00	
Total Owners' Equity, December 31, 20--				177 5 0 0 00	

22-2 WORK TOGETHER (concluded)

[7]

GENERAL JOURNAL   PAGE 15

	DATE	ACCOUNT TITLE	DOC. NO.	POST. REF.	DEBIT	CREDIT	
14		*Closing Entries*					14
15	31	Sales			133510 00		15
16		Income Summary				133510 00	16
17	31	Income Summary			72010 00		17
18		Advertising Expense				2400 00	18
19		Depreciation Expense—Equipment				3063 00	19
20		Depreciation Expense—Truck				2250 00	20
21		Insurance Expense				1225 00	21
22		Miscellaneous Expense				4347 00	22
23		Rent Expense				18000 00	23
24		Supplies Expense—Service				18807 00	24
25		Supplies Expense—Office				3475 00	25
26		Truck Expense				13250 00	26
27		Uncollectible Accounts Exp.				293 00	27
28		Utilities Expense				4900 00	28
29	31	Income Summary			61500 00		29
30		Maria Delgado, Capital				32978 00	30
31		Oren Kelso, Capital				28522 00	31
32	31	Maria Delgado, Capital			17600 00		32
33		Maria Delgado, Drawing				17600 00	33
34	31	Oren Kelson, Capital			10400 00		34
35		Oren Kelso, Drawing				10400 00	35
36							36
37							37
38							38
39							39
40							40
41							41
42							42
43							43

22-2 ON YOUR OWN, p. 618

End-of-fiscal-period-work for a partnership

Lowe and Ray Gallery

Work Sheet

For Year Ended December 31, 20--

				5	6	7	8
	ACCOUNT TITLE			INCOME STATEMENT		BALANCE SHEET	
				DEBIT	CREDIT	DEBIT	CREDIT
13	Jeffery Lowe, Capital						66 0 0 0 00
14	Jeffery Lowe, Drawing					21 0 0 0 00	
15	Mona Ray, Capital						60 0 0 0 00
16	Mona Ray, Drawing					21 0 0 0 00	
17	Income Summary						
18	Sales				115 4 5 0 00		
19	Advertising Expense			1 3 2 0 00			
20	Depr. Expense—Equipment			4 7 3 7 00			
21	Depr. Expense—Truck			3 7 4 0 00			
22	Insurance Expense			8 4 5 00			
23	Miscellaneous Expense			1 9 8 0 00			
24	Rent Expense			18 4 8 0 00			
25	Supplies Expense—Service			12 9 6 2 00			
26	Supplies Expense—Office			2 3 9 6 00			
27	Truck Expense			11 2 7 7 00			
28	Uncollectible Accounts Expense			1 9 8 00			
29	Utilities Expense			2 9 1 5 00			
30				60 8 5 0 00	115 4 5 0 00	250 4 7 6 00	195 8 7 6 00
31	Net Income			54 6 0 0 00			54 6 0 0 00
32				115 4 5 0 00	115 4 5 0 00	250 4 7 6 00	250 4 7 6 00

22-2 **ON YOUR OWN (continued)**

[8]

Lowe and Ray Gallery
Income Statement
For Year Ended December 31, 20--

								% OF NET SALES
Operating Revenue:								
Sales					115	4 5 0 00		100.0
Operating Expenses:								
Advertising Expense	1 3 2 0 00							
Depreciation Expense—Equipment	4 7 3 7 00							
Depreciation Expense—Truck	3 7 4 0 00							
Insurance Expense	8 4 5 00							
Miscellaneous Expense	1 9 8 0 00							
Rent Expense	18 4 8 0 00							
Supplies Expense—Service	12 9 6 2 00							
Supplies Expense—Office	2 3 9 6 00							
Truck Expense	11 2 7 7 00							
Uncollectible Accounts Expense	1 9 8 00							
Utilities Expense	2 9 1 5 00							
Total Operating Expenses					60	8 5 0 00		52.7
Net Income					54	6 0 0 00		47.3

[9]

Lowe and Ray Gallery
Distribution of Net Income Statement
For Year Ended December 31, 20--

Jeffery Lowe:			
8% Interest on Equity	5 2 8 0 00		
Salary	12 0 0 0 00		
Share of Remaining Net Income	8 2 6 0 00		
Total Share of Net Income		25 5 4 0 00	
Mona Ray:			
8% Interest on Equity	4 8 0 0 00		
Salary	16 0 0 0 00		
Share of Remaining Net Income	8 2 6 0 00		
Total Share of Net Income		29 0 6 0 00	
Total Net Income		54 6 0 0 00	

22-2 ON YOUR OWN (continued)

[10]

Lowe and Ray Gallery

Owners' Equity Statement

For Year Ended December 31, 20--

Jeffery Lowe:			
Capital, January 1, 20--		66 0 0 0 00	
Share of Net Income	25 5 4 0 00		
Less Withdrawals	21 0 0 0 00		
Net Increase in Capital		4 5 4 0 00	
Capital, December 31, 20--			70 5 4 0 00
Mona Ray:			
Capital, January 1, 20--		60 0 0 0 00	
Share of Net Income	29 0 6 0 00		
Less Withdrawals	21 0 0 0 00		
Net Increase in Capital		8 0 6 0 00	
Capital, December 31, 20--			68 0 6 0 00
Total Owners' Equity, December 31, 20--			138 6 0 0 00

22-2 ON YOUR OWN (concluded)

[11]

GENERAL JOURNAL   PAGE 12

	DATE	ACCOUNT TITLE	DOC. NO.	POST. REF.	DEBIT	CREDIT	
14		*Closing Entries*					14
15	31	Sales			115 4 5 0 00		15
16		Income Summary				115 4 5 0 00	16
17	31	Income Summary			60 8 5 0 00		17
18		Advertising Expense				1 3 2 0 00	18
19		Depreciation Expense—Equipment				4 7 3 7 00	19
20		Depreciation Expense—Truck				3 7 4 0 00	20
21		Insurance Expense				8 4 5 00	21
22		Miscellaneous Expense				1 9 8 0 00	22
23		Rent Expense				18 4 8 0 00	23
24		Supplies Expense—Service				12 9 6 2 00	24
25		Supplies Expense—Office				2 3 9 6 00	25
26		Truck Expense				11 2 7 7 00	26
27		Uncollectible Accounts Exp.				1 9 8 00	27
28		Utilities Expense				2 9 1 5 00	28
29	31	Income Summary			54 6 0 0 00		29
30		Jeffery Lowe, Capital				25 5 4 0 00	30
31		Mona Roy, Capital				29 0 6 0 00	31
32	31	Jeffery Lowe, Capital			21 0 0 0 00		32
33		Jeffery Lowe, Drawing				21 0 0 0 00	33
34	31	Mona Ray, Capital			21 0 0 0 00		34
35		Mona Ray, Drawing				21 0 0 0 00	35
36							36
37							37
38							38
39							39
40							40
41							41
42							42
43							43

22-3 WORK TOGETHER, p. 623

Liquidation of a partnership

Cash	$12,500.00
Supplies	1,250.00
Office Equipment	15,000.00
Accumulated Depreciation—Office Equipment	8,250.00
Truck	25,500.00
Accumulated Depreciation—Truck	18,300.00
Accounts Payable	1,250.00
Jason Edson, Capital	13,450.00
Peggy Karam, Capital	13,000.00

[3]

GENERAL JOURNAL   PAGE 4

	DATE		ACCOUNT TITLE	DOC. NO.	POST. REF.	DEBIT	CREDIT	
1	20-- May	6	Jason Edson, Capital	M21		4 5 0 00		1
2			Peggy Karam, Capital			3 0 0 00		2
3			Loss and Gain on Realization				7 5 0 00	3
4								4
5								5
6								6
7								7
8								8
9								9
10								10
11								11
12								12
13								13
14								14
15								15
16								16
17								17
18								18
19								19
20								20

22-3 WORK TOGETHER (concluded)

[3]

CASH RECEIPTS JOURNAL

PAGE 6

DATE		ACCOUNT TITLE	DOC. NO.	POST. REF.	GENERAL DEBIT	GENERAL CREDIT	ACCOUNTS RECEIVABLE CREDIT	SALES CREDIT	SALES TAX PAYABLE CREDIT	CASH DEBIT	
20-- May	1	Loss and Gain on Realizatin	R86		750000					6000000	1
		Accum. Depr.—Office Equipment			825000						2
		Office Equipment				1500000					3
	1	Loss and Gain on Realization	R87		300000					95000	4
		Supplies				125000					5
	3	Accum. Depr.—Truck	R88		1830000					750000	6
		Truck				2550000					7
		Loss and Gain on Realization				30000					8
											9
											10
											11
											12

CASH PAYMENTS JOURNAL

PAGE 8

DATE		ACCOUNT TITLE	CK. NO.	POST. REF.	GENERAL DEBIT	GENERAL CREDIT	ACCOUNTS PAYABLE DEBIT	CASH CREDIT	
20-- May	5	✓	116				125000	125000	1
	6	Jason Edson, Capital	117		1300000			1300000	2
		Peggy Karam, Capital	118		1270000			1270000	3
									4
									5
									6
									7
									8
									9

22-3 ON YOUR OWN, p. 623

Liquidation of a partnership

Cash	$ 8,750.00
Supplies	850.00
Office Equipment	17,500.00
Accumulated Depreciation—Office Equipment	9,625.00
Truck	29,750.00
Accumulated Depreciation—Truck	21,350.00
Accounts Payable	875.00
Denise Oxley, Capital	13,000.00
Charles Tatum, Capital	12,000.00

[4]

GENERAL JOURNAL

PAGE 5

	DATE		ACCOUNT TITLE	DOC. NO.	POST. REF.	DEBIT	CREDIT	
1	20– June	6	Denise Oxley, Capital	M29		6 1 5 00		1
2			Charles Tatum, Capital			4 1 0 00		2
3			Loss and Gain on Distribution				1 0 2 5 00	3
4								4
5								5
6								6
7								7
8								8
9								9
10								10
11								11
12								12
13								13
14								14
15								15
16								16
17								17
18								18
19								19
20								20

22-3 ON YOUR OWN (concluded)

[4]

CASH RECEIPTS JOURNAL — PAGE 8

DATE		ACCOUNT TITLE	DOC. NO.	POST. REF.	GENERAL DEBIT	GENERAL CREDIT	ACCOUNTS RECEIVABLE CREDIT	SALES CREDIT	SALES TAX PAYABLE CREDIT	CASH DEBIT	
20-- June	1	Loss and Gain on Realization	R96		16750 00					62000 00	1
		Accum. Depr.—Office Equipment			9625 00						2
		Office Equipment				17500 00					3
	1	Supplies	R97			850 00				9000 00	4
		Gain and Loss on Realization				50 00					5
	3	Accum. Depr.—Truck	R98		21350 00					90000 00	6
		Truck				29750 00					7
		Loss and Gain on Realization				600 00					8
											9
											10
											11
											12

CASH PAYMENTS JOURNAL — PAGE 10

DATE		ACCOUNT TITLE	CK. NO.	POST. REF.	GENERAL DEBIT	GENERAL CREDIT	ACCOUNTS PAYABLE DEBIT	CASH CREDIT	
20-- June	5	✓	125				8750 00	8750 00	1
	6	Denise Oxley	126		12385 00			12385 00	2
		Charles Tatum	127		11590 00			11590 00	3
									4
									5
									6
									7
									8
									9

22-1 APPLICATION PROBLEM, p. 625

Calculating partnership earnings

[1]

Fixed percentage:

	Total Net Income	×	Fixed %	=	Partner's Share of Net Income
Fargo	$80,000.00	×	50%	=	$40,000.00
Kain	80,000.00	×	50%	=	40,000.00
Total net income					$80,000.00

[2]

Percentage of total equity:

	Partner's Equity	÷	Total Equity	=	%	×	Net Income	=	Partner's Share
Fargo	$ 80,000.00	÷	$200,000.00	=	40%	×	$80,000.00	=	$32,000.00
Kain	120,000.00	÷	200,000.00	=	60%	×	80,000.00	=	48,000.00
Total net income									$80,000.00

[3]

Interest on equity plus fixed percentage:

	Partner's Equity	×	Interest Rate	=	Partner's Interest
Fargo	$ 80,000.00	×	12%	=	$ 9,600.00
Kain	120,000.00	×	12%	=	14,400.00
Total interest					$24,000.00

Net Income	–	Total Interest	=	Remaining Net Income
$80,000.00	–	$24,000.00	=	$56,000.00

	Remaining Net Income	×	Fixed %	=	Partner's Share
Fargo	$56,000.00	×	50%	=	$28,000.00
Kain	56,000.00	×	50%	=	28,000.00
Total remaining net income					$56,000.00

	Interest	+	Remaining Net Income	=	Partner's Share
Fargo	$ 9,600.00	+	$28,000.00	=	$37,600.00
Kain	14,400.00	+	28,000.00	=	42,400.00
Total net income					$80,000.00

22-1 APPLICATION PROBLEM (concluded)

[4]

Salary plus fixed percentage:

Salaries for	Fargo	+	Kain	=	Total Salaries
	$24,000.00	+	$30,000.00	=	$54,000.00

Net Income	–	Total Salaries	=	Remaining Net Income
$80,000.00	–	$54,000.00	=	$26,000.00

	Remaining Net Income	×	Fixed %	=	Partner's Share	+	Salary	=	Partner's Total Share
Fargo	$26,000.00	×	40%	=	$10,400.00	+	$24,000.00	=	$34,400.00
Kain	26,000.00	×	60%	=	15,600.00	+	30,000.00	=	45,600.00
Total net income									$80,000.00

[5]

Interest on equity, salary, and fixed percentage:

	Partner's Equity	×	Interest Rate	=	Interest on Equity	+	Salary	=	Total Allowance
Fargo	$ 80,000.00	×	10%	=	$ 8,000.00	+	$24,000.00	=	$32,000.00
Kain	120,000.00	×	8%	=	9,600.00	+	30,000.00	=	39,600.00
Total allowance									$71,600.00

Net Income	–	Total Allowance	=	Remaining Net Income
$80,000.00	–	$71,600.00	=	$8,400.00

	Remaining Net Income	×	Fixed %	=	Partner's Share	+	Total Allowance	=	Partner's Total Share
Fargo	$8,400.00	×	50%	=	$4,200.00	+	$32,000.00	=	$36,200.00
Kain	8,400.00	×	50%	=	4,200.00	+	39,600.00	=	43,800.00
Total net income									$80,000.00

[6]

Interest on equity, salary, and fixed percentage (deficit):

	Partner's Equity	×	Interest Rate	=	Interest on Equity	+	Salary	=	Total Allowance
Fargo	$ 80,000.00	×	15%	=	$12,000.00	+	$30,000.00	=	$42,000.00
Kain	120,000.00	×	15%	=	18,000.00	+	36,000.00	=	54,000.00
Total allowance									$96,000.00

Net Income	–	Total Allowance	=	Deficit
$80,000.00	–	$96,000.00	=	$16,000.00

	Deficit	×	Fixed %	=	Partner's Share		Total Allowance	–	Deficit	=	Partner's Total Share
Fargo	$16,000.00	×	50%	=	$8,000.00		$42,000.00	–	$8,000.00	=	$34,000.00
Kain	16,000.00	×	50%	=	8,000.00		54,000.00	–	8,000.00	=	46,000.00
Total net income											$80,000.00

22-2 APPLICATION PROBLEM, p. 625

Journalizing partners' withdrawals

GENERAL JOURNAL PAGE 6

	DATE		ACCOUNT TITLE	DOC. NO.	POST. REF.	DEBIT	CREDIT	
1	20-- June	5	Janet Agnew, Drawing	M46		4 0 0 00		1
2			Supplies—Office				4 0 0 00	2
3								3
4								4
5								5
6								6
7								7
8								8
9								9
10								10
11								11
12								12
13								13
14								14
15								15
16								16
17								17
18								18
19								19
20								20
21								21
22								22
23								23
24								24
25								25
26								26
27								27
28								28
29								29
30								30
31								31
32								32

22-2   APPLICATION PROBLEM (concluded)

CASH PAYMENTS JOURNAL

PAGE 12

	DATE		ACCOUNT TITLE	CK. NO.	POST. REF.	GENERAL DEBIT	GENERAL CREDIT	ACCOUNTS PAYABLE DEBIT	CASH CREDIT	
1	June 20--	26	Buford Franco, Drawing	284		60000			60000	1
2										2
3										3
4										4
5										5
6										6
7										7
8										8
9										9
10										10
11										11
12										12
13										13
14										14
15										15
16										16
17										17
18										18
19										19
20										20
21										21
22										22
23										23
24										24
25										25

22-3 APPLICATION PROBLEM, p. 625

Completing end-of-fiscal-period work for a partnership

Plantasia
Work Sheet
For Year Ended December 31, 20--

	ACCOUNT TITLE	TRIAL BALANCE DEBIT	TRIAL BALANCE CREDIT	ADJUSTMENTS DEBIT	ADJUSTMENTS CREDIT	INCOME STATEMENT DEBIT	INCOME STATEMENT CREDIT	BALANCE SHEET DEBIT	BALANCE SHEET CREDIT
1	Cash	42711180						42711180	
2	Petty Cash	20000						20000	
3	Accounts Receivable	195266						195266	
4	Allowance for Uncollectible Accounts		1952		(a) 11716				13668
5	Supplies—Plants	911890			(b) 752297			159593	
6	Supplies—Office	180810			(c) 139000			41810	
7	Prepaid Insurance	132271			(d) 49000			83271	
8	Equipment	1225400						1225400	
9	Accum. Depr.—Equipment		232500		(e) 122500				355000
10	Truck	600000						600000	
11	Accum. Depr.—Truck		183000		(f) 90000				273000
12	Accounts Payable		594852						594852
13	Susan Poole, Capital		2340000						2340000
14	Susan Poole, Drawing	440000						440000	
15	Ann Dodd, Capital		1260000						1260000
16	Ann Dodd, Drawing	260000						260000	
17	Income Summary								
18	Sales		5340409				5340409		
19	Advertising Expense	96000				96000			
20	Depr. Expense—Equipment			(e) 122500		122500			
21	Depr. Expense—Truck			(f) 90000		90000			
22	Insurance Expense			(d) 49000		49000			
23	Miscellaneous Expense	173896				173896			
24	Rent Expense	720000				720000			
25	Supp. Expense—Plants			(b) 752297		752297			
26	Supplies Expense—Office			(c) 139000		139000			
27	Truck Expense	530000				530000			
28	Uncollectible Accounts Expense			(a) 11716		11716			
29	Utilities Expense	196000				196000			
30		9952713	9952713	1164513	1164513	2880409	5340409	7296520	4836520
31	Net Income					2460000			2460000
32						5340409	5340409	7296520	7296520
33									
34									

22-3 APPLICATION PROBLEM (continued)

[1]

Plantasia

Income Statement

For Year Ended December 31, 20--

			% OF NET SALES
Operating Revenue:			
Sales		53 4 0 4 09	100.0
Operating Expenses:			
Advertising Expense	9 6 0 00		
Depreciation Expense—Equipment	1 2 2 5 00		
Depreciation Expense—Truck	9 0 0 00		
Insurance Expense	4 9 0 00		
Miscellaneous Expense	1 7 3 8 96		
Rent Expense	7 2 0 0 00		
Supplies Expense—Plants	7 5 2 2 97		
Supplies Expense—Office	1 3 9 0 00		
Truck Expense	5 3 0 0 00		
Uncollectible Accounts Expense	1 1 7 16		
Utilities Expense	1 9 6 0 00		
Total Operating Expenses		28 8 0 4 09	53.9
Net Income		24 6 0 0 00	46.1

[2]

Plantasia

Distribution of Net Income Statement

For Year Ended December 31, 20--

Susan Poole:		
65.0% of Net Income	15 9 9 0 00	
Ann Dodd:		
35.0% of Net Income	8 6 1 0 00	
Total Net Income		24 6 0 0 00

22-3 APPLICATION PROBLEM (continued)

[3]

Plantasia

Owners' Equity Statement

For Year Ended December 31, 20--

Susan Poole:			
Capital, January 1, 20--		23 4 0 0 00	
Share of Net Income	15 9 9 0 00		
Less Withdrawals	4 4 0 0 00		
Net Increase in Capital		11 5 9 0 00	
Capital, December 31, 20--			34 9 9 0 00
Ann Dodd:			
Capital, January 1, 20--		12 6 0 0 00	
Share of Net Income	8 6 1 0 00		
Less Withdrawals	2 6 0 0 00		
Net Increase in Capital		6 0 1 0 00	
Capital, December 31, 20--			18 6 1 0 00
Total Owners' Equity, December 31, 20--			53 6 0 0 00

22-3 APPLICATION PROBLEM (continued)

[4]

Plantasia

Balance Sheet

December 31, 20--

ASSETS					
Current Assets:					
Cash			42 7 1 1 80		
Petty Cash			2 0 0 00		
Accounts Receivable	1 9 5 2 66				
Less Allowance for Uncollectible Accounts	1 3 6 68		1 8 1 5 98		
Supplies—Plants			1 5 9 5 93		
Supplies—Office			4 1 8 10		
Prepaid Insurance			8 3 2 71		
Total Current Assets				47 5 7 4 52	
Plant Assets:					
Equipment	12 2 5 4 00				
Less Accumulated Depr.—Equipment	3 5 5 0 00		8 7 0 4 00		
Truck	6 0 0 0 00				
Less Accumulated Depr.—Truck	2 7 3 0 00		3 2 7 0 00		
Total Plant Assets				11 9 7 4 00	
Total Assets				59 5 4 8 52	
LIABILITIES					
Accounts Payable				5 9 4 8 52	
OWNERS' EQUITY					
Susan Poole, Capital			34 9 9 0 00		
Ann Dodd, Capital			18 6 1 0 00		
Total Owners' Equity				53 6 0 0 00	
Total Liabilities and Owners' Equity				59 5 4 8 52	

22-3 APPLICATION PROBLEM (continued)

[5, 6]

GENERAL JOURNAL   PAGE 12

	DATE		ACCOUNT TITLE	DOC. NO.	POST. REF.	DEBIT	CREDIT	
1			**Adjusting Entries**					1
2	20-- Dec.	31	Uncollectible Accounts Expense			1 1 7 16		2
3			Allowance for Uncollectible Accounts				1 1 7 16	3
4		31	Supplies Expense—Plants			7 5 2 2 97		4
5			Supplies—Plants				7 5 2 2 97	5
6		31	Supplies Expense—Office			1 3 9 0 00		6
7			Supplies—Office				1 3 9 0 00	7
8		31	Insurance Expense			4 9 0 00		8
9			Prepaid Insurance				4 9 0 00	9
10		31	Depreciation Expense—Equipment			1 2 2 5 00		10
11			Accumulated Depreciation—Equipment				1 2 2 5 00	11
12		31	Depreciation Expense—Truck			9 0 0 00		12
13			Accumulated Depreciation—Truck				9 0 0 00	13
14			**Closing Entries**					14
15		31	Sales			53 4 0 4 09		15
16			Income Summary				53 4 0 4 09	16
17		31	Income Summary			28 8 0 4 09		17
18			Advertising Expense				9 6 0 00	18
19			Depreciation Expense—Equipment				1 2 2 5 00	19
20			Depreciation Expense—Truck				9 0 0 00	20
21			Insurance Expense				4 9 0 00	21
22			Miscellaneous Expense				1 7 3 8 96	22
23			Rent Expense				7 2 0 0 00	23
24			Supplies Expense—Plants				7 5 2 2 97	24
25			Supplies Expense—Office				1 3 9 0 00	25
26			Truck Expense				5 3 0 0 00	26
27			Uncollectible Accounts Expense				1 1 7 16	27
28			Utilities Expense				1 9 6 0 00	28
29		31	Income Summary			24 6 0 0 00		29
30			Susan Poole, Capital				15 9 9 0 00	30
31			Ann Dodd, Capital				8 6 1 0 00	31
32		31	Susan Poole, Capital			4 4 0 0 00		32
33			Susan Poole, Drawing				4 4 0 0 00	33
34		31	Ann Dodd, Capital			2 6 0 0 00		34
35			Ann Dodd, Drawing				2 6 0 0 00	35

22-3 APPLICATION PROBLEM

Extra form

GENERAL JOURNAL   PAGE _____

	DATE	ACCOUNT TITLE	DOC. NO.	POST. REF.	DEBIT	CREDIT	
1							1
2							2
3							3
4							4
5							5
6							6
7							7
8							8
9							9
10							10
11							11
12							12
13							13
14							14
15							15
16							16
17							17
18							18
19							19
20							20
21							21
22							22
23							23
24							24
25							25
26							26
27							27
28							28
29							29
30							30
31							31
32							32
33							33
34							34
35							35

Name _____ Date _____ Class _____

22-4 APPLICATION PROBLEM, p. 626

Liquidating a partnership

GENERAL JOURNAL   PAGE 7

	DATE	ACCOUNT TITLE	DOC. NO.	POST. REF.	DEBIT	CREDIT	
1	20-- July 6	Donald Winn, Capital	M34		39000		1
2		Judy Reed, Capital			21000		2
3		Loss and Gain on Realization				60000	3
4							4
5							5
6							6
7							7
8							8
9							9
10							10
11							11
12							12
13							13
14							14
15							15
16							16
17							17
18							18
19							19
20							20
21							21
22							22
23							23
24							24
25							25
26							26
27							27
28							28
29							29
30							30
31							31

22-4 APPLICATION PROBLEM (concluded)

CASH RECEIPTS JOURNAL

PAGE 13

	DATE	ACCOUNT TITLE	DOC. NO.	POST. REF.	GENERAL DEBIT	GENERAL CREDIT	ACCOUNTS RECEIVABLE CREDIT	SALES CREDIT	SALES TAX PAYABLE CREDIT	CASH DEBIT	
1	20-- July 1	Loss and Gain on Realization	R114		50000					4000000	1
2		Accum. Depr.—Office Equipment			550000						2
3		Office Equipment				1000000					3
4	1	Loss and Gain on Realization	R115		300000					200000	4
5		Supplies				50000					5
6	3	Accumulated Depreciation—Truck	R116		1220000					500000	6
7		Truck				1700000					7
8		Loss and Gain on Realization				200000					8
9											9
10											10
11											11
12											12

CASH PAYMENTS JOURNAL

PAGE 13

	DATE	ACCOUNT TITLE	CK. NO.	POST. REF.	GENERAL DEBIT	GENERAL CREDIT	ACCOUNTS PAYABLE DEBIT	CASH CREDIT	
1	20-- July 5	Accounts Payable	156		500000			500000	1
2	6	Donald Winn, Capital	157		691000			1370000	2
3		Judy Reed, Capital	158		679000				3
4									4
5									5
6									6
7									7
8									8
9									9

22-5 MASTERY PROBLEM, p. 627

Completing end-of-fiscal-period work for a partnership

J & L Service
Work Sheet
For Year Ended December 31, 20--

#	ACCOUNT TITLE	TRIAL BALANCE DEBIT	TRIAL BALANCE CREDIT	ADJUSTMENTS DEBIT	ADJUSTMENTS CREDIT	INCOME STATEMENT DEBIT	INCOME STATEMENT CREDIT	BALANCE SHEET DEBIT	BALANCE SHEET CREDIT
1	Cash	3016584						3016584	
2	Petty Cash	30000						30000	
3	Accounts Receivable	179938						179938	
4	Allowance for Uncollectible Accounts		2798		(a) 10700				13498
5	Supplies—Service	840307			(b) 693242			147065	
6	Supplies—Office	160000			(c) 128089			31911	
7	Prepaid Insurance	121887			(d) 45155			76732	
8	Equipment	1362100						1362100	
9	Accum. Depr.—Equipment		214100		(e) 136200				350300
10	Truck	1200000						1200000	
11	Accum. Depr.—Truck		271500		(f) 160000				431500
12	Accounts Payable		549032						549032
13	Sarah Saxon, Capital		1500000						1500000
14	Sarah Saxon, Drawing	800000						800000	
15	Jane Rolf, Capital		1200000						1200000
16	Jane Rolf, Drawing	1000000						1000000	
17	Income Summary								
18	Sales		8283826				8283826		
19	Advertising Expense	80000				80000			
20	Depr. Expense—Equipment			(e) 136200		136200			
21	Depr. Expense—Truck			(f) 160000		160000			
22	Insurance Expense			(d) 45155		45155			
23	Miscellaneous Expense	1602440				1602440			
24	Rent Expense	960000				960000			
25	Supplies Expense—Service			(b) 693242		693242			
26	Supplies Expense—Office			(c) 128089		128089			
27	Truck Expense	488000				488000			
28	Uncollectible Accounts Expense			(a) 10700		10700			
29	Utilities Expense	180000				180000			
30		12021256	12021256	1173386	1173386	4483826	8283826	7844330	4044330
31	Net Income					3800000			3800000
32						8283826	8283826	7844330	7844330

22-5 MASTERY PROBLEM (continued)

[1]

J & L Service
Income Statement
For Year Ended December 31, 20--

							% OF NET SALES
Operating Revenue:							
Sales				82 8 3 8 26		100.0
Operating Expenses:							
Advertising Expense	8 0 0 00					
Depreciation Expense—Equipment	1 3 6 2 00					
Depreciation Expense—Truck	1 6 0 0 00					
Insurance Expense	4 5 1 55					
Miscellaneous Expense	16 0 2 4 40					
Rent Expense	9 6 0 0 00					
Supplies Expense—Service	6 9 3 2 42					
Supplies Expense—Office	1 2 8 0 89					
Truck Expense	4 8 8 0 00					
Uncollectible Accounts Expense	1 0 7 00					
Utilities Expense	1 8 0 0 00					
Total Operating Expenses				44 8 3 8 26		54.1
Net Income				38 0 0 0 00		45.9

[2]

J & L Service
Distribution of Net Income Statement
For Year Ended December 31, 20--

Sarah Saxon:		
10.0% Interest on Equity	1 5 0 0 00	
Salary	10 0 0 0 00	
Share of Remaining Net income	5 1 5 0 00	
Total Share of Net Income		16 6 5 0 00
Jane Rolf:		
10.0% Interest on Equity	1 2 0 0 00	
Salary	15 0 0 0 00	
Share of Remaining Net income	5 1 5 0 00	
Total Share of Net Income		21 3 5 0 00
Total Net Income		38 0 0 0 00

22-5 MASTERY PROBLEM (continued)

[3]

J & L Service

Owners' Equity Statement

For Year Ended December 31, 20--

Sarah Saxon:			
Capital, January 1, 20--		15 0 0 0 00	
Share of Net Income	16 6 5 0 00		
Less Withdrawals	8 0 0 0 00		
Net Increase in Capital		8 6 5 0 00	
Capital, December 31, 20--			23 6 5 0 00
Jane Rolf:			
Capital, January 1, 20--		12 0 0 0 00	
Share of Net Income	21 3 5 0 00		
Less Withdrawals	10 0 0 0 00		
Net Increase in Capital		11 3 5 0 00	
Capital, December 31, 20--			23 3 5 0 00
Total Owners' Equity, December 31, 20--			47 0 0 0 00

22-5 MASTERY PROBLEM (continued)

[4]

J & L Service

Balance Sheet

December 31, 20--

ASSETS					
Current Assets:					
Cash			30 1 6 5 84		
Petty Cash			3 0 0 00		
Accounts Receivable	1 7 9 9 38				
Less Allowance for Uncollectible Accounts	1 3 4 98		1 6 6 4 40		
Supplies—Service			1 4 7 0 65		
Supplies—Office			3 1 9 11		
Prepaid Insurance			7 6 7 32		
Total Current Assets				34 6 8 7 32	
Plant Assets:					
Equipment	13 6 2 1 00				
Less Accumulated Depr.—Equipment	3 5 0 3 00		10 1 1 8 00		
Truck	12 0 0 0 00				
Less Accumulated Depr.—Truck	4 3 1 5 00		7 6 8 5 00		
Total Plant Assets				17 8 0 3 00	
Total Assets				52 4 9 0 32	
LIABILITIES					
Accounts Payable				5 4 9 0 32	
OWNERS' EQUITY					
Sarah Saxon, Capital			23 6 5 0 00		
Jane Rolf, Capital			23 3 5 0 00		
Total Owners' Equity				47 0 0 0 00	
Total Liabilities and Owners' Equity				52 4 9 0 32	

22-5 MASTERY PROBLEM (continued)

[5, 6]

GENERAL JOURNAL   PAGE 12

	DATE		ACCOUNT TITLE	DOC. NO.	POST. REF.	DEBIT	CREDIT	
1			*Adjusting Entries*					1
2	20-- Dec.	31	Uncollectible Accounts Expense			1 0 7 00		2
3			Allowance for Uncollectible Accounts				1 0 7 00	3
4		31	Supplies Expense—Service			6 9 3 2 42		4
5			Supplies—Service				6 9 3 2 42	5
6		31	Supplies Expense—Office			1 2 8 0 89		6
7			Supplies—Office				1 2 8 0 89	7
8		31	Insurance Expense			4 5 1 55		8
9			Prepaid Insurance				4 5 1 55	9
10		31	Depreciation Expense—Equipment			1 3 6 2 00		10
11			Accumulated Depreciation—Equipment				1 3 6 2 00	11
12		31	Depreciation Expense—Truck			1 6 0 0 00		12
13			Accumulated Depreciation—Truck				1 6 0 0 00	13
14			*Closing Entries*					14
15		31	Sales			82 8 3 8 26		15
16			Income Summary				82 8 3 8 26	16
17		31	Income Summary			44 8 3 8 26		17
18			Advertising Expense				8 0 0 00	18
19			Depreciation Expense—Equipment				1 3 6 2 00	19
20			Depreciation Expense—Truck				1 6 0 0 00	20
21			Insurance Expense				4 5 1 55	21
22			Miscellaneous Expense				16 0 2 4 40	22
23			Rent Expense				9 6 0 0 00	23
24			Supplies Expense—Service				6 9 3 2 42	24
25			Supplies Expense—Office				1 2 8 0 89	25
26			Truck Expense				4 8 8 0 00	26
27			Uncollectible Accounts Expense				1 0 7 00	27
28			Utilities Expense				1 8 0 0 00	28
29		31	Income Summary			38 0 0 0 00		29
30			Sarah Saxon, Capital				16 6 5 0 00	30
31			Jane Rolf, Capital				21 3 5 0 00	31
32		31	Sarah Saxon, Capital			8 0 0 0 00		32
33			Sarah Saxon, Drawing				8 0 0 0 00	33
34		31	Jane Rolf, Capital			10 0 0 0 00		34
35			Jane Rolf, Drawing				10 0 0 0 00	35

22-5 MASTERY PROBLEM

Extra form

GENERAL JOURNAL   PAGE _____

	DATE		ACCOUNT TITLE	DOC. NO.	POST. REF.	DEBIT	CREDIT	
1								1
2								2
3								3
4								4
5								5
6								6
7								7
8								8
9								9
10								10
11								11
12								12
13								13
14								14
15								15
16								16
17								17
18								18
19								19
20								20
21								21
22								22
23								23
24								24
25								25
26								26
27								27
28								28
29								29
30								30
31								31
32								32
33								33
34								34
35								35

22-6 CHALLENGE PROBLEM, p. 627

Completing end-of-fiscal-period work for a partnership

D & E Sales
Work Sheet
For Year Ended December 31, 20--

#	Account Title	TB Debit	TB Credit	Adj. Debit	Adj. Credit	IS Debit	IS Credit	BS Debit	BS Credit
1	Cash	6806999						6806999	
2	Petty Cash	40000						40000	
3	Accounts Receivable	560036						560036	
4	Allowance for Uncollectible Accounts		1233		(a) 3452				4685
5	Merchandise Inventory	1264640			(b) 35469			1229171	
6	Supplies—Sales	128546			(c) 62988			65558	
7	Supplies—Office	91494			(d) 41172			50322	
8	Prepaid Insurance	126072			(e) 64297			61775	
9	Equipment	1159700						1159700	
10	Accum. Depr.—Equipment		233100		(f) 115970				349070
11	Truck	734000						734000	
12	Accum. Depr.—Truck		151204		(g) 73400				224604
13	Accounts Payable		483902						483902
14	Theresa Doron, Capital		2425000						2425000
15	Theresa Doron, Drawing	600000						600000	
16	Roy Eden, Capital		2150000						2150000
17	Roy Eden, Drawing	500000						500000	
18	Income Summary			(b) 35469		35469			
19	Sales		4417674				4417674		
20	Purchases	2886938				2886938			
21	Purchases Returns and Allowances		31756				31756		
22	Advertising Expense	75000				75000			
23	Depr. Expense—Equipment			(f) 115970		115970			
24	Depr. Expense—Truck			(g) 73400		73400			
25	Insurance Expense			(e) 64297		64297			
26	Miscellaneous Expense	92800				92800			
27	Rent Expense	840000				840000			
28	Supplies Expense—Sales			(c) 62988		62988			
29	Supplies Expense—Office			(d) 41172		41172			
30	Truck Expense	522794				522794			
31	Uncollectible Accounts Expense			(a) 3452		3452			
32	Utilities Expense	95150				95150			
33		9893869	9893869	396748	396748	4909430	4449430	5177261	5637261
34	Net Loss						460000	460000	
35						4909430	4909430	5637261	5637261

22-6 CHALLENGE PROBLEM (continued)

[1]

D & E Sales

Income Statement

For Year Ended December 31, 20--

					% OF NET SALES
Operating Revenue:					
Sales				44 1 7 6 74	100.0
Cost of Merchandise Sold:					
Merchandise Inventory, Jan. 1, 20--			12 6 4 6 40		
Purchases	28 8 6 9 38				
Less Purchases Returns & Allowances	3 1 7 56	28 5 5 1 82			
Total Cost of Mdse. Available for Sale		41 1 9 8 22			
Less Mdse. Inventory, Dec. 31, 20--		12 2 9 1 71			
Cost of Merchandise Sold				28 9 0 6 51	65.4
Gross Profit on Operations				15 2 7 0 23	34.6
Operating Expenses:					
Advertising Expense		7 5 0 00			
Depreciation Expense—Equipment		1 1 5 9 70			
Depreciation Expense—Truck		7 3 4 00			
Insurance Expense		6 4 2 97			
Miscellaneous Expense		9 2 8 00			
Rent Expense	8 4 0 0 00				
Supplies Expense—Sales		6 2 9 88			
Supplies Expense—Office		4 1 1 72			
Truck Expense	5 2 2 7 94				
Uncollectible Accounts Expense		3 4 52			
Utilities Expense		9 5 1 50			
Total Operating Expenses				19 8 7 0 23	45.0
Net Loss				(4 6 0 0 00)	-10.4

Name _____ Date _____ Class _____

22-6   CHALLENGE PROBLEM (continued)

[2]

D & E Sales

Distribution of Net Income Statement

For Year Ended December 31, 20--

Theresa Doran:			
10% Interest on Equity	2 4 2 5 00		
Salary	12 0 0 0 00	14 4 2 5 00	
Less Share of Net Deficit		17 1 4 6 25	
Total Share of Net Loss			2 7 2 1 25
Roy Eden:			
10% Interest on Equity	2 1 5 0 00		
Salary	10 0 0 0 00	12 1 5 0 00	
Less Share of Net Deficit		14 0 2 8 75	
Total Share of Net Loss			1 8 7 8 75
Total Net Loss			4 6 0 0 00

Computation of share of net deficit:

		Shares of Deficit Distribution
Total Interest and Salary Distribution	$14,425.00	Doran—
	12,150.00	$31,175 × 55% = $17,146.25
	$26,575.00	Eden—
Plus Net Loss	4,600.00	$31,175 × 45% = $14,028.75
Total Net Deficit to Distribution	$31,175.00	

[3]

D & E Sales

Owners' Equity Statement

For Year Ended December 31, 20--

Theresa Doran:			
Capital, January 1, 20--		24 2 5 0 00	
Share of Net Loss	2 7 2 1 25		
Plus Withdrawals	6 0 0 0 00		
Net Decrease in Capital		8 7 2 1 25	
Capital, December 31, 20--			15 5 2 8 75
Roy Eden:			
Capital, January 1, 20--		21 5 0 0 00	
Share of Net Loss	1 8 7 8 75		
Plus Withdrawals	5 0 0 0 00		
Net Decrease in Capital		6 8 7 8 75	
Capital, December 31, 20--			14 6 2 1 25
Total Owners' Equity, December 31, 20--			30 1 5 0 00

22-6 CHALLENGE PROBLEM (concluded)

[4]

D & E Sales

Balance Sheet

December 31, 20--

ASSETS						
Current Assets:						
Cash			6 8 0 6 99			
Petty Cash			4 0 0 00			
Accounts Receivable	5 6 0 36					
Less Allowance for Uncollectible Accounts	4 6 85		5 1 3 51			
Merchandise Inventory			12 2 9 1 71			
Supplies—Sales			6 5 5 58			
Supplies—Office			5 0 3 22			
Prepaid Insurance			6 1 7 75			
Total Current Assets					21 7 8 8 76	
Plant Assets:						
Equipment	11 5 9 7 00					
Less Accumulated Depr.—Equipment	3 4 9 0 70		8 1 0 6 30			
Truck	7 3 4 0 00					
Less Accumulated Depr.—Truck	2 2 4 6 04		5 0 9 3 96			
Total Plant Assets					13 2 0 0 26	
Total Assets					34 9 8 9 02	
LIABILITIES						
Accounts Payable					4 8 3 9 02	
Total Liabilities					4 8 3 9 02	
OWNERS' EQUITY						
Theresa Doran, Capital			15 5 2 8 75			
Roy Eden, Capital			14 6 2 1 25			
Total Owners' Equity					30 1 5 0 00	
Total Liabilities and Owners' Equity					34 9 8 9 02	

23-1 WORK TOGETHER
ON YOUR OWN, p. 640

Journalizing governmental operating budgets   [6, 7]

Work Together 23-1

JOURNAL   PAGE 12

DATE		ACCOUNT TITLE	DOC. NO.	POST. REF.	GENERAL DEBIT	GENERAL CREDIT	CASH DEBIT	CASH CREDIT
20-- Jan.	1	Estimated Revenues			843000000			
		Appropriations				836800000		
		Budgetary Fund Balance				6200000		

On Your Own 23-1

JOURNAL   PAGE 14

DATE		ACCOUNT TITLE	DOC. NO.	POST. REF.	GENERAL DEBIT	GENERAL CREDIT	CASH DEBIT	CASH CREDIT
20-- Jan.	1	Estimated Revenues			2461000000			
		Appropriations				2423000000		
		Budgetary Fund Balance				38000000		

Name _____ Date _____ Class _____

WORK TOGETHER
ON YOUR OWN

Extra form

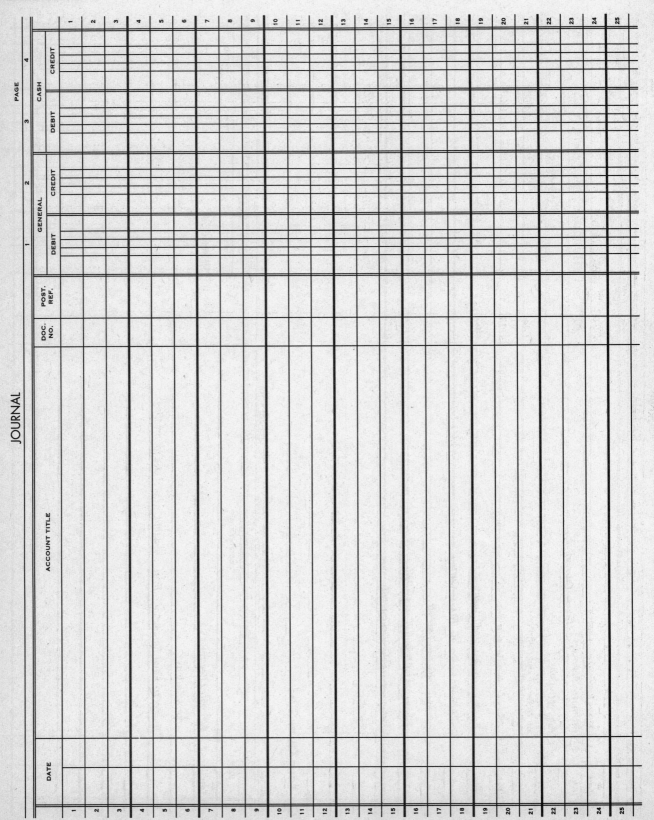

JOURNAL

23-2 WORK TOGETHER, p. 644

Journalizing governmental revenue transactions [4]

JOURNAL PAGE 1

	DATE		ACCOUNT TITLE	DOC. NO.	POST. REF.	GENERAL DEBIT (1)	GENERAL CREDIT (2)	CASH DEBIT (3)	CASH CREDIT (4)
1	Jan.	1	Taxes Receivable—Current	M34		2400000000			
2			Allowance for Uncoll. Taxes—Current				2400000		
3			Property Tax Revenue				237600000		
4		14	Other Revenue	R84			135400	135400	
5	Feb.	11	Taxes Receivable—Current	R113			97300000	97300000	
6	Mar.	1	Taxes Receivable—Delinquent	M68		9620000			
7			Allowance for Uncoll. Taxes—Current			2400000			
8			Taxes Receivable—Current				9620000		
9			Allowance for Uncoll. Taxes—Delinquent				2400000		
10		12	Taxes Receivable—Delinquent	R157			30300000	30300000	
11		12	Totals			2520200000	352485400	100465400	
12									
13									
14									
15									
16									
17									
18									
19									
20			Note: Totals are not specifically required, but are provided for proofing.						
21									
22									
23									
24									
25									

23-2 WORK TOGETHER

Extra form

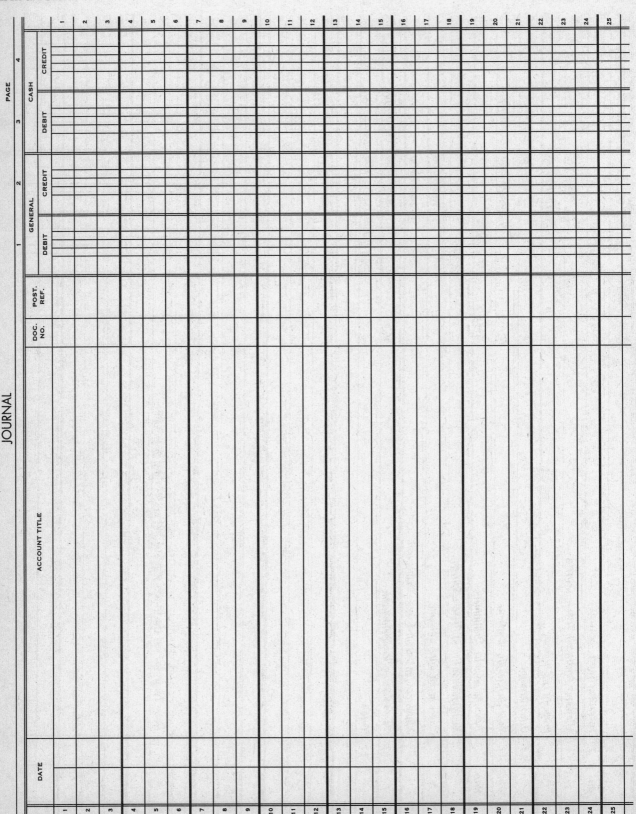

JOURNAL

23-2 ON YOUR OWN, p. 644

Journalizing governmental revenue transactions [5]

JOURNAL — PAGE 1

	DATE		ACCOUNT TITLE	DOC. NO.	POST. REF.	GENERAL DEBIT (1)	GENERAL CREDIT (2)	CASH DEBIT (3)	CASH CREDIT (4)	
1	20-- Jan.	1	Taxes Receivable—Current	M163		120000000				1
2			Allowance for Uncoll. Taxes—Current				1200000			2
3			Property Tax Revenue				118800000			3
4		20	Other Revenue	R541			89400	89400		4
5	Feb.	11	Taxes Receivable—Current	R596			48520000	48520000		5
6	Mar.	1	Taxes Receivable—Delinquent	M225		4810000				6
7			Allowance for Uncoll. Taxes—Current			12000000				7
8			Taxes Receivable—Current				4810000			8
9			Allowance for Uncoll. Taxes—Delinquent				1200000			9
10		15	Taxes Receivable—Delinquent	R628			1515000	1515000		10
11		15	Totals			126010000	176134400	50124400		11
12										12
13										13
14										14
15										15
16										16
17										17
18										18
19										19
20			Note: Totals are not specifically required, but are provided for proofing.							20
21										21
22										22
23										23
24										24
25										25

23-2 ON YOUR OWN

Extra form

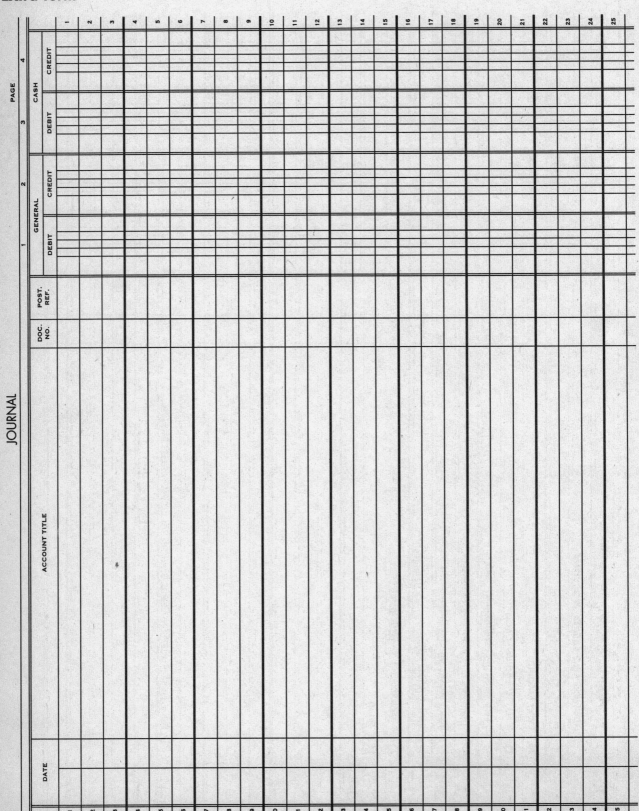

23-3 WORK TOGETHER, p. 651

Journalizing governmental encumbrances, expenditures, and other transactions [5]

JOURNAL   PAGE 1

DATE	ACCOUNT TITLE	DOC. NO.	POST. REF.	GENERAL DEBIT	GENERAL CREDIT	CASH DEBIT	CASH CREDIT	
20-- Jan. 11	Expenditure—Other Charges, Public Works	C482		2 3 8 00			2 3 8 00	1
16	Encumbrance—Supplies, Public Safety	M111		1 5 5 00				2
	Reserve for Encumbrance—Current Year				1 5 5 00			3
19	Notes Payable	NP15			20 0 0 0 0 00	20 0 0 0 0 00		4
27	Reserve for Encumbrance—Current Year	M125		1 5 5 00				5
	Encumbrance—Supplies, Public Safety				1 5 5 00			6
27	Expenditure—Supplies, Public Safety	C497		1 5 1 00			1 5 1 00	7
Feb. 6	Expenditure—Capital Outlays, Gen. Gov't.	C520		3 9 5 00			3 9 5 00	8
19	Notes Payable	C538		20 0 0 0 0 00			20 2 0 0 0 00	9
	Expenditure—Other Charges, Gen. Gov't.			2 0 0 0 00				10
Mar. 16	Investments—Short Term	C567		15 0 0 0 0 00			15 0 0 0 0 00	11
Jun. 16	Investments—Short Term	R312			15 0 0 0 0 00	15 3 7 5 0 00		12
	Interest Revenue				3 7 5 0 00			13
16	Totals			35 3 0 9 4 00	35 4 0 6 0 00	35 3 7 5 0 00	35 2 7 8 4 00	14
								15
								16
								17
								18
								19
								20
								21
								22
								23
								24
								25

Note: Totals are not specifically required, but are provided for proofing.

23-3 WORK TOGETHER

Extra form

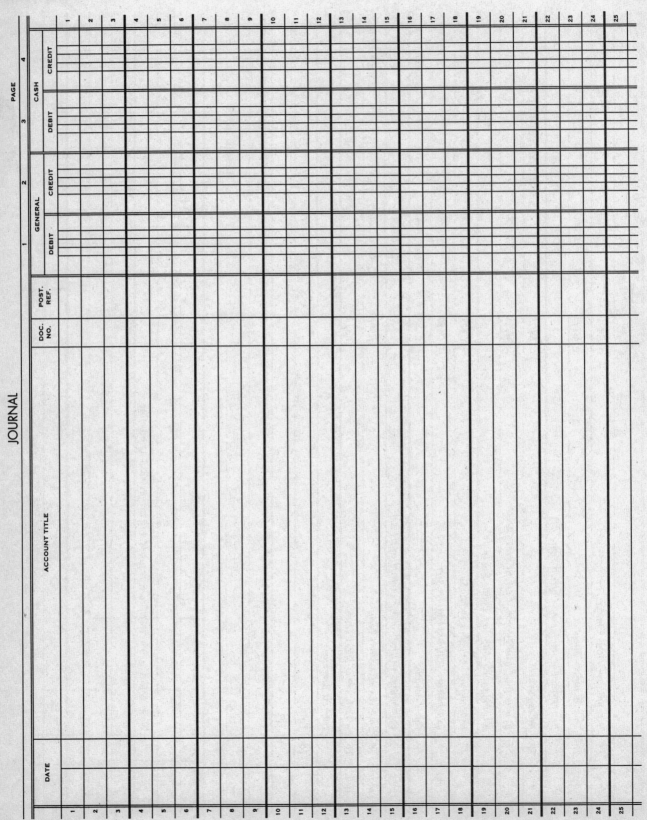

JOURNAL

23-3 ON YOUR OWN, p. 652

Journalizing governmental encumbrances, expenditures, and other transactions [6]

JOURNAL

PAGE 1

DATE		ACCOUNT TITLE	DOC. NO.	POST. REF.	GENERAL DEBIT	GENERAL CREDIT	CASH DEBIT	CASH CREDIT	
20–									
Jan.	12	Expenditure—Personnel, Recreation	C267		500000			500000	1
	17	Encumbrance—Supplies, Public Works	M88		21500				2
		Reserve for Encumbrance—Current Year				21500			3
	20	Notes Payable	NP10			5000000	5000000		4
	28	Reserve for Encumbrance—Current Year	M95		21500				5
		Encumbrance—Supplies, Public Works				21500			6
	28	Expenditure—Supplies, Public Works	C282		21100			21100	7
Feb.	7	Expenditure—Capital Outlays, Public Safety	C294		37500			37500	8
	20	Notes Payable	C322		5000000			5041667	9
		Expenditure—Other Charges, Gen. Gov't.			41667				10
Mar.	17	Investments—Short Term	C351		7500000			7500000	11
Jun.	17	Investments—Short Term	R101			7500000	7575000		12
	17	Interest Revenue				75000			13
	17	Totals			12693267	12618000	12575000	12650267	14

Note: Totals are not specifically required, but are provided for proofing.

23-3 ON YOUR OWN

Extra form

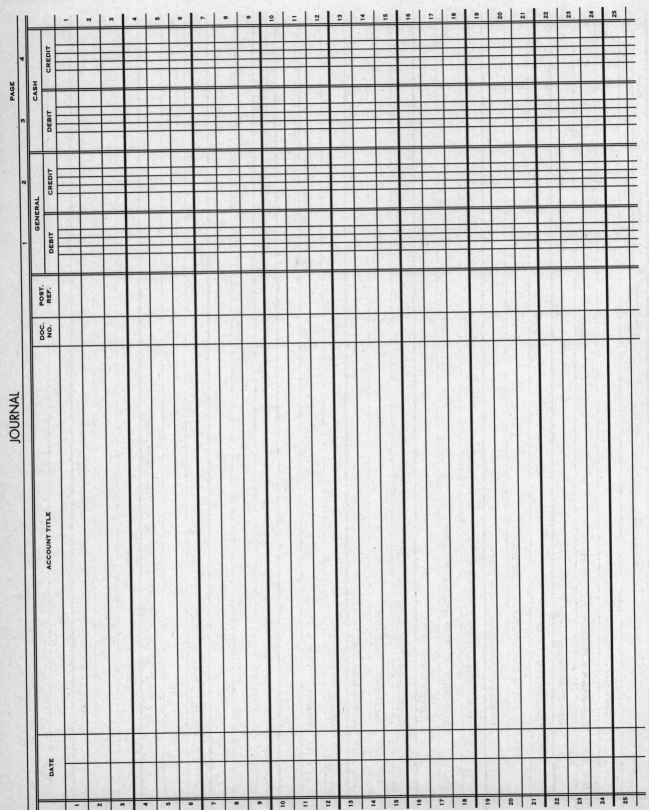

23-1 APPLICATION PROBLEM, p. 654

Journalizing governmental operating budgets

JOURNAL   PAGE 1

	DATE	ACCOUNT TITLE	DOC. NO.	POST. REF.	GENERAL DEBIT	GENERAL CREDIT	CASH DEBIT	CASH CREDIT	
1		a. APPLETON							1
2	20-- Jan. 1	Estimated Revenues			2050000000				2
3		Appropriations				2009000000			3
4		Budgetary Fund Balance				41000000			4
5									5
6		b. MILLTOWN							6
7	20-- Jan. 1	Estimated Revenues			79450000				7
8		Appropriations				78920000			8
9		Budgetary Fund Balance				530000			9
10									10
11		c. WILSON							11
12	20-- Jan. 1	Estimated Revenues			175400000				12
13		Appropriations				172250000			13
14		Budgetary Fund Balance				3150000			14
15	1	Totals			459850000	459850000			15
16									16
17									17
18									18
19									19
20									20
21									21
22									22
23									23
24									24
25									25

Note: Totals are not specifically required, but are provided for proofing.

Name _____ Date _____ Class _____

23-1 APPLICATION PROBLEM

Extra form

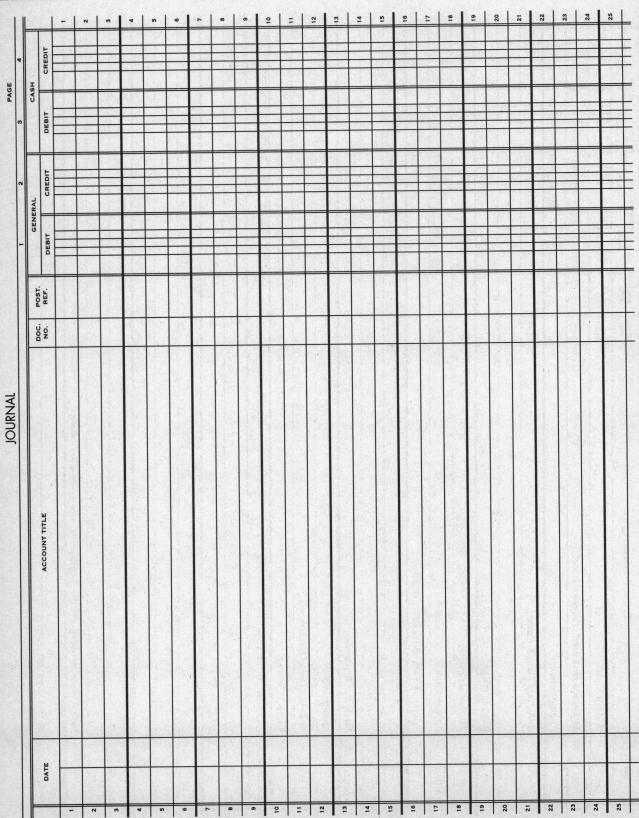

JOURNAL

					PAGE

23-2 APPLICATION PROBLEM, p. 654

Journalizing governmental revenue transactions

JOURNAL PAGE 1

	DATE		ACCOUNT TITLE	DOC. NO.	POST. REF.	GENERAL DEBIT	GENERAL CREDIT	CASH DEBIT	CASH CREDIT	
1	Jan.	1	Taxes Receivable—Current	M88		110000000				1
2			Allowance for Uncoll. Taxes—Current				11000000			2
3			Property Tax Revenue				108900000			3
4		8	Taxes Receivable—Current	R134			9760000	9760000		4
5		14	Other Revenue	R147			5600	5600		5
6	Feb.	11	Taxes Receivable—Current	R194			17235000	17235000		6
7		16	Other Revenue	R212			274450	274450		7
8	Mar.	1	Taxes Receivable—Delinquent	M107		5680000				8
9			Allowance for Uncoll. Taxes—Current			11000000				9
10			Taxes Receivable—Current				5680000			10
11			Allowance for Uncoll. Taxes—Delinquent				11000000			11
12		12	Taxes Receivable—Delinquent	R259			1070000	1070000		12
13		12	Totals			116780000	144878050	28098050		13
14										14
15										15
16										16
17										17
18										18
19										19
20										20
21										21
22										22
23										23
24										24
25										25

Note: Totals are not specifically required, but are provided for proofing.

23-2 APPLICATION PROBLEM

Extra form

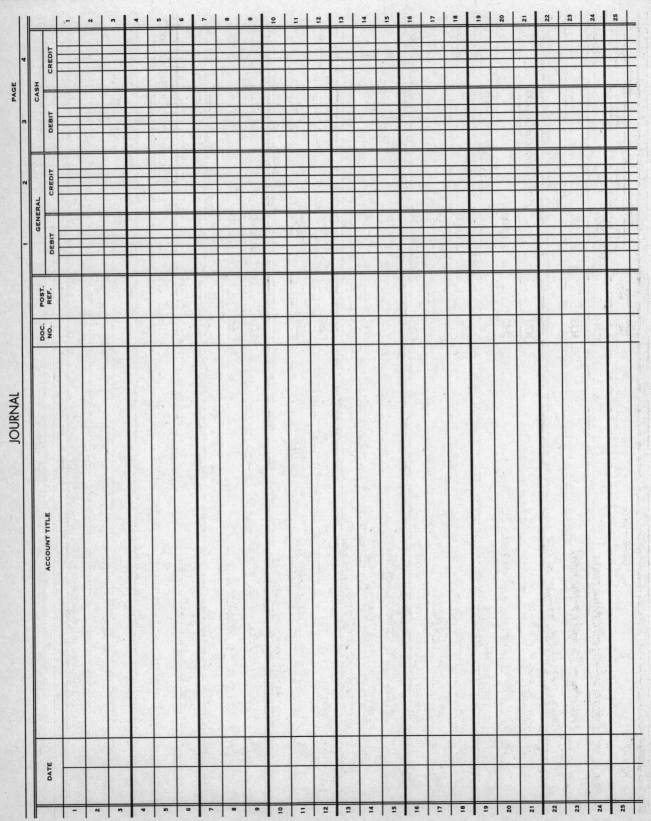

23-3 APPLICATION PROBLEM, p. 654

Journalizing governmental encumbrances, expenditures, and other transactions

JOURNAL
PAGE 1

	DATE		ACCOUNT TITLE	DOC. NO.	POST. REF.	GENERAL DEBIT	GENERAL CREDIT	CASH DEBIT	CASH CREDIT	
1	20-- Jan.	11	Expenditure—Supplies, Public Works	C244		2055 00			2055 00	1
2		15	Encumbrance—Supplies, Public Safety	M33		235 00				2
3			Reserve for Encumbrances—Current Year				235 00			3
4		16	Notes Payable	NP6			15000 00 00	15000 00 00		4
5		28	Reserve for Encumbrances—Current Year	M40		235 00				5
6			Encumbrance—Supplies, Public Safety				235 00			6
7		28	Expenditure—Supplies, Public Safety	C258		232 00			232 00	7
8	Feb.	5	Expenditure—Capital Outlays, Gen. Gov't.	C267		255 00			255 00	8
9		16	Notes Payable	C279		15000 00 00			1512 50 00	9
10			Expenditure—Other Charges, Gen. Gov't.			1250 00				10
11		28	Encumbrance—Supplies, Public Works	M49		276 00				11
12			Reserve for Encumbrances—Current Year				276 00			12
13	Mar.	15	Investments—Short Term	C296		2000 00 00			2000 00 00	13
14		18	Reserve for Encumbrances—Current Year	M58		276 00				14
15			Encumbrance—Supplies, Public Works				276 00			15
16		18	Expenditure—Supplies, Public Works	C315		278 00			278 00	16
17		21	Expenditure—Personnel, Recreation	C322		360 00			360 00	17
18	Jun.	15	Investments—Short Term	R184			2000 00 00	2040 00 00		18
19			Interest Revenue				400 00 00			19
20		15	Totals			3536 02 00	3550 22 00	3540 00 000	3525 80 00	20
21										21
22										22
23			Note: Totals are not specifically required, but are provided for proofing.							23
24										24
25										25

23-3 APPLICATION PROBLEM

Extra form

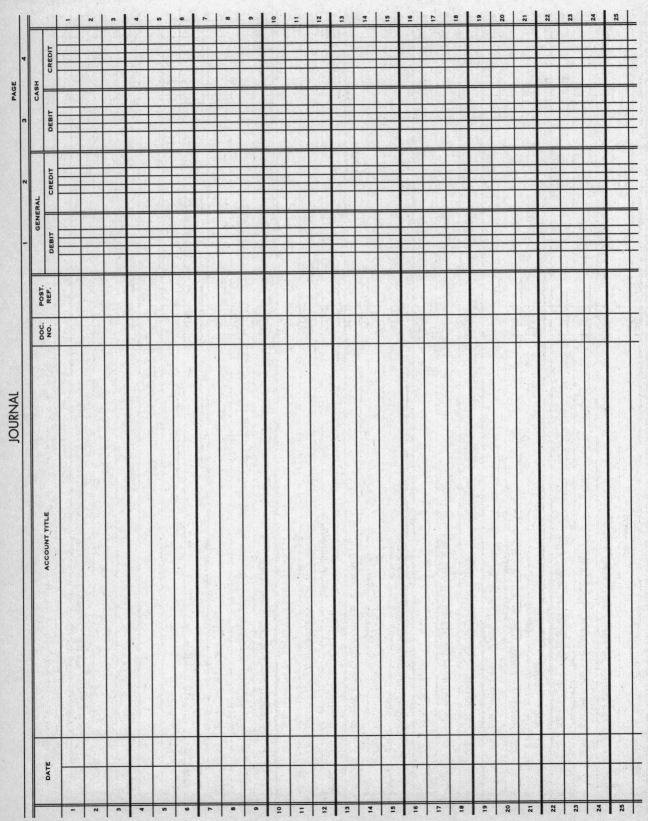

23-4 MASTERY PROBLEM, p. 655

Journalizing governmental transactions

JOURNAL
PAGE 1

	DATE	ACCOUNT TITLE	DOC. NO.	POST. REF.	GENERAL DEBIT	GENERAL CREDIT	CASH DEBIT	CASH CREDIT
1	Jan. 2	Estimated Revenues	M42		1270000000			
2		Appropriations				1224000000		
3		Budgetary Fund Balance				46000000		
4	2	Taxes Receivable—Current	M43		1220000000			
5		Allowance for Uncoll. Taxes—Current				12200000		
6		Property Tax Revenue				1207800000		
7	9	Taxes Receivable—Current	R105			5730000	57300000	
8	11	Expenditure—Other Charges, Gen. Gov't	C168		234400			234400
9	12	Notes Payable	NP7			200000000	200000000	
10	16	Encumbrance—Supplies, Public Works	M54		16500			
11		Reserve for Encumbrances—Current Year				16500		
12	20	Other Revenue	R111			22500	22500	
13	30	Expenditure—Capital Outlays, Public Works	C182		45000			45000
14	Feb. 6	Reserve for Encumbrances—Current Year	M58		16500			
15		Encumbrance—Supplies, Public Works				16500		
16	6	Expenditure—Supplies, Public Works	C190		17000			17000
17	24	Encumbrance—Supplies, Recreation	M69		13300			
18		Reserve for Encumbrances—Current Year				13300		
19	Mar. 1	Taxes Receivable—Delinquent	M76		5140000			
20		Allowance for Uncoll. Taxes—Current			1220000			
21		Taxes Receivable—Current				5140000		
22		Allowance for Uncoll. Taxes—Delinquent				1220000		
23	12	Notes Payable	C222		200000000			203000000
24		Expenditure—Other Charges, Gen. Gov't			3000000			

23-4 MASTERY PROBLEM (concluded)

JOURNAL

PAGE 1 (cont.)

	DATE	ACCOUNT TITLE	DOC. NO.	POST. REF.	GENERAL DEBIT	GENERAL CREDIT	CASH DEBIT	CASH CREDIT	
25	20	Investments—Short Term	C234		40000000			40000000	25
26	22	Reserve for Encumbrances—Current Year	M88		13300				26
27		Encumbrance—Supplies, Recreation				13300			27
28	22	Expenditure—Supplies, Recreation	C241		13100			13100	28
29	Apr. 10	Taxes Receivable—Delinquent	R355			2100000	2100000		29
30	25	Expenditure—Personnel, Recreation	C266		50000			50000	30
31	June 20	Investments—Short Term	R497			40000000	40800000		31
32		Interest Revenue				800000			32
33	20	Totals			31586 8100	32407 2100	68652 5500	60448 5500	33
34									34
35									35
36									36
37									37
38									38
39									39
40									40
41									41
42									42
43									43
44									44
45									45
46									46
47									47
48									48

Note: Totals are not specifically required, but are provided for proofing.

23-5 CHALLENGE PROBLEM, p. 656

Journalizing governmental transactions

JOURNAL
PAGE 1

DATE		ACCOUNT TITLE	DOC. NO.	POST. REF.	GENERAL DEBIT	GENERAL CREDIT	CASH DEBIT	CASH CREDIT	
20-- Jan.	2	Estimated Revenues	M88		152800000				1
		Budgetary Fund Balance			1410000				2
		Appropriations				154210000			3
	2	Taxes Receivable—Current	M89		145200000				4
		Allowance for Uncoll. Taxes—Current				1452000			5
		Property Tax Revenue				143748000			6
	9	Taxes Receivable—Current	R111			6470000	6470000		7
	17	Expenditure—Other Charges, Public Works	C131		28600			28600	8
	20	Notes Payable	NP14			17500000	17500000		9
	25	Encumbrance—Supplies, Public Safety	M102		17000				10
		Reserve for Encumbrances—Current Year				17000			11
Feb.	3	Other Revenue	R152			115800	115800		12
	10	Reserve for Encumbrances—Current Year	M130		17000				13
		Encumbrance—Supplies, Public Safety				17000			14
	10	Expenditure—Supplies, Public Safety	C188		16200			16200	15
	21	Expenditure—Capital Outlays, Recreation	C199		575500			575500	16
Mar.	1	Taxes Receivable—Delinquent	M154		15810000				17
		Allowance for Uncoll. Taxes—Current			1452000				18
		Taxes Receivable—Current				15810000			19
		Allowance for Uncoll. Taxes—Delinquent				1452000			20
	15	Investments—Short Term	C220		50000000			50000000	21
	20	Notes Payable	C230		17500000			17850000	22
		Expenditure—Other Charges, Gen. Gov't			350000				23
	21	Taxes Receivable—Delinquent	R206			22500000	22500000		24

23-5 CHALLENGE PROBLEM (concluded)

JOURNAL

PAGE 1 (cont.)

DATE		ACCOUNT TITLE	DOC. NO.	POST. REF.	GENERAL DEBIT	GENERAL CREDIT	CASH DEBIT	CASH CREDIT	
Apr.	4	Encumbrances—Capital Outlays, Gen. Gov't.	M178		880 00				25
		Reserve for Encumbrances—Current Year				880 00			26
	16	Reserve for Encumbrances—Current Year	M190		880 00				27
		Encumbrance—Capital Outlays, Gen. Gov't.				880 00			28
	16	Expenditure—Capital Outlays, Gen. Gov't.	C267		898 00			898 00	29
July	15	Investments—Short Term	R289			5000000 00	5150000 00		30
		Interest Revenue				150000 00			31
	15	Totals			3849241 00	3947178 00	778358 00	680421 00	32
									33
									34
									35
									36
									37
									38
									39
									40
									41
									42
									43
									44
									45
									46
									47
									48

Note: Totals are not specifically required, but are provided for proofing.

24-1 WORK TOGETHER, p. 667

Preparing a work sheet for a governmental organization   [5, 6]

Town of Anoka General Fund
Work Sheet
For Year Ended December 31, 20--

#	Account Title	Trial Balance Debit	Trial Balance Credit	Adjustments Debit	Adjustments Credit	Revenues/Expenditures Debit	Revenues/Expenditures Credit	Balance Sheet Debit	Balance Sheet Credit
1	Cash	7165100						7165100	
2	Taxes Receivable—Current								
3	Allow. for Uncoll. Taxes—Current								
4	Taxes Receivable—Delinquent	1219700						1219700	
5	Allow. for Uncoll. Taxes—Delinquent		682400						682400
6	Interest Receivable			(b)249000				249000	
7	Allow. for Uncoll. Interest				(b)49800				49800
8	Inventory of Supplies			(a)292500				292500	
9	Investments—Short Term								
10	Accounts Payable		3310800						3310800
11	Notes Payable								
12	Unreserved Fund Balance		855000						855000
13	Reserve for Encumb.—Current Year		1550000	(c)1550000			1550000		
14	Reserve for Encumb.—Prior Year				(c)1550000				
15	Reserve for Inventory of Supplies				(a)292500				292500
16	Property Tax Revenue		160041100		(b)199200		160041100		
17	Interest Revenue		748500				947700		
18	Other Revenue		223000				223000		
19	Expend.—Personnel, Gen. Gov't	25847200				25847200			
20	Expend.—Supplies, Gen. Gov't	1049500				1049500			
21	Expend.—Other Chgs., Gen. Gov't	11306000				11306000			
22	Expend.—Cap. Outlays, Gen. Gov't	1697800				1697800			
23	Expend.—Personnel, Pub. Saf.	54971200				39900500 / 54971200			
24	Expend.—Supplies, Pub. Saf.	1866300				1866300			
25	Expend.—Other Chgs., Pub. Saf.	15381800				15381800			
26	Expend.—Cap. Outlays, Pub. Saf.	8749300				8749300			
27	Expend.—Personnel, Pub. Wks.	11218600				80968600 / 11218600			

24-1 WORK TOGETHER (concluded)

[5, 6]

#	ACCOUNT TITLE	TRIAL BALANCE DEBIT	TRIAL BALANCE CREDIT	ADJUSTMENTS DEBIT	ADJUSTMENTS CREDIT	REVENUES/EXPENDITURES DEBIT	REVENUES/EXPENDITURES CREDIT	BALANCE SHEET DEBIT	BALANCE SHEET CREDIT
28	Expend.—Supplies, Pub. Wks.	5 895 00				5 895 00			
29	Expend.—Other Chgs., Pub. Wks.	96 224 00				96 224 00			
30	Expend.—Cap. Outlays, Pub. Wks.	50 781 00				50 781 00			
31	Expend.—Personnel, Rec.	564 000 00				2650 86 00 / 564 00 00			
32	Expend.—Supplies, Rec.	4 708 00				4 708 00			
33	Expend.—Other Chgs., Rec.	25 545 00				25 545 00			
34	Expend.—Cap. Outlays, Rec.	14 330 00				14 330 00			
35	Estimated Revenues	1611 45 000				1009 83 00 / 1611 45 0 00			
36	Appropriations		1579 051 00				1579 051 00		
37	Budgetary Fund Balance		32 399 00				32 399 00		
38	Encumb.—Supplies, Pub. Wks.	1 550 00				1 550 00			
39		3271 608 00	3271 608 00	6965 00	6965 00	3187 76 00	3225 118 00	892 63 00	519 05 00
40						37 358 00			37 358 00
41	*Excess of Rev. Over Expend.*					3225 118 00		892 63 00	892 63 00
42									
43									
44									
45									
46									
47									
48									
49									
50									
51									
52									
53									
54									

24-1 ON YOUR OWN, p. 667

Preparing a work sheet for a governmental organization [7, 8]

Town of Annandale General Fund
Work Sheet
For Year Ended December 31, 20--

#	ACCOUNT TITLE	Trial Balance DEBIT	Trial Balance CREDIT	Adjustments DEBIT	Adjustments CREDIT	Revenues/Expenditures DEBIT	Revenues/Expenditures CREDIT	Balance Sheet DEBIT	Balance Sheet CREDIT
1	Cash	7718700						7718700	
2	Taxes Receivable—Current								
3	Allow. for Uncoll. Taxes—Current								
4	Taxes Receivable—Delinquent	1058600						1058600	
5	Allow. for Uncoll. Taxes—Delinquent		591800						591800
6	Interest Receivable			(b)218000				218000	
7	Allow. for Uncoll. Interest				(b)43600				43600
8	Inventory of Supplies			(a)187000				187000	
9	Investments—Short Term								
10	Accounts Payable		3571400						3571400
11	Notes Payable								
12	Unreserved Fund Balance		2731900						2731900
13	Reserve for Encumb.—Current Year		190000	(c)190000					
14	Reserve for Encumb.—Prior Year				(c)190000		190000		187000
15	Reserve for Inventory of Supplies				(a)187000				
16	Property Tax Revenue		149019500				149019500		
17	Interest Revenue		651500		(b)174400		825900		
18	Other Revenue		379000				379000		
19	Expend.—Personnel, Gen. Gov't	23140400				23140400			
20	Expend.—Supplies, Gen. Gov't	1127700				1127700			
21	Expend.—Other Chgs., Gen. Gov't	11088800				11088800			
22	Expend.—Cap. Outlays, Gen. Gov't	1566300				1566300			
23	Expend.—Personnel, Pub. Saf.	53879000				53879000			
24	Expend.—Supplies, Pub. Saf.	1692100				1692100			
25	Expend.—Other Chgs., Pub. Saf.	15009300				15009300			
26	Expend.—Cap. Outlays, Pub. Saf.	8750000				8750000			
27	Expend.—Personnel, Pub. Wks.	11196200				11196200			

24-1 ON YOUR OWN (concluded)

[7, 8]

#	ACCOUNT TITLE	TRIAL BALANCE DEBIT	TRIAL BALANCE CREDIT	ADJUSTMENTS DEBIT	ADJUSTMENTS CREDIT	REVENUES/EXPENDITURES DEBIT	REVENUES/EXPENDITURES CREDIT	BALANCE SHEET DEBIT	BALANCE SHEET CREDIT
28	Expend.—Supplies, Pub. Wks.	4 9 2 4 00				4 9 2 4 00			
29	Expend.—Other Chgs., Pub. Wks.	95 6 7 5 00				95 6 7 5 00			
30	Expend.—Cap. Outlays, Pub. Wks.	50 0 0 0 00				50 0 0 0 00			
31	Expend.—Personnel, Rec.	140 0 0 0 00				262 5 6 1 00 / 140 0 0 0 00			
32	Expend.—Supplies, Rec.	3 9 4 3 00				3 9 4 3 00			
33	Expend.—Other Chgs., Rec.	24 8 5 6 00				24 8 5 6 00			
34	Expend.—Cap. Outlays, Rec.	13 7 8 2 00				13 7 8 2 00			
35	Estimated Revenues	1501 5 0 0 00				56 5 8 1 00 / 1501 5 0 0 00			
36	Appropriations		1485 0 0 0 00				1485 0 0 0 00		
37	Budgetary Fund Balance		16 5 0 0 00				16 5 0 0 00		
38	Encumb.—Supplies, Recreation	1 9 0 0 00				1 9 0 0 00			
39		3072 8 5 1 00	3072 8 5 1 00	5 9 5 0 00	5 9 5 0 00	2985 0 7 8 00 / 3005 6 4 4 00	3005 6 4 4 00	91 8 2 3 00	71 2 5 7 00
40	Excess of Rev. Over Expend.					20 5 6 6 00			20 5 6 6 00
41						3005 6 4 4 00	3005 6 4 4 00	91 8 2 3 00	91 8 2 3 00
42									
43									
44									
45									
46									
47									
48									
49									
50									
51									
52									
53									
54									

24-2 WORK TOGETHER, p. 671

Preparing financial statements for a governmental organization

The work sheet from Work Together 24-1 is needed to complete this problem.

Town of Anoka Annual Operating Budget—General Fund For Year Ended December 31, 20--		
ESTIMATED REVENUES		
Property Tax	$ 1,600,411.00	
Interest	9,000.00	
Other	2,039.00	
Total Estimated Revenues		$ 1,611,450.00
ESTIMATED EXPENDITURES AND **BUDGETARY FUND BALANCE**		
General Government:		
Personnel	$ 268,550.00	
Supplies	63,800.00	
Other Charges	27,925.00	
Capital Outlays	39,725.00	
Total General Government		$ 400,000.00
Public Safety:		
Personnel	$ 398,500.00	
Supplies	125,750.00	
Other Charges	126,250.00	
Capital Outlays	160,500.00	
Total Public Safety		811,000.00
Public Works:		
Personnel	$ 135,800.00	
Supplies	49,250.00	
Other Charges	56,775.00	
Capital Outlays	24,726.00	
Total Public Works		266,551.00
Recreation:		
Personnel	$ 38,600.00	
Supplies	23,800.00	
Other Charges	16,550.00	
Capital Outlays	22,550.00	
Total Recreation		101,500.00
Total Estimated Expenditures		$ 1,579,051.00
Budgetary Fund Balance		32,399.00
Total Estimated Expenditures and Budgetary Fund Balance		$ 1,611.450.00

24-2 WORK TOGETHER (continued)

[5]

Town of Anoka General Fund

Statement of Revenues, Expenditures, and Changes in Fund Balance—Budget and Actual

For Year Ended December 31, 20--

	BUDGET	ACTUAL	VARIANCE—FAVORABLE (UNFAVORABLE)
Revenues:			
Property Tax Revenue	1600 4 1 1 00	1600 4 1 1 00	—
Interest Revenue	9 0 0 0 00	9 4 7 7 00	4 7 7 00
Other Revenue	2 0 3 9 00	2 2 3 0 00	1 9 1 00
Total Revenues	1611 4 5 0 00	1612 1 1 8 00	6 6 8 00
Expenditures:			
General Government	400 0 0 0 00	399 0 0 5 00	9 9 5 00
Public Safety	811 0 0 0 00	809 6 8 6 00	1 3 1 4 00
Public Works	266 5 5 1 00	265 0 8 6 00	1 4 6 5 00
Recreation	101 5 0 0 00	100 9 8 3 00	5 1 7 00
Total Expenditures	1579 0 5 1 00	1574 7 6 0 00	4 2 9 1 00
Excess of Revenues Over Expenditures	32 3 9 9 00	37 3 5 8 00	4 9 5 9 00
Less Outstanding Encumbrances, Dec. 31, 20--	—	1 5 5 0 00	(1 5 5 0 00)
Increase in Unreserved Fund Balance for Year	32 3 9 9 00	35 8 0 8 00	3 4 0 9 00
Unreserved Fund Balance, Jan. 1, 20--	8 5 5 0 00	8 5 5 0 00	—
Unreserved Fund Balance, Dec. 31, 20--	40 9 4 9 00	44 3 5 8 00	3 4 0 9 00

24-2 WORK TOGETHER (concluded)

[6]

Town of Anoka General Fund

Balance Sheet

December 31, 20--

ASSETS													
Cash								71	6	5	1	00	
Taxes Receivable—Delinquent	12	1	9	7	00								
Less Allowance for Uncoll. Taxes —Delinquent	6	8	2	4	00		5	3	7	3	00	
Interest Receivable	2	4	9	0	00								
Less Allowance for Uncollectible Interest		4	9	8	00		1	9	9	2	00	
Inventory of Supplies								2	9	2	5	00	
Total Assets								81	9	4	1	00	
LIABILITIES AND FUND EQUITY													
Liabilities:													
Accounts Payable								33	1	0	8	00	
Fund Equity:													
Unreserved Fund Balance	44	3	5	8	00								
Reserve for Encumbrances—Prior Year	1	5	5	0	00								
Reserve for Inventory of Supplies	2	9	2	5	00								
Total Fund Equity								48	8	3	3	00	
Total Liabilities and Fund Equity								81	9	4	1	00	

Name _____ Date _____ _ Class _____

24-2 WORK TOGETHER

Extra form

24-2 ON YOUR OWN, p. 671

Preparing financial statements for a governmental organization

The work sheet from On Your Own 24-1 is needed to complete this problem.

Town of Annandale Annual Operating Budget—General Fund For Year Ended December 31, 20--		
ESTIMATED REVENUES		
Property Tax	$ 1,490,195.00	
Interest.	7,638.00	
Other	3,667.00	
Total Estimated Revenues.		$ 1,501,500.00
ESTIMATED EXPENDITURES AND BUDGETARY FUND BALANCE		
General Government:		
Personnel	$ 259,250.00	
Supplies	54,500.00	
Other Charges	23,775.00	
Capital Outlays	31,873.00	
Total General Government		$ 369,398.00
Public Safety:		
Personnel	$ 425,550.00	
Supplies	101,375.00	
Other Charges	118,266.00	
Capital Outlays	150,000.00	
Total Public Safety.		795,191.00
Public Works:		
Personnel	$ 127,900.00	
Supplies	54,921.00	
Other Charges	55,316.00	
Capital Outlays	25,550.00	
Total Public Works		263,687.00
Recreation:		
Personnel	$ 19,650.00	
Supplies	10,950.00	
Other Charges	7,624.00	
Capital Outlays	18,500.00	
Total Recreation		56,724.00
Total Estimated Expenditures		$ 1,485,000.00
Budgetary Fund Balance.		16,500.00
Total Estimated Expenditures and Budgetary Fund Balance		$ 1,501.500.00

24-2 ON YOUR OWN (continued)

[7]

Town of Annandale General Fund

Statement of Revenues, Expenditures, and Changes in Fund Balance—Budget and Actual

For Year Ended December 31, 20--

	BUDGET	ACTUAL	VARIANCE—FAVORABLE (UNFAVORABLE)
Revenues:			
Property Tax Revenue	1490 1 9 5 00	1490 1 9 5 00	——
Interest Revenue	7 6 3 8 00	8 2 5 9 00	6 2 1 00
Other Revenue	3 6 6 7 00	3 7 9 0 00	1 2 3 00
Total Revenues	1501 5 0 0 00	1502 2 4 4 00	7 4 4 00
Expenditures:			
General Government	369 3 9 8 00	369 2 3 2 00	1 6 6 00
Public Safety	795 1 9 1 00	793 3 0 4 00	1 8 8 7 00
Public Works	263 6 8 7 00	262 5 6 1 00	1 1 2 6 00
Recreation	56 7 2 4 00	56 5 8 1 00	1 4 3 00
Total Expenditures	1485 0 0 0 00	1481 6 7 8 00	3 3 2 2 00
Excess of Revenues Over Expenditures	16 5 0 0 00	20 5 6 6 00	4 0 6 6 00
Less Outstanding Encumbrances, Dec. 31, 20--	——	1 9 0 0 00	(1 9 0 0 00)
Increase in Unreserved Fund Balance for Year	16 5 0 0 00	18 6 6 6 00	2 1 6 6 00
Unreserved Fund Balance, Jan. 1, 20--	27 3 1 9 00	27 3 1 9 00	——
Unreserved Fund Balance, Dec. 31, 20--	43 8 1 9 00	45 9 8 5 00	2 1 6 6 00

24-2 ON YOUR OWN (concluded)

[8]

Town of Annandale General Fund

Balance Sheet

December 31, 20--

ASSETS										
Cash							77	1 8 7	00
Taxes Receivable—Delinquent	10	5 8 6	00						
Less Allowance for Uncoll. Taxes —Delinquent	5	9 1 8	00		4	6 6 8	00	
Interest Receivable	2	1 8 0	00					
Less Allowance for Uncollectible Interest		4 3 6	00		1	7 4 4	00	
Inventory of Supplies					1	8 7 0	00	
Total Assets					85	4 6 9	00	
LIABILITIES AND FUND EQUITY								
Liabilities:								
Accounts Payable					35	7 1 4	00	
Fund Equity:								
Unreserved Fund Balance	45	9 8 5	00					
Reserve for Encumbrances—Prior Year	1	9 0 0	00					
Reserve for Inventory of Supplies	1	8 7 0	00					
Total Fund Equity					49	7 5 5	00	
Total Liabilities and Fund Equity					85	4 6 9	00	

24-2 ON YOUR OWN

Extra form

24-3 WORK TOGETHER, p. 674

Journalizing adjusting and closing entries for a governmental organization [5, 6]

The work sheet from Work Together 24-1 is needed to complete this problem.

JOURNAL

PAGE 40

	DATE	ACCOUNT TITLE	DOC. NO.	POST. REF.	GENERAL DEBIT	GENERAL CREDIT	CASH DEBIT	CASH CREDIT	
1		*Adjusting Entries*							1
2	20-- Dec. 31	Inventory of Supplies			2 9 2 5 00				2
3		Reserve for Inventory of Supplies				2 9 2 5 00			3
4	31	Interest Receivable			2 4 9 0 00				4
5		Allowance for Uncollectible Interest				4 9 8 00			5
6		Interest Revenue				1 9 9 2 00			6
7	31	Reserve for Encumbrances—Current Year			1 5 5 0 00				7
8		Reserve for Encumbrances—Prior Year				1 5 5 0 00			8
9		*Closing Entries*							9
10	31	Property Tax Revenue			1600 4 1 1 00				10
11		Interest Revenue			9 4 7 7 00				11
12		Other Revenue			2 2 3 0 00				12
13		Unreserved Fund Balance				1612 1 1 8 00			13
14	31	Unreserved Fund Balance			1574 7 6 0 00				14
15		Expenditure—Personnel, Gen. Gov't				258 4 7 2 00			15
16		Expenditure—Supplies, Gen. Gov't				10 4 9 5 00			16
17		Expenditure—Other Charges, Gen. Gov't				113 0 6 0 00			17
18		Expenditure—Capital Outlays, Gen. Gov't				16 9 7 8 00			18
19		Expenditure—Personnel, Public Safety				549 7 1 2 00			19
20		Expenditure—Supplies, Public Safety				18 6 6 3 00			20
21		Expenditure—Other Charges, Public Safety				153 8 1 8 00			21
22		Expenditure—Capital Outlays, Public Safety				87 4 9 3 00			22
23		Expenditure—Personnel, Public Works				112 1 8 6 00			23
24		Expenditure—Supplies, Public Works				5 8 9 5 00			24

24-3 WORK TOGETHER (concluded)

[5, 6]

JOURNAL

PAGE 40 (cont.)

	DATE	ACCOUNT TITLE	DOC. NO.	POST. REF.	GENERAL DEBIT	GENERAL CREDIT	CASH DEBIT	CASH CREDIT	
25		Expenditure—Other Charges, Public Works				9622400			25
26		Expenditure—Capital Outlays, Public Works				5078100			26
27		Expenditure—Personnel, Recreation				5640000			27
28		Expenditure—Supplies, Recreation				470800			28
29		Expenditure—Other Charges, Recreation				2554500			29
30		Expenditure—Capital Outlays, Recreation				1433000			30
31	31	Appropriations			15790 5100				31
32		Budgetary Fund Balance			3239900				32
33		Estimated Revenues				16114 5000			33
34	31	Unreserved Fund Balance			155000				34
35		Encumbrance—Supplies, Public Works				155000			35
36									36
37									37
38									38
39									39
40									40
41									41
42									42
43									43
44									44
45									45
46									46
47									47
48									48

Name _____ Date _____ Class _____

24-3 ON YOUR OWN, p. 674

Journalizing adjusting and closing entries for a governmental organization [7, 8]

The work sheet from On Your Own 24-1 is needed to complete this problem.

JOURNAL   PAGE 52

	DATE	DOC. NO.	POST. REF.	ACCOUNT TITLE	GENERAL DEBIT	GENERAL CREDIT	CASH DEBIT	CASH CREDIT
1				*Adjusting Entries*				
2	20-- Dec. 31			Inventory of Supplies	1 87000			
3				Reserve for Inventory of Supplies		1 87000		
4	31			Interest Receivable	2 18000			
5				Allowance for Uncollectible Interest		43600		
6				Interest Revenue		1 74400		
7	31			Reserve for Encumbrances—Current Year	1 90000			
8				Reserve for Encumbrances—Prior Year		1 90000		
9				*Closing Entries*				
10	31			Property Tax Revenue	1490 1 9500			
11				Interest Revenue	8 25900			
12				Other Revenue	3 79000			
13				Unreserved Fund Balance		1502 2 4400		
14	31			Unreserved Fund Balance	1481 6 7800			
15				Expenditure—Personnel, Gen. Gov't		231 4 0400		
16				Expenditure—Supplies, Gen. Gov't		11 2 7700		
17				Expenditure—Other Charges, Gen. Gov't		110 8 8800		
18				Expenditure—Capital Outlays, Gen. Gov't		15 6 6300		
19				Expenditure—Personnel, Public Safety		538 7 9000		
20				Expenditure—Supplies, Public Safety		16 9 2100		
21				Expenditure—Other Charges, Public Safety		150 0 9300		
22				Expenditure—Capital Outlays, Public Safety		87 5 0000		
23				Expenditure—Personnel, Public Works		111 9 6200		
24				Expenditure—Supplies, Public Works		4 92400		

24-3 ON YOUR OWN (concluded)

[7, 8]

JOURNAL

PAGE 52 (cont.)

	DATE	ACCOUNT TITLE	DOC. NO.	POST. REF.	GENERAL DEBIT	GENERAL CREDIT	CASH DEBIT	CASH CREDIT	
25		Expenditure—Other Charges, Public Works				9567500			25
26		Expenditure—Capital Outlays, Public Works				5000000			26
27		Expenditure—Personnel, Recreation				14000000			27
28		Expenditure—Supplies, Recreation				394300			28
29		Expenditure—Other Charges, Recreation				2485600			29
30		Expenditure—Capital Outlays, Recreation				1378200			30
31	31	Appropriations			148500000				31
32		Budgetary Fund Balance			1650000				32
33		Estimated Revenues				150150000			33
34	31	Unreserved Fund Balance			190000				34
35		Encumbrance—Supplies, Recreation				190000			35
36									36
37									37
38									38
39									39
40									40
41									41
42									42
43									43
44									44
45									45
46									46
47									47
48									48

24-1 APPLICATION PROBLEM, p. 676

Preparing a work sheet for a governmental organization

[1, 2]

The work sheet prepared in this problem is needed to complete Application Problems 24-2 and 24-3.

Town of Winona General Fund
Work Sheet
For Year Ended December 31, 20--

	ACCOUNT TITLE	TRIAL BALANCE DEBIT	TRIAL BALANCE CREDIT	ADJUSTMENTS DEBIT	ADJUSTMENTS CREDIT	REVENUES/EXPENDITURES DEBIT	REVENUES/EXPENDITURES CREDIT	BALANCE SHEET DEBIT	BALANCE SHEET CREDIT
1	Cash	7413000						7413000	
2	Taxes Receivable—Current								
3	Allow. for Uncoll. Taxes—Current								
4	Taxes Receivable—Delinquent	1770000						1770000	
5	Allow. for Uncoll. Taxes—Delinquent		796000						796000
6	Interest Receivable			(b) 290000				290000	
7	Allow. for Uncoll. Interest				(b) 58000				58000
8	Inventory of Supplies			(a) 353400				353400	
9	Investments—Short Term								
10	Accounts Payable		3432000						3432000
11	Notes Payable								
12	Unreserved Fund Balance		4124400						4124400
13	Reserve for Encumb.—Current Year		2240000	(c) 224000					
14	Reserve for Encumb.—Prior Year				(c) 224000		224000		
15	Reserve for Inventory of Supplies				(a) 353400				353400
16	Property Tax Revenue		145900000				145900000		
17	Interest Revenue		475600		(b) 232000		707600		
18	Other Revenue		902000				902000		
19	Expend.—Personnel, Gen. Gov't	25005000				25005000			
20	Expend.—Supplies, Gen. Gov't	1210000				1210000			
21	Expend.—Other Chgs., Gen. Gov't	12451000				12451000			
22	Expend.—Cap. Outlays, Gen. Gov't	1450000				1450000			
23	Expend.—Personnel, Pub. Saf.	41470000				4011600 / 41470000			
24	Expend.—Supplies, Pub. Saf.	2185000				2185000			
25	Expend.—Other Chgs., Pub. Saf.	16842000				16842000			
26	Expend.—Cap. Outlays, Pub. Saf.	8098000				8098000			
27	Expend.—Personnel, Pub. Wks.	15773000				6859500 / 15773000			

24-1 APPLICATION PROBLEM (concluded)

[1, 2]

	ACCOUNT TITLE	TRIAL BALANCE DEBIT (1)	TRIAL BALANCE CREDIT (2)	ADJUSTMENTS DEBIT (3)	ADJUSTMENTS CREDIT (4)	REVENUES/EXPENDITURES DEBIT (5)	REVENUES/EXPENDITURES CREDIT (6)	BALANCE SHEET DEBIT (7)	BALANCE SHEET CREDIT (8)
28	Expend.—Supplies, Pub. Wks.	6150 00				6150 00			
29	Expend.—Other Chgs., Pub. Wks.	5217 00				5217 00			
30	Expend.—Cap. Outlays, Pub. Wks.	4630 00				4630 00			
31	Expend.—Personnel, Rec.	5525 00				2623 5 00 / 552 5 00			
32	Expend.—Supplies, Rec.	2157 00				2157 00			
33	Expend.—Other Chgs., Rec.	2775 00				2775 00			
34	Expend.—Cap. Outlays, Rec.	1044 00				1044 00			
35	Estimated Revenues	14769 50 00				1150 10 00 / 14769 50 00			
36	Appropriations		14675 40 00				14675 40 00		
37	Budgetary Fund Balance		941 00 00				941 00 00		
38	Encumb.—Supplies, Gen Gov't	224 0 00				224 0 00			
39		30354 90 00	30354 90 00	8 674 00	8 674 00	29436 00 00	29542 86 00	9826 40 0	8763 80 0
40	Excess of Rev. Over Expend.					1062 600			1062 600
41						29542 86 00	29542 86 00	9826 40 0	9826 40 0
42									
43									
44									
45									
46									
47									
48									
49									
50									
51									
52									
53									
54									

24-2 APPLICATION PROBLEM p. 676

Preparing financial statements for a governmental organization [1]

The work sheet prepared in Application Problems 24-1 is needed to complete this problem.

Town of Winona General Fund

Statement of Revenues, Expenditures, and Changes in Fund Balance—Budget and Actual

For Year Ended December 31, 20--

	BUDGET	ACTUAL	VARIANCE— FAVORABLE (UNFAVORABLE)
Revenues:			
Property Tax Revenue	1459 0 0 0 00	1459 0 0 0 00	—
Interest Revenue	8 9 5 0 00	7 0 7 6 00	(1 8 7 4 00)
Other Revenue	9 0 0 0 00	9 0 2 0 00	2 0 00
Total Revenues	1476 9 5 0 00	1475 0 9 6 00	(1 8 5 4 00)
Expenditures:			
General Government	402 8 2 0 00	401 1 6 0 00	1 6 6 0 00
Public Safety	686 4 7 0 00	685 9 5 0 00	5 2 0 00
Public Works	262 4 9 0 00	262 3 5 0 00	1 4 0 00
Recreation	115 7 6 0 00	115 0 1 0 00	7 5 0 00
Total Expenditures	1467 5 4 0 00	1464 4 7 0 00	3 0 7 0 00
Excess of Revenues Over Expenditures	9 4 1 0 00	10 6 2 6 00	1 2 1 6 00
Less Outstanding Encumbrances, Dec. 31, 20--	—	2 2 4 0 00	(2 2 4 0 00)
Increase in Unreserved Fund Balance for Year	9 4 1 0 00	8 3 8 6 00	(1 0 2 4 00)
Unreserved Fund Balance, Jan. 1, 20--	41 2 4 4 00	41 2 4 4 00	—
Unreserved Fund Balance, Dec. 31, 20--	50 6 5 4 00	49 6 3 0 00	(1 0 2 4 00)

Name _____ Date _____ Class _____

24-2 APPLICATION PROBLEM (concluded)

Town of Winona General Fund

Balance Sheet

December 31, 20--

ASSETS			
Cash			74 1 3 0 00
Taxes Receivable—Delinquent	17 7 0 0 00		
Less Allowance for Uncoll. Taxes —Delinquent	7 9 6 0 00	9 7 4 0 00	
Interest Receivable	2 9 0 0 00		
Less Allowance for Uncollectible Interest	5 8 0 00	2 3 2 0 00	
Inventory of Supplies		3 5 3 4 00	
Total Assets		89 7 2 4 00	
LIABILITIES AND FUND EQUITY			
Liabilities:			
Accounts Payable		34 3 2 0 00	
Fund Equity:			
Unreserved Fund Balance	49 6 3 0 00		
Reserve for Encumbrances—Prior Year	2 2 4 0 00		
Reserve for Inventory of Supplies	3 5 3 4 00		
Total Fund Equity		55 4 0 4 00	
Total Liabilities and Fund Equity		89 7 2 4 00	

24-3 APPLICATION PROBLEM, p. 676

Journalizing adjusting and closing entries for a governmental organization   [1, 2]

The work sheet prepared in Application Problem 24-1 is needed to complete this problem.

JOURNAL   PAGE 23

	DATE	ACCOUNT TITLE	DOC. NO.	POST. REF.	GENERAL DEBIT	GENERAL CREDIT	CASH DEBIT	CASH CREDIT	
1		*Adjusting Entries*							1
2	20-- Dec. 31	Inventory of Supplies			3534 00				2
3		Reserve for Inventory of Supplies				3534 00			3
4	31	Interest Receivable			2900 00				4
5		Allowance for Uncollectible Interest				580 00			5
6		Interest Revenue				2320 00			6
7	31	Reserve for Encumbrances—Current Year			2240 00				7
8		Reserve for Encumbrances—Prior Year				2240 00			8
9		*Closing Entries*							9
10	31	Property Tax Revenue			1459000 00				10
11		Interest Revenue			7076 00				11
12		Other Revenue			9020 00				12
13		Unreserved Fund Balance				1475096 00			13
14	31	Unreserved Fund Balance			1464470 00				14
15		Expenditure—Personnel, Gen. Gov't				250050 00			15
16		Expenditure—Supplies, Gen. Gov't				12100 00			16
17		Expenditure—Other Charges, Gen. Gov't				124510 00			17
18		Expenditure—Capital Outlays, Gen. Gov't				14500 00			18
19		Expenditure—Personnel, Public Safety				414700 00			19
20		Expenditure—Supplies, Public Safety				21850 00			20
21		Expenditure—Other Charges, Public Safety				168420 00			21
22		Expenditure—Capital Outlays, Public Safety				80980 00			22
23		Expenditure—Personnel, Public Works				157730 00			23
24		Expenditure—Supplies, Public Works				6150 00			24

24-3 APPLICATION PROBLEM (concluded)

[1, 2]

JOURNAL

PAGE 23 (cont.)

	DATE	ACCOUNT TITLE	DOC. NO.	POST. REF.	GENERAL DEBIT	GENERAL CREDIT	CASH DEBIT	CASH CREDIT	
25		Expenditure—Other Charges, Public Works				5217000			25
26		Expenditure—Capital Outlays, Public Works				4630000			26
27		Expenditure—Personnel, Recreation				5525000			27
28		Expenditure—Supplies, Recreation				2157000			28
29		Expenditure—Other Charges, Recreation				2775000			29
30		Expenditure—Capital Outlays, Recreation				1044000			30
31	31	Appropriations			146754000				31
32		Budgetary Fund Balance			941000				32
33		Estimated Revenues				147695000			33
34	31	Unreserved Fund Balance			224000				34
35		Encumbrance—Supplies, Gen. Gov't				224000			35
36									36
37									37
38									38
39									39
40									40
41									41
42									42
43									43
44									44
45									45
46									46
47									47
48									48

24-4 MASTERY PROBLEM, p. 677

Completing the end-of-fiscal-period work for a governmental organization [1, 2]

Town of Duluth General Fund
Work Sheet
For Year Ended December 31, 20--

#	ACCOUNT TITLE	TRIAL BALANCE DEBIT	TRIAL BALANCE CREDIT	ADJUSTMENTS DEBIT	ADJUSTMENTS CREDIT	REVENUES/EXPENDITURES DEBIT	REVENUES/EXPENDITURES CREDIT	BALANCE SHEET DEBIT	BALANCE SHEET CREDIT
1	Cash	10339000						10339000	
2	Taxes Receivable—Current								
3	Allow. for Uncoll. Taxes—Current								
4	Taxes Receivable—Delinquent	1043000						1043000	
5	Allow. for Uncoll. Taxes—Delinquent		694000						694000
6	Interest Receivable			(b) 235000				235000	
7	Allow. for Uncoll. Interest				(b) 47000				47000
8	Inventory of Supplies			(a) 290000				290000	
9	Investments—Short Term								
10	Accounts Payable		2934000						2934000
11	Notes Payable								
12	Unreserved Fund Balance		3555000						3555000
13	Reserve for Encumb.—Current Year		187000	(c) 187000					
14	Reserve for Encumb.—Prior Year				(c) 187000		187000		
15	Reserve for Inventory of Supplies				(a) 290000		290000		
16	Property Tax Revenue		126500000				126500000		
17	Interest Revenue		668000		(b) 188000		856000		
18	Other Revenue		812000				812000		
19	Expend.—Personnel, Gen. Gov't.	21164000				21164000			
20	Expend.—Supplies, Gen. Gov't.	1049000				1049000			
21	Expend.—Other Chgs., Gen. Gov't.	10655000				10655000			
22	Expend.—Cap. Outlays, Gen. Gov't.	1230000				1230000			
23	Expend.—Personnel, Pub. Saf.	39754000				3409800 / 3975400			
24	Expend.—Supplies, Pub. Saf.	1862000				1862000			
25	Expend.—Other Chgs., Pub. Saf.	14415000				14415000			
26	Expend.—Cap. Outlays, Pub. Saf.	7230000				7230000			
27	Expend.—Personnel, Pub. Wks.	9220000				6326100 / 9220000			

	ACCOUNT TITLE	TRIAL BALANCE DEBIT	TRIAL BALANCE CREDIT	ADJUSTMENTS DEBIT	ADJUSTMENTS CREDIT	REVENUES/EXPENDITURES DEBIT	REVENUES/EXPENDITURES CREDIT	BALANCE SHEET DEBIT	BALANCE SHEET CREDIT
28	Expend.—Supplies, Pub. Wks.	5 25 000				5 25 000			
29	Expend.—Other Chgs., Pub. Wks.	44 75 000				44 75 000			
30	Expend.—Cap. Outlays, Pub. Wks.	39 60 000				39 60 000			
31	Expend.—Personnel, Rec.	48 22 000				1818 0 0 00 / 48 2 0 00			
32	Expend.—Supplies, Rec.	1 85 000				1 85 000			
33	Expend.—Other Chgs., Rec.	23 48 000				23 48 000			
34	Expend.—Cap. Outlays, Rec.	8 87 000				8 87 000			
35	Estimated Revenues	1280 000 00				824 2 0 00 / 1280 0 0 00			
36	Appropriations		1240 000 00 00				1240 00 000		
37	Budgetary Fund Balance		40 00 000				40 00 000		
38	Encumb.—Supplies, Gen Gov't	1 87 000			7 12 000	1 87 000			
39		2633 5 0 000	2633 5 0 000	7 12 000	7 12 000	2519 6 8 000	2563 5 5 000	119 07 000	75 20 000
40						43 87 000			43 87 000
41	*Excess of Rev. Over Expend.*					2563 5 5 000	2563 5 5 000	119 07 000	119 07 000
42									
43									
44									
45									
46									
47									
48									
49									
50									
51									
52									
53									
54									

24-4 **MASTERY PROBLEM (continued)**

[3]

Town of Duluth General Fund

Statement of Revenues, Expenditures, and Changes in Fund Balance—Budget and Actual

For Year Ended December 31, 20--

	BUDGET	ACTUAL	VARIANCE—FAVORABLE (UNFAVORABLE)
Revenues:			
Property Tax Revenue	1265 0 0 0 00	1265 0 0 0 00	—
Interest Revenue	7 2 5 0 00	8 5 6 0 00	1 3 1 0 00
Other Revenue	7 7 5 0 00	8 1 2 0 00	3 7 0 00
Total Revenues	1280 0 0 0 00	1281 6 8 0 00	1 6 8 0 00
Expenditures:			
General Government	342 2 0 0 00	340 9 8 0 00	1 2 2 0 00
Public Safety	633 1 0 0 00	632 6 1 0 00	4 9 0 00
Public Works	182 0 0 0 00	181 8 0 0 00	2 0 0 00
Recreation	82 7 0 0 00	82 4 2 0 00	2 8 0 00
Total Expenditures	1240 0 0 0 00	1237 8 1 0 00	2 1 9 0 00
Excess of Revenues Over Expenditures	40 0 0 0 00	43 8 7 0 00	3 8 7 0 00
Less Outstanding Encumbrances, Dec. 31, 20--	—	1 8 7 0 00	(1 8 7 0 00)
Increase in Unreserved Fund Balance for Year	40 0 0 0 00	42 0 0 0 00	2 0 0 0 00
Unreserved Fund Balance, Jan. 1, 20--	35 5 5 0 00	35 5 5 0 00	—
Unreserved Fund Balance, Dec. 31, 20--	75 5 5 0 00	77 5 5 0 00	2 0 0 0 00

Town of Duluth General Fund

Balance Sheet

December 31, 20--

ASSETS										
Cash						103	3	9	0	00
Taxes Receivable—Delinquent	10	4	3	0	00					
Less Allowance for Uncoll. Taxes —Delinquent	6	9	4	0	00	3	4	9	0	00
Interest Receivable	2	3	5	0	00					
Less Allowance for Uncollectible Interest		4	7	0	00	1	8	8	0	00
Inventory of Supplies						2	9	0	0	00
Total Assets						111	6	6	0	00
LIABILITIES AND FUND EQUITY										
Liabilities:										
Accounts Payable						29	3	4	0	00
Fund Equity:										
Unreserved Fund Balance	77	5	5	0	00					
Reserve for Encumbrances—Prior Year	1	8	7	0	00					
Reserve for Inventory of Supplies	2	9	0	0	00					
Total Fund Equity						82	3	2	0	00
Total Liabilities and Fund Equity						111	6	6	0	00

24-4 MASTERY PROBLEM (continued)

[5, 6]

JOURNAL
PAGE 42

DATE		ACCOUNT TITLE	DOC. NO.	POST. REF.	GENERAL DEBIT	GENERAL CREDIT	CASH DEBIT	CASH CREDIT
		Adjusting Entries						
20-- Dec.	31	Inventory of Supplies			2 900 00			
		Reserve for Inventory of Supplies				2 900 00		
	31	Interest Receivable			2 350 00			
		Allowance for Uncollectible Interest				470 00		
		Interest Revenue				1 880 00		
	31	Reserve for Encumbrances—Current Year			1 870 00			
		Reserve for Encumbrances—Prior Year				1 870 00		
		Closing Entries						
	31	Property Tax Revenue			1 265 000 00			
		Interest Revenue			8 560 00			
		Other Revenue			8 120 00			
		Unreserved Fund Balance				1 281 680 00		
	31	Unreserved Fund Balance			1 237 810 00			
		Expenditure—Personnel, Gen. Gov't				211 640 00		
		Expenditure—Supplies, Gen. Gov't				10 490 00		
		Expenditure—Other Charges, Gen. Gov't				106 550 00		
		Expenditure—Capital Outlays, Gen. Gov't				12 300 00		
		Expenditure—Personnel, Public Safety				397 540 00		
		Expenditure—Supplies, Public Safety				18 620 00		
		Expenditure—Other Charges, Public Safety				144 150 00		
		Expenditure—Capital Outlays, Public Safety				72 300 00		
		Expenditure—Personnel, Public Works				92 200 00		
		Expenditure—Supplies, Public Works				5 250 00		

24-4 MASTERY PROBLEM (concluded)

[5, 6]

JOURNAL

PAGE 42 (cont.)

	DATE	ACCOUNT TITLE	DOC. NO.	POST. REF.	GENERAL DEBIT	GENERAL CREDIT	CASH DEBIT	CASH CREDIT	
25		Expenditure—Other Charges, Public Works				4475000			25
26		Expenditure—Capital Outlays, Public Works				3960000			26
27		Expenditure—Personnel, Recreation				4822000			27
28		Expenditure—Supplies, Recreation				185000			28
29		Expenditure—Other Charges, Recreation				2348000			29
30		Expenditure—Capital Outlays, Recreation				887000			30
31	31	Appropriations			124000000				31
32		Budgetary Fund Balance			4000000				32
33		Estimated Revenues				128000000			33
34	31	Unreserved Fund Balance			187000				34
35		Encumbrance—Supplies, Gen. Gov't				187000			35
36									36
37									37
38									38
39									39
40									40
41									41
42									42
43									43
44									44
45									45
46									46
47									47
48									48

24-5 CHALLENGE PROBLEM, p. 679

Completing end-of-fiscal-period work for a governmental organization [1, 2]

Town of Plymouth General Fund
Work Sheet
For Year Ended December 31, 20--

#	ACCOUNT TITLE	TRIAL BALANCE DEBIT	TRIAL BALANCE CREDIT	ADJUSTMENTS DEBIT	ADJUSTMENTS CREDIT	REVENUES/EXPENDITURES DEBIT	REVENUES/EXPENDITURES CREDIT	BALANCE SHEET DEBIT	BALANCE SHEET CREDIT
1	Cash	56148 00						56148 00	
2	Taxes Receivable—Current								
3	Allow. for Uncoll. Taxes—Current								
4	Taxes Receivable—Delinquent	28074 00						28074 00	
5	Allow. for Uncoll. Taxes—Delinquent		11225 00						11225 00
6	Interest Receivable			(b) 6080 00				6080 00	
7	Allow. for Uncoll. Interest				(b) 1216 00				1216 00
8	Inventory of Supplies			(a) 3382 00				3382 00	
9	Investments—Short Term								
10	Accounts Payable		35816 00						35816 00
11	Notes Payable		63450 00						63450 00
12	Unreserved Fund Balance								
13	Reserve for Encumb.—Current Year		1076 00	(c) 1076 00					
14	Reserve for Encumb.—Prior Year				(c) 1076 00		1076 00		
15	Reserve for Inventory of Supplies				(a) 3382 00				3382 00
16	Property Tax Revenue		1455900 00				1455900 00		
17	Interest Revenue		9885 00		(b) 4864 00		14749 00		
18	Other Revenue		15973 00				15973 00		
19	Expend.—Personnel, Gen. Gov't.	260520 00				260520 00			
20	Expend.—Supplies, Gen. Gov't.	14394 00				14394 00			
21	Expend.—Other Chgs., Gen. Gov't.	129975 00				129975 00			
22	Expend.—Cap. Outlays, Gen. Gov't.	15168 00				15168 00			
23	Expend.—Personnel, Pub. Saf.	483590 0				483590 0			
24	Expend.—Supplies, Pub. Saf.	21973 00				21973 00			
25	Expend.—Other Chgs., Pub. Saf.	175843 00				175843 00			
26	Expend.—Cap. Outlays, Pub. Saf.	85745 00				85745 00			
27	Expend.—Personnel, Pub. Wks.	113225 00				113225 00			

24-5 CHALLENGE PROBLEM (continued)

[1, 2]

	ACCOUNT TITLE	TRIAL BALANCE DEBIT (1)	TRIAL BALANCE CREDIT (2)	ADJUSTMENTS DEBIT (3)	ADJUSTMENTS CREDIT (4)	REVENUES/EXPENDITURES DEBIT (5)	REVENUES/EXPENDITURES CREDIT (6)	BALANCE SHEET DEBIT (7)	BALANCE SHEET CREDIT (8)
28	Expend.—Supplies, Pub. Wks.	6687 00				6687 00			
29	Expend.—Other Chgs., Pub. Wks.	52684 00				52684 00			
30	Expend.—Cap. Outlays, Pub. Wks.	48820 00				48820 00			
31	Expend.—Personnel, Rec.	56855 00				221416 00 / 56855 00			
32	Expend.—Supplies, Rec.	2678 00				2678 00			
33	Expend.—Other Chgs., Rec.	28910 00				28910 00			
34	Expend.—Cap. Outlays, Rec.	10960 00				10960 00			
35	Estimated Revenues	1485840 00				99403 00 / 1485840 00	1511160 00		
36	Appropriations		1511160 00						
37	Budgetary Fund Balance	25320 00				25320 00	21405 00		
38	Encumb.—Supplies, Pub. Saf.	1076 00				1076 00			
39		3104485 00	3104485 00	10538 00	10538 00	3020263 00	2998858 00	93684 00	115089 00
40	Excess of Expend. Over Rev.						21405 00	21405 00	
41						3020263 00	3020263 00	115089 00	115089 00
42									
43									
44									
45									
46									
47									
48									
49									
50									
51									
52									
53									
54									

24-5 CHALLENGE PROBLEM (continued)

[3]

Town of Plymouth General Fund

Statement of Revenues, Expenditures, and Changes in Fund Balance—Budget and Actual

For Year Ended December 31, 20--

	BUDGET	ACTUAL	VARIANCE— FAVORABLE (UNFAVORABLE)
Revenues:			
Property Tax Revenue	1455 9 0 0 00	1455 9 0 0 00	——
Interest Revenue	13 3 6 0 00	14 7 4 9 00	1 3 8 9 00
Other Revenue	16 5 8 0 00	15 9 7 3 00	(6 0 7 00)
Total Revenues	1485 8 4 0 00	1486 6 2 2 00	7 8 2 00
Expenditures:			
General Government	420 1 3 0 00	420 0 5 7 00	7 3 00
Public Safety	769 5 3 0 00	767 1 5 1 00	2 3 7 9 00
Public Works	221 9 5 5 00	221 4 1 6 00	5 3 9 00
Recreation	99 5 4 5 00	99 4 0 3 00	1 4 2 00
Total Expenditures	1511 1 6 0 00	1508 0 2 7 00	3 1 3 3 00
Excess of Expenditures Over Revenues	25 3 2 0 00	21 4 0 5 00	3 9 1 5 00
Plus Outstanding Encumbrances, Dec. 31, 20--	——	1 0 7 6 00	(1 0 7 6 00)
Decrease in Unreserved Fund Balance for Year	25 3 2 0 00	22 4 8 1 00	2 8 3 9 00
Unreserved Fund Balance, Jan. 1, 20--	63 4 5 0 00	63 4 5 0 00	——
Unreserved Fund Balance, Dec. 31, 20--	38 1 3 0 00	40 9 6 9 00	2 8 3 9 00

24-5 CHALLENGE PROBLEM (continued)

[4]

Town of Plymouth General Fund

Balance Sheet

December 31, 20--

ASSETS			
Cash			56 1 4 8 00
Taxes Receivable—Delinquent	28 0 7 4 00		
Less Allowance for Uncoll. Taxes —Delinquent	11 2 2 5 00	16 8 4 9 00	
Interest Receivable	6 0 8 0 00		
Less Allowance for Uncollectible Interest	1 2 1 6 00	4 8 6 4 00	
Inventory of Supplies		3 3 8 2 00	
Total Assets		81 2 4 3 00	
LIABILITIES AND FUND EQUITY			
Liabilities:			
Accounts Payable		35 8 1 6 00	
Fund Equity:			
Unreserved Fund Balance	40 9 6 9 00		
Reserve for Encumbrances—Prior Year	1 0 7 6 00		
Reserve for Inventory of Supplies	3 3 8 2 00		
Total Fund Equity		45 4 2 7 00	
Total Liabilities and Fund Equity		81 2 4 3 00	

JOURNAL

PAGE 40

	DATE	ACCOUNT TITLE	DOC. NO.	POST. REF.	GENERAL DEBIT	GENERAL CREDIT	CASH DEBIT	CASH CREDIT	
1		*Adjusting Entries*							1
2	20-- Dec. 31	Inventory of Supplies			3 38200				2
3		Reserve for Inventory of Supplies				3 38200			3
4	31	Interest Receivable			6 08000				4
5		Allowance for Uncollectible Interest				1 21600			5
6		Interest Revenue				4 86400			6
7	31	Reserve for Encumbrances—Current Year			1 07600				7
8		Reserve for Encumbrances—Prior Year				1 07600			8
9		*Closing Entries*							9
10	31	Property Tax Revenue			1455 90000				10
11		Interest Revenue			14 74900				11
12		Other Revenue			15 97300				12
13		Unreserved Fund Balance				1486 62200			13
14	31	Unreserved Fund Balance			1508 02700				14
15		Expenditure—Personnel, Gen. Gov't				260 52000			15
16		Expenditure—Supplies, Gen. Gov't				14 39400			16
17		Expenditure—Other Charges, Gen. Gov't				129 97500			17
18		Expenditure—Capital Outlays, Gen. Gov't				15 16800			18
19		Expenditure—Personnel, Public Safety				483 59000			19
20		Expenditure—Supplies, Public Safety				21 97300			20
21		Expenditure—Other Charges, Public Safety				175 84300			21
22		Expenditure—Capital Outlays, Public Safety				85 74500			22
23		Expenditure—Personnel, Public Works				113 22500			23
24		Expenditure—Supplies, Public Works				6 68700			24

24-5 CHALLENGE PROBLEM (concluded)

[5, 6]

JOURNAL

PAGE 40 (cont.)

	DATE	ACCOUNT TITLE	DOC. NO.	POST. REF.	GENERAL DEBIT	GENERAL CREDIT	CASH DEBIT	CASH CREDIT	
25		Expenditure—Other Charges, Public Works				5268400			25
26		Expenditure—Capital Outlays, Public Works				4882000			26
27		Expenditure—Personnel, Recreation				5685500			27
28		Expenditure—Supplies, Recreation				267800			28
29		Expenditure—Other Charges, Recreation				2891000			29
30		Expenditure—Capital Outlays, Recreation				1096000			30
31	31	Appropriations			151116000				31
32		Budgetary Fund Balance				2532000			32
33		Estimated Revenues				148584000			33
34	31	Unreserved Fund Balance			107600				34
35		Encumbrance—Supplies, Public Safety				107600			35
36									36
37									37
38									38
39									39
40									40
41									41
42									42
43									43
44									44
45									45
46									46
47									47
48									48

24-5 CHALLENGE PROBLEM

Extra form

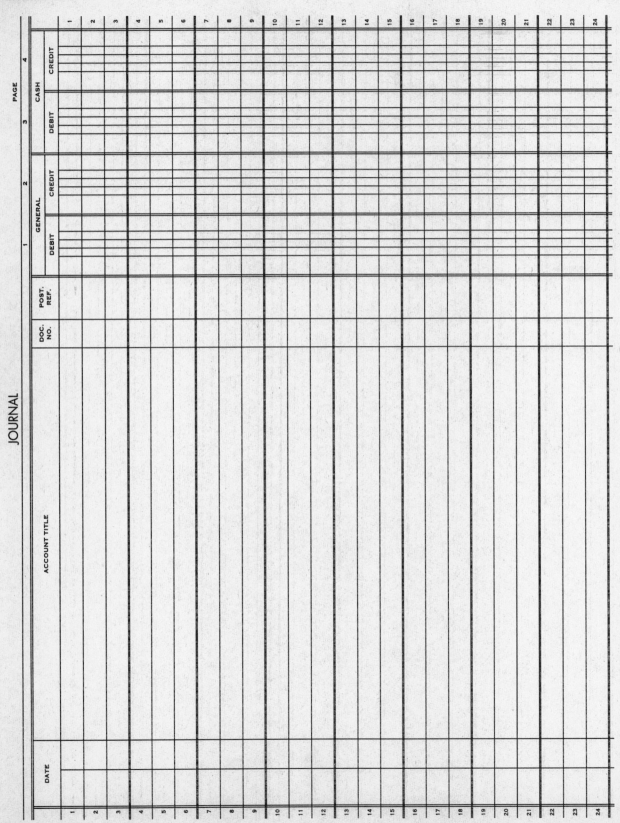

JOURNAL

24-5 CHALLENGE PROBLEM

Extra form

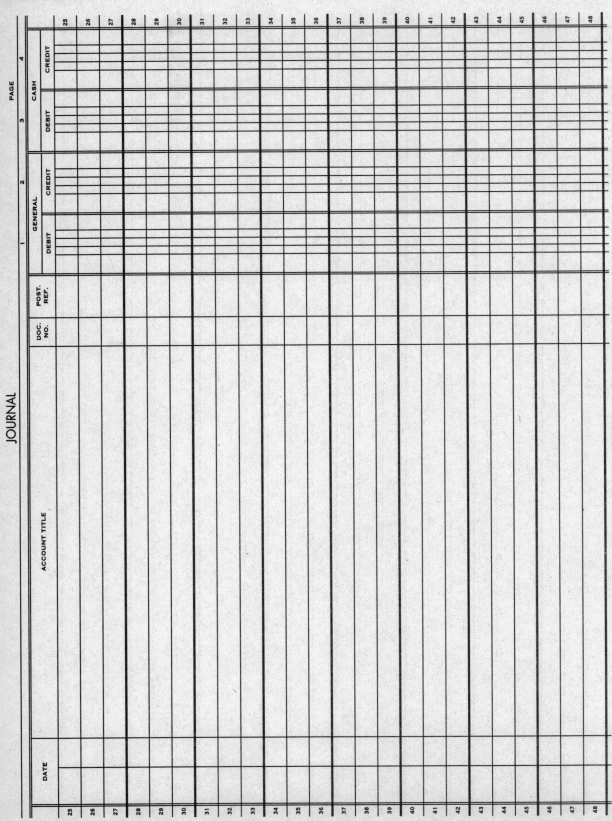

JOURNAL